Man and the Changing Landscape

A study of Occupation and Palaeo Environment
in the Central Pennines

Bernard Barnes, MA, BPHIL

Work Notes 3

Editor
Joan J. Taylor, BA, PHD, FSA
Rankin Lecturer in Prehistoric Archaeology
University of Liverpool

Merseyside County Council/Merseyside County Museums
University of Liverpool Department of Prehistoric Archaeology

ISBN 0 906367 12 3

Set in Monophoto Times New Roman by
August Filmsetting, Warrington, Cheshire

Printed by
Eaton Press, Wallasey, Merseyside

Designed by Barrie Jones
Design Dept, Merseyside County Museums

Contents

Figure 1. Frontispiece

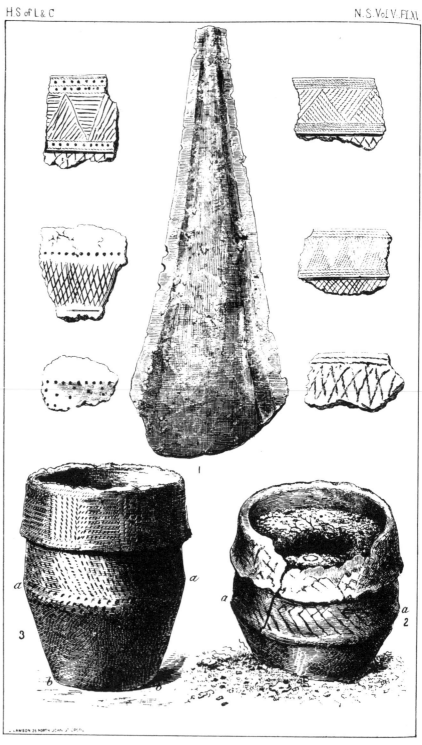

BRITISH REMAINS, FOUND AT DARWEN AND EXTWISTLE.

List of Tables and Figures

Foreword

Bernard Barnes, Senior Lecturer in Geography at the City of Manchester College of Higher Education, presents an integrated landscape study of Man's involvement through time in the naturally defined area of the Central Pennines. This is the first research to combine the distribution of sites in a landscape study with all the evidence available of Man's activities in the region, including radiocarbon dates. The work was initially presented as a B.Phil. in Prehistoric Archaeology dissertation, for which it was awarded a distinction from the University of Liverpool. Presented here reworked, it also contains an appendix by Miss R.L. Brown on the pollen evidence from several Hunter/Gatherer Mesolithic sites in the area. Professor Frank Oldfield not only supervised her collection of samples, but also her laboratory preparation, which was presented in part for a Geography B.A. dissertation, University of Liverpool. Again this appendix was recognised as a very competent piece of research, and is presented here as a complementary essay to the main study. To increase the value of this volume as a primary source, Bernard Barnes has exhaustively brought together in the second appendix all the non-perished remains of Man from the region which are now housed in various museums or recorded elsewhere.

The continuing cooperation of the Merseyside County Museums with the Department of Prehistoric Archaeology, University of Liverpool, has enabled the standard of this series to be maintained. The cost of publication has been kept down through the very kind generosity of the Barbinder Trust of Lord Leverhulme, Chancellor of the University of Liverpool, and the Robert Kiln Charitable Trust. The financial assistance by Lord Leverhulme has permitted the two institutions to make the series available in the true spirit of its founder Professor T.G.E. Powell, who wished to make available important information normally too long for a journal, but too short for publication as a book, to as many interested individuals as possible. The two institutions have judged this third volume to be a significant contribution to this aim, containing not only a collection of all previously recorded objects from this area, but also much new information, making it a source of primary importance.

Editor
Joan J. Taylor, BA, PHD, FSA
Rankin Senior Lecturer in Prehistoric Archaeology
University of Liverpool

Preface

My interest in the evolution of the Pennine landscape, both man-made and physical, goes back many years, but this study arose specifically from investigations into Mesolithic occupation sites on the high moorland plateaux between Saddleworth and Marsden. Questions arose from this research concerning environmental changes in early post glacial times, and these were gradually widened to involve an examination of the complex relationship between man and the landscape throughout prehistoric times in the Pennines and their adjacent areas.

This study would not have been possible without the ready cooperation of museum curators and individuals who so freely made their collections and information available to me. Grateful thanks are due to the following: Philip Mayes, County Archaeologist, and Jeny Keighley of the West Yorkshire Archaeological Unit; Stephen Kerry, Bradford, Metropolitan District Council Museums; Angela P. Thomas, Bolton Metropolitan Borough Museums; Michael Pitman, Rochdale Metropolitan Borough Museum; John A. Gilks, Tolson Memorial Museum, Huddersfield; the Director, Philip Holdsworth, and Adrian Tindall of the Greater Manchester Archaeological Unit; and staffs at the Manchester Museum and at the Towneley Hall Museum, Burnley. The opportunity to pursue this interest was made possible when I was granted leave of absence from my work at the City of Manchester College of Higher Education for a year in order to undertake post graduate study at Liverpool University in 1977-8.

My special thanks are due to Dr J. J. Taylor, Rankin Senior Lecturer in Prehistoric Archaeology at the University of Liverpool, for her scholarly advice, kind encouragement and understanding. I would also like to thank Dr V. R. Switsur for making available radiocarbon dates in advance of publication; Professor Frank Oldfield for his interest and advice; Miss Louise Brown for her work on pollen analysis; Mr N. Tyson for permission to reproduce Fig. 32; Mr C. Burgess for permission to reproduce Fig. 35; and Miss K. Lancaster for re-drawing the figures and diagrams. Margaret Warhurst, Keeper of Antiquities, Merseyside County Museums, was helpful with the representative collection of Francis Buckley's material, now housed with them, a collection which Buckley put together to replace a more comprehensive one which was destroyed during World War II.

The kindly help of Dr W. P. B. Stonehouse has been most valuable: he has unhesitatingly put his detailed knowledge of prehistoric sites on the gritstone moors at my disposal. Lastly, but not least, to my wife and family, whose weekends and other 'holidays' have often been spent on visits to museums and lonely moorland sites, often in very adverse weather, I can only express my deepest gratitude for their support in the compilation of this work.

Greenfield, Saddleworth
March 1981.

Note

The radiocarbon dates quoted within the text are left uncalibrated. A distinction is made between radiocarbon dates, which are expressed as b.c., and calendar years, which are expressed as B.C. After sites and artefacts, a number in parentheses refers to its appropriate reference in Appendix 2 the Index of Archaeological Discoveries.

Both imperial and metric measurements appear in the text as the measurements given are taken directly from the various sources quoted. The tables below give the equivalents:

Imperial Measurements with Metric Equivalents
1 inch   = 2.54 centimetres
1 foot = 12 inches   = 30.48 centimetres
1 yard = 3 feet   = 91.44 centimetres
                                = 0.9144 metre

Metric Measurements with Imperial Equivalents
1 millimetre   = 0.039 inch
1 centimetre = 10 mm   = 0.394 inch
1 metre   = 100 centimetres = 1.094 yards
              = 1000 millimetres

Abbreviations
With the exception of those listed below, the abbreviations used in this work follow the current international practice recommended by the Council for British Archaeology.

CAGB	Bradford City Art Gallery and Museum (Cartwright Museum) Archaeological Group Bulletin
GMAG	Greater Manchester Archaeological Group
HAS	Halifax Antiquarian Society Transactions
LAS	Littleborough Archaeological Society
O.D.	Ordnance Datum
O.S.	Ordnance Survey
Progr. Geogr.	Progress in Geography: International Reviews of Current Research
THSLC	Transactions of the Historic Society of Lancashire and Cheshire
TLCAS	Transactions of the Lancashire and Cheshire Antiquarian Society
WYAU	Index of the West Yorkshire Archaeological Unit
YAJ	Yorkshire Archaeological Journal

Introduction

In 1874, while searching for glacial erratics, John Aitken of Bacup and James Binns of Halifax discovered flints on their local moors and recognised them as the remains of early man (Aitken 1875; Roth 1906, 289). Their work incited the discoveries of J. W. Davis in the Halifax area (Davis 1881) and of Law and Horsfall in a wider area of the Central Pennines. The latter noted in particular the very small size of some of the implements, and began a series of investigations to ascertain the distribution of these 'pygmy' flints and to determine the precise level at which they occurred beneath the peat (Law & Horsfall 1882 and 1886–8). Publication of their work encouraged a great number of other investigations (eg March 1887b; Wrigley 1911), while many more casual collectors were also at work. One of the first to excavate in a more scientific manner was Francis Buckley of Greenfield, Saddleworth, and, although his methods have sometimes been decried (Hallam 1960, 33), his flint typology was acknowledged by Graham Clark (Clark 1932, 23). Buckley re examined most of the earlier sites besides discovering many new ones in a detailed exploration of the moors between Longdendale (Tintwistle Low Moor) to the south, Soyland Moor to the north and Knowl Moor to the west (Buckley 1921, 1922, 1924a and Mss.), and museums all over the country have their 'Buckley flints', one of the finest collections being that destroyed during the Second World War at Liverpool Museum. Since Buckley's time collectors have continued to 'scour' the moors for flint implements.

Thus the Millstone Grit uplands of the Central Pennines – the area, generally speaking, to the east and north of Manchester and to the west of Leeds (Fig. 2) – have been recognised as a prolific source of 'pygmy flints' or Mesolithic microliths for over 100 years. This area today, however, consists largely of bleak and windswept peaty wastes, far too extreme and barren for human settlement, where even the sheep struggle to gain a livelihood. In the ameliorating climate of the post glacial period, from about 8,000 b.c. to 3,400 b.c., Mesolithic hunters and gatherers frequented the uplands in an environment which must have been quite different to that existing today. Indeed, there is increasing evidence to demonstrate that from this time man began to exert a more or less significant role in the evolution of the Pennine moorlands. Yet it is the changing function of these very moorlands during prehistoric times that in many ways stimulated this study. From being a favoured area in Mesolithic times, they later presented a more hostile front to human activities. Because of this, the Central Pennines are by no means famed for their archaeological sites and monuments: these are generally unimpressive where they have survived the settlement growth and the industrial and agricultural activities of more recent times. Both sites and artefacts demonstrate a relative backwardness when compared with other, more favoured, areas: in many ways this district was a backwater, the uplands because of their hostility and even the foothill zones were comparatively marginal. The region was not avoided entirely, however, and, indeed, it assumed a peculiar attraction at different times in prehistory. This begs the question concerning the dominance or otherwise of environmental changes when they are compared to changes in human activities, and an interesting contrast arises and is repeated again and again between the microenvironments of the Pennine fringes, the foothill and valley zones, and those of the uplands proper, so far as human exploitation and settlement are concerned, and it is this which will receive special attention here.

Thus while Mesolithic artefacts are plentiful on certain parts of the uplands, the other prehistoric periods are poorly represented on the gritstone moors; even in the foothill areas the remains, which include burials, evidence of settlements and casual finds, are comparatively scattered, both in space and time, and are often poorly representative. During the preceding Palaeolithic period, the activities of man had been greatly restricted by glacial conditions, and his remains are almost entirely confined to a few limestone caves in Derbyshire, occupied presumably for

Figure 2.

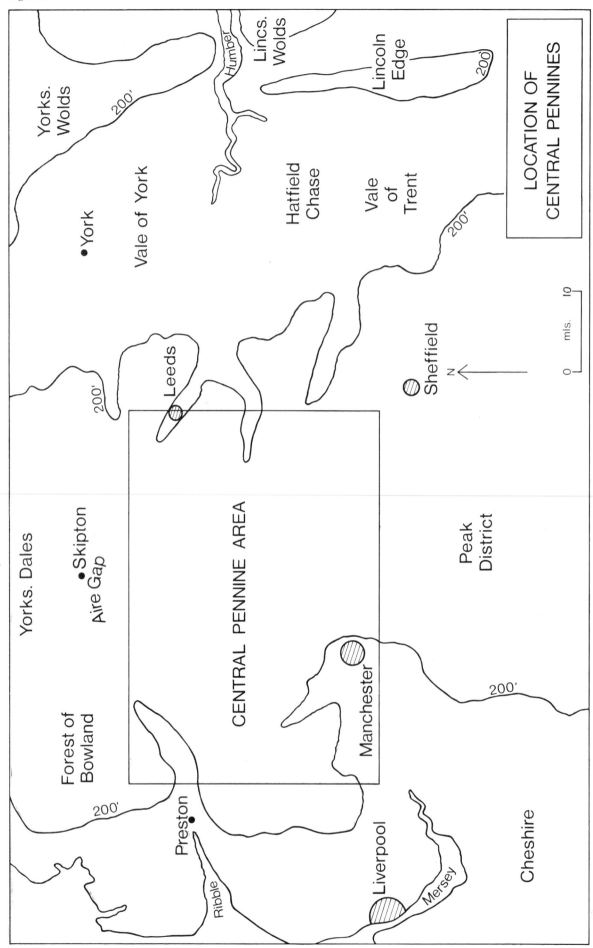

LOCATION OF CENTRAL PENNINES

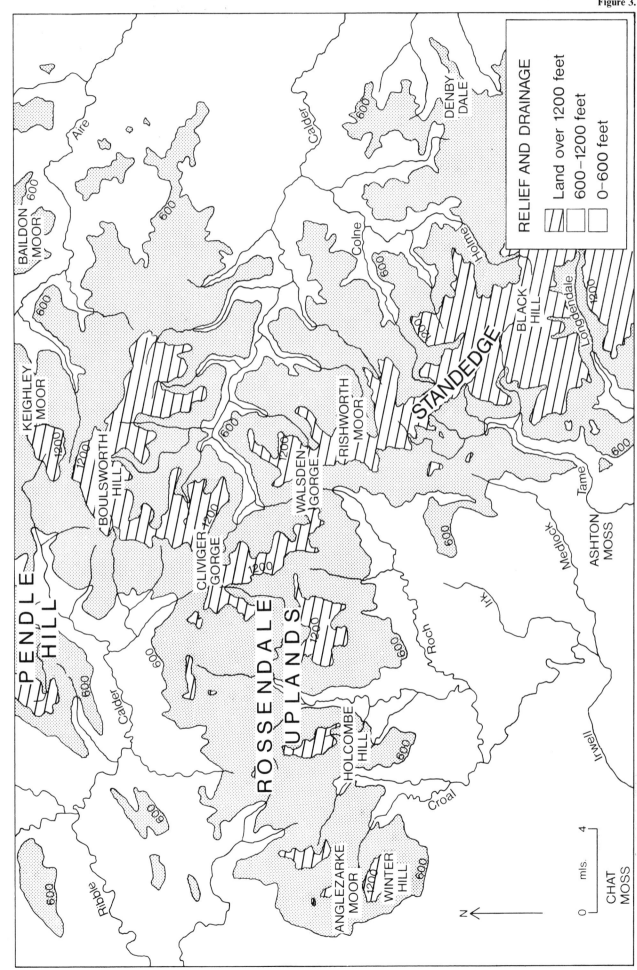

Figure 3.

short periods of time. The Carboniferous Limestone areas of the Yorkshire Dales to the north, and, more especially, the Peak District to the south, also overshadow the uplands and foothills of the Central Pennines in post Mesolithic times, and, as mentioned above, the extent to which this can be ascribed to environmental influences will be discussed in more detail later.

The specific area under discussion comprises the Pennines and adjacent areas between Longdendale in the south and Boulsworth Hill in the north, and includes the extension of the higher land through the Rossendale Uplands westwards to Winter Hill (Fig. 3). The boundaries are arbitrary in many respects, chosen to include as much of the Central Pennine uplands as possible, and yet at the same time to achieve a manageable unit for discussion. Thus they include some low-lying land in the Manchester area to the south west, and exclude some foothill areas and outlying uplands, particularly in the east and north. The use of the term 'Central Pennines' should perhaps be defended. Some writers (eg Jacobi *et al* 1976) would include this area under the general title of 'Southern Pennines', but here the latter term is taken to mean the Derbyshire Hills, the area to the south of Longdendale (the area generally known as the Peak District), while the Central Pennines are as defined by the Geological Survey, the Millstone Grit uplands lying to the south of the Aire Gap (Edwards & Trotter 1954, Fig. 1).

The Pennines form the primary watershed of England, on the west the streams draining to the Irish Sea and on the east to the North Sea. This fact, in addition to the effects of topographical and other environmental factors, has probably contributed significantly to the characteristic cultural attributes of this upland area, both in prehistoric times and in later ages. Although the hills rarely rise to over 2,000 feet O.D., and in the Central Pennines they seldom reach 1,700 feet O.D., nevertheless they have always featured as a significant barrier, a divide in more senses than one, so far as both environmental factors and human activities are concerned. Contrasts have therefore arisen between the areas on each side of the watershed, contrasts, however, which have varied through time in their impact on the landscape, as will be seen.

This study attempts to provide a synopsis of the archaeological material of this area from the beginning of the Mesolithic period to the end of the Iron Age, (a span of over eight millennia beginning before 7600 b.c.), and to assess it in the context of our present studies into the palaeoenvironment. For convenience and ease of comparison, the traditional divisions of the prehistoric period – Mesolithic and Neolithic periods, Bronze Age and Iron Age – have been utilised. While it is recognised that the value of these divisions has been questioned for a number of years (and aspects of their artificiality will become apparent in this description of the Central Pennine area), it is not the prime purpose to further the discussion here. An emphasis is placed on the value of environmental evidence in its relationship to human activity, and, conversely, in recognising the human factor in a 'natural' succession. In recent times, environmental archaeology has made great headway in the Pennines, favoured by the occurrence of peat in the uplands which is valuable for reconstructing by means of pollen analysis the botanical environment and the effects of early man on soils and vegetation, though the acid soils have generally led to a lack of preservation of bone and wood. Not all the evidence from the two fields is in complete agreement: a full synthesis is not yet possible, largely due to dating difficulties in both the archaeological and environmental investigations, but it is hoped that this study will provide a useful summary of current knowledge.

Works of synthesis, like this, inevitably owe much to many, as is evidenced by the bibliography and the acknowledgements. Nearly all the archaeological and environmental evidence presented here is what Ashbee described as 'indirect knowledge', knowledge gained by the critical appreciation of the descriptions, reports and narratives prepared by others (Ashbee 1960, 2).

Chapter One
Man and the Palaeoenvironment

It is axiomatic to view the environment of early man in Britain, with all its ramifications, as having an obvious bearing on his activities, setting clear limits to what was technically feasible for a particular cultural group. How influential it was varied both through time and space. Though the relationship between human activities and environment generally was symbiotic, born of economic circumstances (Evans 1975, xiv), in uplands like the Central Pennines, marginal areas so far as human occupation is concerned, environmental factors played the dominant role. Thus fluctuating sea levels, the initial amelioration of the climate in post glacial times and its subsequent variations, the consequential changes in vegetation, geological and structural factors and their influence on topography at various times, and the effects of all these on soils, all have a relevance in the study of prehistoric occupancy of an area. The work of geographers and others in related disciplines can not only bring much light to bear on these aspects, the background to colonisation by early man, but also on its wider spatial context, by the analysis of the interconnection between individual archaeological sites, rather than emphasising the details of their particular artefact assemblages. All this has relevance in the study of man, his social organisation and his organisation of the landscape in prehistoric times, particularly as it is increasingly realised that 'the English landscape is much older than we have ever conceived', and that it is 'prehistoric in outline, and its development cannot be understood if this is not appreciated' (Taylor 1980). It has been realised for some years, and is ever more apparent, that there is a need to investigate archaeological sites using all these interdisciplinary methods directed to the explanation of how man adapted and varied through time.

The spatial analysis of archaeological distributions depends on the results of much field investigation. These distributions are, of course, relict in character, dependent on subsequent survival, the ease of discovery, and the number of investigators at work in particular areas. Nevertheless, the patterns often – and not least in this area of study – reveal geological and topographical correlations with sites and artefacts, seemingly suggesting a conscious preference for certain areas. Similarly, climatic and related forms of environmental change may be reflected in the landscape by the distribution of occupation sites connected or linked together at a particular point in time. The pattern of Mesolithic sites on the uplands of the Central Pennines and the poverty of subsequent Neolithic evidence offers unequivocal testimony to the significance of the climatic changes which have occurred during the last 5,000 years; changes, yet to be described, which enhanced the environmental changes inflicted because of man's activities. Even a slight deterioration in climatic conditions would have the effect of rendering large areas of the gritstone uplands marginal in character, particularly insofar as cultivation and permanent settlement were concerned. Thus the new Neolithic society, with its emphasis away from hunting and gathering, and towards crop production and animal grazing, which in turn allowed permanent settlement, found itself circumscribed in the Central Pennine district by limits imposed because of the unfavourable environmental conditions. The predictability of land use reinforces the predictability of sites that arises from our increasing knowledge of the changing significance of certain topographical and soil characteristics and other environmental paradigms. In this body of knowledge, palynological evidence has a vital role, particularly when studied in conjunction with the site distribution and management. Thus while the survival of such valuable indicators of occupation and land use as burial mounds and field boundaries may be fortuitous, and subsequent reworking of the landscape may have destroyed a good deal of the evidence (an important factor to bear in mind in the foothill areas of the Central Pennines), environmental records, such as those afforded by pollen cores from peat bogs provide an independent tool for the study of former landscapes. Indeed, pollen studies have made a remarkable contribution to our knowledge of vegetation changes with the pollen grains of flowering plants and the spores of ferns and mosses being preserved in peat and other sedimentary deposits, owing to their wetness and acidity. While the distribution of suitable deposits is variable across the country, the frequency of peat bogs on plateau summits means that the selection of a relatively small study area, like the Central Pennines which incorporates such an upland environment, gives unique evidence for the work of palynologists, which can be buttressed by radiocarbon datings. In many cases continuous pollen records can be considered within certain limits with other environmental studies such as topographical and climatic change. We have gained insight by these comparisons into how the landscape has evolved since the late glacial period. Palynological investigation, thereby, provides evidence of the ability of various groups of people to adapt to and make use of their immediate environment for their own ends.

Thus much useful primary data regarding problems such as forest clearance, the development of agriculture and changes in the intensity of land use can be provided. An illustration of the value of this type of material can be mentioned here, although this will be examined in more detail later. The evidence from pollens, particularly when tied in with the examination of the spatial analysis of sites and artefacts, increasingly points to the conclusion that the degeneration of formerly forested areas in the uplands into peat bog and heath is by no means due entirely to climatic factors: as early as 6,000 B.C. Mesolithic man was no longer just a hunter and gatherer, but had begun to clear small patches of woodland by fire and to initiate the whole process of animal husbandry. Hence, without going to the other extreme and denying that the general deterioration in climate during later prehistoric times did not play at least a contributory role, there exists the possibility that man himself may have interfered with or even cut short the natural Flandrian (or post glacial) progression of vegetation in the earlier immigration phase, as opposed simply to interference with mature deciduous forest after its establishment (Smith 1979, 22).

Only those human activities which were intensive and sustained will survive in the pollen record. Hence palynology directed at discovering the impact of Mesolithic man should be concentrated near accredited Mesolithic sites rather than probing at random. Again the Central Pennine area is a very pertinent study area in this respect, providing as it does a marked concentration of microlithic flint sites belonging both to the early and to the later phases of the period occurring beneath extensive peat bogs. For this reason this study contains a summary of the results of an investigation into pollen cores taken from three such sites by Louise Brown, sites which were chosen because they had also been dated previously by radio-carbon methods, and her findings are presented in Appendix 1. An increasing volume of material is being gathered together concerning pollen work in the upland areas of the Pennines as well as further afield, in North Yorkshire for example, and this has been used throughout this study because of the environ-mental information it provides and to corroborate field evidence – although, as will be seen, the two do not always necessarily concur.

The understanding of changes in the human occupancy of the Central Pennines and of former landscapes in general cannot be achieved without the application of techniques such as palynology, just as the analysis of site distribution is not fully legitimised without detailed work to determine the attributes of individual sites, not least in their relationship to the prevailing environmental circumstances.

Chapter Two
The Physical Environment

The Central Pennines, part of the range of hills popularly known as 'the backbone of England', consist of a dissected plateau which is generally over 1,200 feet O.D. This plateau is moulded from a markedly asymmetrical upfold or anticline which has a steep western limb and gently dipping rocks to the east. Consequently, many of the highest points are found close to the western flanks of the uplands, which rise to 1,900 feet O.D. at Black Hill in the south and to 1,700 feet O.D. at Boulsworth Hill in the north (Fig. 3). The rocks comprising the Central Pennines are Upper Carboniferous in age, with the Millstone Grit series being the most characteristic rocks. These consist of bands of hard gritstone separated by soft, quickly rotting shales, the differential erosion of grit and shale producing the 'stepped' landscapes so typical of the area. The central moorlands are flanked on either side by Lower Coal Measure rocks which consist chiefly of shales separating beds of sandstones, themselves hardly distinguishable from those of the Millstone Grit series (Fig. 4).

On the eastern flanks of the Pennines, where the moorlands of West Yorkshire fall gently away from the watershed, erosion of the slightly tilted Millstone Grit and Lower Coal Measure rocks has given rise to a series of west facing escarpments which gradually decrease in height away from the uplands. Prominent among these are the Lower Coal Measure escarpments in the vicinity of Halifax and to the south of Huddersfield, the latter including the impressive prominence of Castle Hill, Almondbury, with its Iron Age fort. In the north east of our area, the gritstone mass of Rombalds Moor overlooks the Aire valley which separates the moor from the Pennine uplands proper (Fig. 3).

The Rossendale Uplands form a westerly extension of the Pennines: they are the surface expression of another anticline which trends from north east to south west (Wright *et al* 1927). Millstone Grits are exposed at its crest to form the level plateau summits of the moorland core, which rises to altitudes as great as 1,500 feet O.D. and is gashed by deep valleys such as that of the upper Irwell and those to the north of Bolton. Round the flanks of the upland the Lower Coal Measures form lower plateaux and benches.

To the north of the Rossendale Uplands, the Carboniferous rocks are disturbed by tight folding (Earp *et al* 1961). A deep downfold or syncline, lying against the northern edge of the anticline, is drained by the Calder and Darwen rivers and forms a broad lowland, but beyond this the Millstone Grits are raised to form a bold ridge with a north east to south west trend overlooking the Ribble valley. This ridge forms the higher ground north of Blackburn at Revidge and Wilpshire, and culminates in the magnificent gritstone mass of Pendle Hill to the north of our area. South of the Rossendale Uplands, the lowlands of the Manchester embayment are floored by Coal Measure rocks and on the south western fringes of our area by Permo Triassic sandstones.

The key to much of the minor relief of those lowlands, however, lies in the varied overlay of unconsolidated glacial deposits of 'North Western' origin, which contain erratic boulders from the Lake District and the southern uplands of Scotland. These cover the 'solid' landscape of pre glacial times. Boulder clays predominate, but in places, notably north of Manchester between Prestwich and Rochdale, they were subsequently covered during the retreat phase of the ice by sand and gravel deposits (Fig. 5). The term 'boulder clay', however, encompasses a wide variety of deposits. These clays can range from extremely stiff to very sandy varieties, and from almost stoneless clays to others which are so stoney as to constitute a gravel with a clayey matrix. In general they give rise to relatively flat landscapes, as in south Lancashire, whereas the sand and gravels are dissected by even the slightest brooks, giving rise to an undulating landscape with haphazardly arranged hillocks and hollows. In places, however, hollows also occur in the boulder clay cover: these were possibly the sites of ephemeral lakes in post glacial

Figure 4.

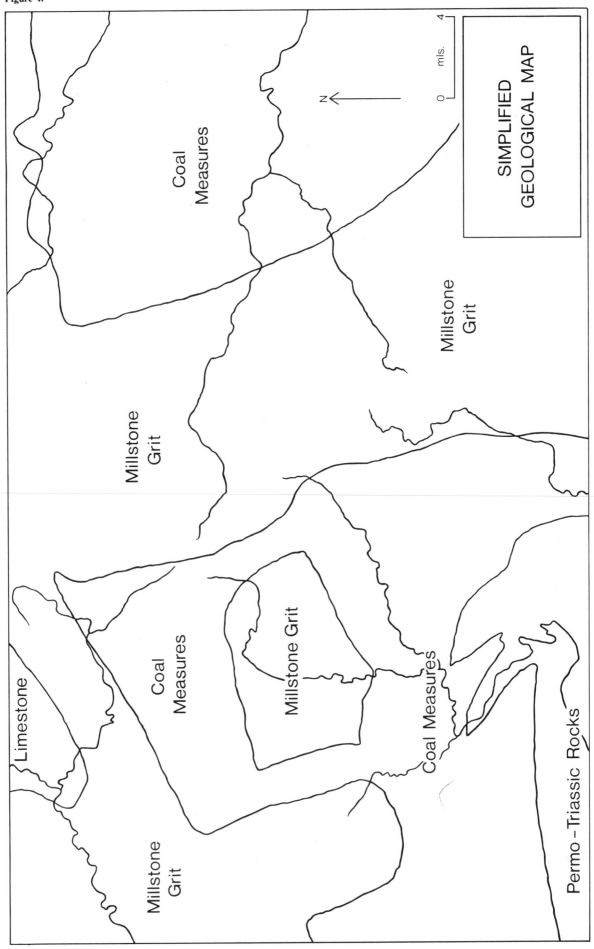

SIMPLIFIED GEOLOGICAL MAP

times, and later saw the accumulation of raised bog as at Ashton Moss and Chat Moss.

Much of the lower ground in the northern part of our area was also covered by glacial deposits, but this time not from North Western Ice but from glaciers moving south down Ribblesdale. The ice breached the Pennine watershed in the Cliviger Gorge south east of Burnley, and penetrated a little way down the valley of the Yorkshire Calder. Ice also reached through the Aire Gap and down the Aire valley (Raistrick 1933a, Plate XV). Boulder clay deposits again predominate, reaching a thickness of 150 feet near Stephen Hey on the north side of the Thursden valley near Burnley (Earp et al 1961, 229), though small patches of sand overlie the clay in places. The Ribblesdale drift is a stiff clay, full of limestone and chert boulders, materials which are rare in North Western drift (Wright et al 1927, 133).

On the western flanks of the Pennines glacial deposits and erratics indicate the minimum altitude which the ice reached: around the Manchester embayment this was generally between 1,200 and 1,300 feet O.D. (Johnson 1969, 196), but further north in the Gorple area, Ribblesdale drift is found at over 1,500 feet O.D. (Wright et al 1927, 134). In the Boulsworth Hill area, for example, small fragments of dark chert, found in deposits around 1,500 feet O.D. were almost certainly ice-borne (Earp et al 1961, 233). On the other side of the Pennines, however, the absence of drift suggests that much of the eastern side of our area was unglaciated. It is unsafe to assume, however, that any part of the Pennines escaped glaciation since much of the highest ice was probably drift-free (Palmer 1967, 19). Striated limestone boulders, however, do occur on Wadsworth Moor (Spencer 1893), while the sporadic nature of high level drift may indicate that much of it was removed by solifluction.

What is certain is that the higher ground was exposed to periglacial conditions for long periods at the end of the Ice Age, and evidence of this is apparent when the peat cover is removed, as it is, for example, by wind erosion after burning (Radley 1965). Large areas of the higher plateaux and the slopes below the 'edges' are covered by felsenmeer (angular, frost-riven boulders), and the lower plateau tops by a sandy regolith, the result of intense periglacial rotting of the bed rock. Great thicknesses of this sandy material are found in moorland hollows and on the lower valley sides where it has been brought down by solifluction, forming 'head' deposits.

The late glacial environment must have been one of chronic instability and sharp diversity (Taylor 1973, 309). Massive accumulations of torrent gravels were brought down to the lowlands by the rivers, and many temporary channels were cut by melt and flood waters. Ephemeral ice-dammed lakes may have occupied parts of some valleys, although this is doubted by many (eg Johnson 1965a). A glacial lake does seem to have occupied the Vale of York, however, reaching up the lower sections of the east Pennine valleys with a shore line around 100 feet O.D. (Palmer 1966, 98), and it left a cover of varied deposits (Radley & Simms 1967, 21; Radley 1974, 10). The area was especially favourable for the formation of landslides at this time, largely on account of its geological structure, together with the presence of boulder clay on the lower slopes of many western valleys ensuring the maintenance of a high water table. Such slope failure seems to have occurred over a long period in post glacial times, and not just in the late glacial period, the steep, western slopes of the Pennines being particularly susceptible. Pollen analysis indicates that many landslip movements were triggered off during periods of increasing rainfall, as in the late Boreal period and the beginning of the sub Atlantic period (see Table 1) (Franks & Johnson 1964; Johnson 1965b, 124).

In post glacial times, therefore, with drainage possibly less well integrated than it is today on the newly deposited glacial drifts and solifluction deposits, one can envisage the existence of ill drained hollows, particularly on the fringes of the hills and at valley heads. Such conditions may well have existed, for example, in the area around Denshaw in the upper reaches of the Tame valley and in the upper parts of the Colne and its tributary valleys west of Marsden. The significance of these so far as early man was concerned will be discussed later.

In the areas of glacial deposition west of the Pennines there is a considerable

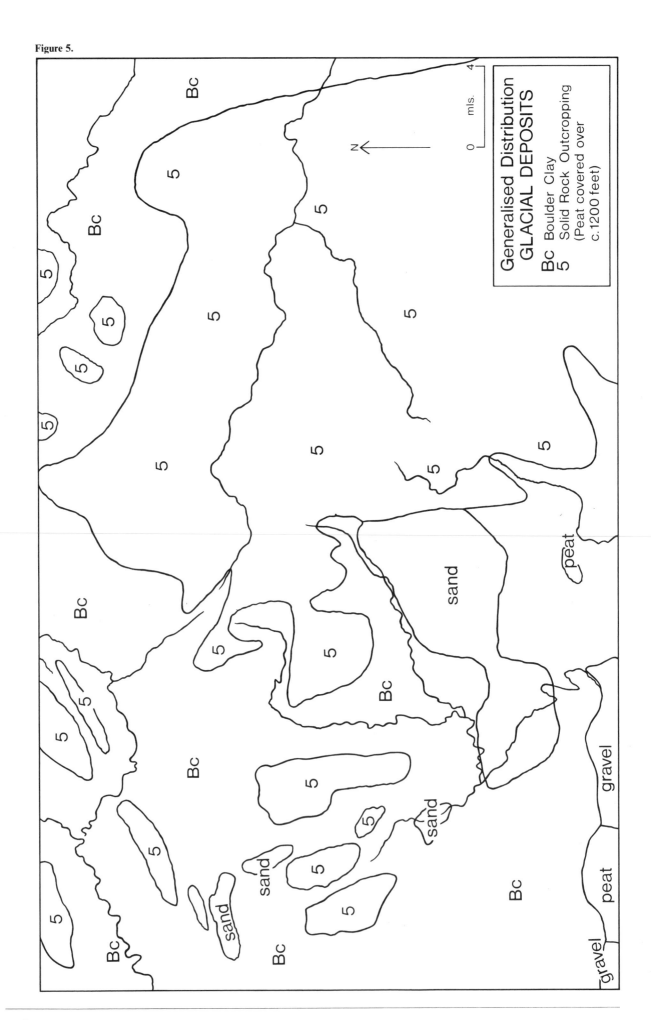

Figure 5.

Generalised Distribution
GLACIAL DEPOSITS

Bc Boulder Clay
5   Solid Rock Outcropping
    (Peat covered over
    c.1200 feet)

N

0   4
mls.

Table 1 Summary of post glacial climatic and environmental changes

Stage	Time (Radiocarbon dating) b.c.	Pollen Zone	Blytt and Sernander Periods	Vegetation Changes (Pennine area)
		VIII	Sub Atlantic	Widespread upland peat formation; clearances on slopes
Flandrian (Post Glacial)	1,000 2,000 3,000	VIIb	Sub Boreal	Increase in ash and birch
	4,000 5,000	VIIa	Atlantic	Increase in alder. Peat formation on higher parts.
	6,000 7,000	VI V	Boreal	Development of mixed oak woodland with hazel and pine.
	8,000	IV	Pre Boreal	Birch and pine
Late Devensian (Late Glacial)	9,000 10,000 11,000	III II I	Upper Dryas Allerød Lower Dryas	Tundra

variation in soil types, ranging from poorly drained, heavy boulder clays and areas of raised bog, to lighter, more freely drained sandy areas (Fig. 5). The fluvio-glacial sands which sometimes cover the boulder clay deposits in the Manchester area have already been mentioned. Of particular significance so far as prehistoric settlement was concerned were the coarse, sandy soils which often mantle the sides of the main valleys, such as that of the Irwell in the Radcliffe and Kearsley areas and the Ribble at Hurst Green (Hall & Folland 1970, 107), and the fluvio-glacial gravels which occur in the Bolton area, amongst others (Tonks et al 1931, 183–4). Generally speaking, however, one can regard much of the lowland area as being relatively poorly drained and covered with scrub, forest, bog or marsh throughout much of the prehistoric period. The plateau summits and flatter watershed areas in the Pennines are peat covered at the present day, and the development of blanket bog in these areas will be discussed in more detail later. On the lower Millstone Grit foothills on both sides of the Pennines, soils over the gritstones are shallower and drier than those over the shales which weather to a heavy, impervious clay; both are deficient in mineral bases, however, and tend to sourness. Very mixed soils occur east of the Pennines, with considerable areas of light, well drained soils derived from the Coal Measure sandstones, and much heavier and poorly drained soils on the shales (Holliday 1967, 67; Carroll et al 1979).

The primary watershed of England is well defined by the main Pennine ridge (Fig. 3). On the western side, the Rossendale Uplands divide the Ribble and Mersey/Irwell drainage basins. The eastern slopes of the Pennines are drained mainly by the Rivers Aire and Calder and their tributaries. Valleys everywhere in the uplands are deeply incised into the plateau surfaces, particularly where, like that of the Yorkshire Calder, they were considerably over deepened by the action of flood waters escaping from melting ice. The watershed was breached by these meltwaters, forming the deep gorges at Cliviger and Walsden at the head of the Yorkshire Calder valley in the Todmorden area, later providing convenient routeways through the hills. The easiest crossing of the Pennines, however, is just to the north of our area where, between the Ribble and the Aire valleys, the Pennine divide is at a lower level, about 425 feet O.D., than at any other point along its entire length. Other crossings of the hills – later exploited by packhorse roads and turnpike roads – are those at Blackstone Edge, Standedge and Woodhead, all around 1,200 feet O.D., and the significance of these will be discussed later. What is noticeable is that, although the upland area is easily penetrated from the east and west, movement in a north-south direction is much more difficult, against the grain of the relief and often across high, inhospitable plateau areas.

A useful division of the Central Pennines into altitudinal zones was suggested by

Woodhead (1931, 17–18). He described three such zones, each characterised by particular types of scenery and vegetation. They were the summit plateaux at altitudes over 1,200 feet; the foothills and spurs between 600 and 1,200 feet; and the valleys and lowlands below 600 feet (Fig. 3). As will emerge later, each of these zones has exerted its own peculiar influence, at times hostile to man but at other times favourable, both during prehistoric and more recent times.

Climatic contrasts between upland and lowland at the present day rest on rainfall rather than temperature. Mean monthly temperatures are only a few degrees lower at upland stations, but there is a steep precipitation gradient against the hill flanks, particularly on the western side which stands in the path of wet Atlantic airstreams (Freeman *et al* 1966, 22–3). Over most of the Lancashire lowlands the rainfall average is between 32 and 36 inches, but on the ascent to the moorland plateaux of the Pennines and the Rossendale Uplands, rainfall totals rapidly increase: the 40 and 45 inch isohyets follow the lower slopes of the fells, and on the summits totals of 60 or even 70 inches are recorded, although some valleys are deep enough to be local rain shadows, with totals as low as 40 inches. It is on the eastern flanks of the hills, however, that rain shadow conditions are most effective. The Huddersfield–Halifax area averages 39 inches while the Dewsbury–Leeds district, in the extreme eastern sector of our area, experiences averages as low as 25 to 27 inches. Possibly of greater significance is the frequency of rainfall rather than its duration (Crowe 1962, 29). The number of 'days with rain' tends to be greater in the hills and on their western flanks than in the eastern side of the area, and closely allied to this, of course, is the incidence of cloud and total amount of sunshine recorded by any one station. Generally speaking, at altitudes above 750 feet climatic conditions are very precarious for cereals at present; there are difficulties in ripening due to the length of the growing season and cloudiness, not to mention the adverse effects of the high percipitation. It is at these altitudes then that land use has always been most sensitive to climatic change (see also Hawke-Smith 1979, 72).

Thus environmentally speaking, while there are obvious contrasts between the upland and lowland parts of the Central Pennine area, there are also important differences between the lowlands and foothills east and west of the Pennines respectively, and these differences played significant roles in prehistoric times.

Chapter Three
Mesolithic Evidence

Introduction

Although the improvement in climate at the end of the last Ice Age commenced as early as 14,000 b.c., the amelioration continued for a long time into the Flandrian (or post glacial) period (Table 1). Initially, at the end of the Ice Age, there would have been remnant snow patches lingering on in sheltered hollows in the Pennines, but after about 8,300 b.c. these would have disappeared. It was between this time and around 5,000 b.c. – the earlier part of the Mesolithic period – that the major modifications in climate occurred, though it was the consequent changes in vegetation and fauna which were of greater significance to man than the actual temperature changes.

During the early Boreal period temperatures were still rising sharply and the climate became drier and more continental. It may be inferred that the altitudinal variations in temperature were less apparent, with a consequent reduction in habitat contrasts between lowlands and uplands at this time, though this would be countered to some extent by longer winters (Taylor 1975, 12). The later part of the Mesolithic coincided with the Atlantic period. Rainfall was then some 11 % above present day levels, while average temperatures were approximately 2–3°C above those of today (Taylor 1975, 313). This was the 'climatic optimum', although the lowlands and sheltered valley sites were probably favoured. In the uplands the higher rainfall would have been amplified by years with totals 25 % or even 50 % above average, while the effect of altitude upon temperatures would have hindered evaporation, summer temperatures in the uplands being up to 2°C lower on average than those of the lowlands (Simmons 1979, 113).

The crucial effect of these climatic changes was the replacement of open tundra by forests, ultimately to considerable altitudes in the uplands. Changes in food supplies resulted in radical changes in the types of animal population. Open country forms disappeared, apparently abruptly in most cases, and were replaced by woodland species such as red and roe deer, elk, auroch and wild pig. It has often been pointed out (eg Mellars 1974, 80) that the biomass (the overall density of the animal population) in forested areas is much less than that of open environments, and that forest species are also less gregarious in their habits. Thus the easily culled herds of reindeer, for example, were replaced by a more diffuse population of red deer and aurochs in particular, animals which were far less receptive to man's presence and thus less easy to exploit. A greater range of animals existed, however, including a whole variety of aquatic creatures, birds, and large and small mammals. There was also a more varied plant diet for both man and his prey.

The increasing rainfall of later Mesolithic times also had important consequences so far as soil and vegetation in the uplands were concerned, and an outline of these will be given later. The increasing oceanity in the climate was exacerbated by rising sea levels which finally insulated Britain and reached their maximum in late Atlantic times. Estuarine habitats extended a considerable distance inland, particularly along the lower parts of the Mersey and Ribble valleys, and perhaps offered richer subsistence opportunities for gatherers and fishermen.

Faced with all these environmental changes, man widened his range in the food quest during the Mesolithic period and in the process developed new tools and weapons.

Archaeological Evidence

Evidence of man's presence in the Central Pennines during the first five millennia of post glacial times consists almost solely of small, usually discrete, scatters of flints: their discovery about one hundred years ago has been described in the Introduction. Although wood and bone must also have been used, their relative

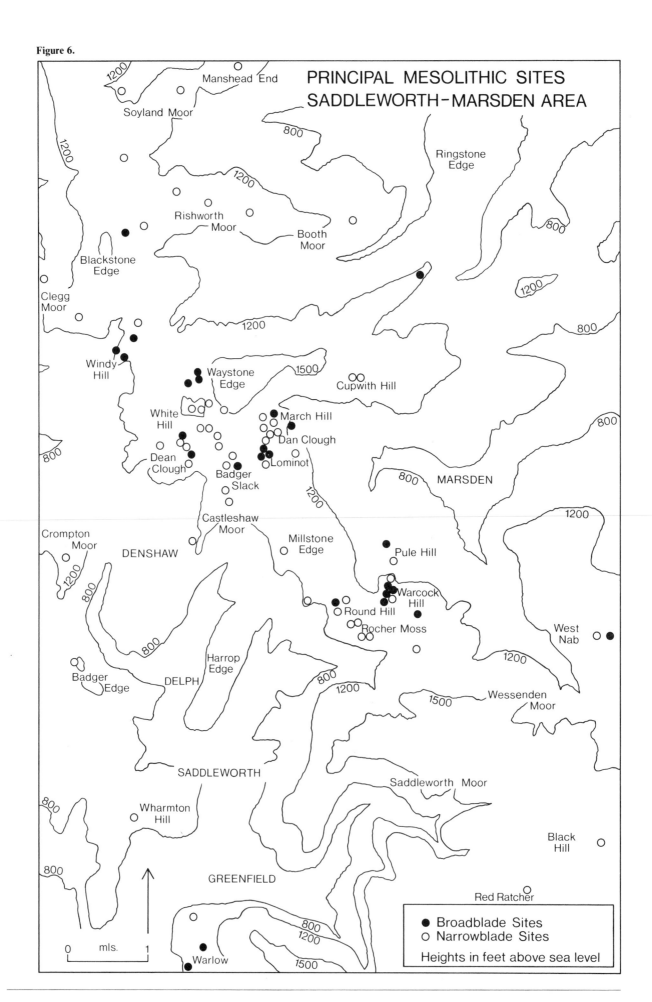

Figure 6.

PRINCIPAL MESOLITHIC SITES
SADDLEWORTH–MARSDEN AREA

Manshead End

Soyland Moor

Ringstone Edge

1200

800

1200

Rishworth Moor

Booth Moor

Blackstone Edge

1200

Clegg Moor

800

1200

800

Windy Hill

Waystone Edge

1500

Cupwith Hill

White Hill

March Hill

Dan Clough

Dean Clough

Lominot

800

MARSDEN

Badger Slack

Castleshaw Moor

1200

1200

Crompton Moor

DENSHAW

Millstone Edge

Pule Hill

Warcock Hill

1200

1500

800

Round Hill

Rocher Moss

West Nab

800

Badger Edge

DELPH

Harrop Edge

800

1200

1500

Wessenden Moor

SADDLEWORTH

Saddleworth Moor

800

Wharmton Hill

Black Hill

800

GREENFIELD

Red Ratcher

800

800
1200

• Broadblade Sites
○ Narrowblade Sites

Warlow

1500

Heights in feet above sea level

0   mls.   1

importance is unknown due to man's occupation of open sites where exposure would accelerate the decay of organic material. The ultimate disappearance of this material was ensured by subsequent peat accumulation on top of the flint sites. Thus the quantity of evidence is small: only the lithic component of material culture survives, and perhaps only an incomplete aspect of that component.

More than 540 sites have been recorded above 1,200 feet O.D. in the Central and Southern Pennines: this may well be an underestimate (Jacobi *et al* 1976, 308), while many more await discovery. They are concentrated in slightly less than 12% (152 square miles) of the study area (which totals 1,290 square miles). They occur in greatest numbers on the moors of the Pennine watershed between Saddleworth and Marsden (Fig. 6). Outside this 'core' area, upland sites have been found to the west on the Rossendale moors (eg Garstang 1906, 215; Baldwin 1903), to the north on the moorlands east of Burnley and north of Calderdale (eg Deans 1933; Leach 1951; Watson 1952, 30–5), and on Rombalds Moor which overlaps the northern perimeter of our area (Cowling 1946, Plate V) (Fig. 7). Further north still, outlying sites have been explored at Malham (Raistrick & Holmes 1963, 75), Blubberhouses Moor (Davies 1963b) and Grassington (Walker 1956). In the South Pennines, Mesolithic sites occur on the north eastern gritstone fringes of the Peak District (eg Radley & Marshall 1963), though none has been recorded on the western side. While finds from the limestone area of the Peak District are scanty (Manby 1962), and few working floors have been discovered (Radley 1968b), parts of this district were exploited as sources of raw material – chert – and this aspect will be discussed later.

It must be noted that important and significant sites occur at lower altitudes on the flanks of the Pennines, one near Charlestown in the Aire valley at Baildon (SE 165388) (Fig. 7) being explored at the time of writing (1978). Outside the immediate area under discussion here, intermediate 'foothill' localities have been found between the uplands proper and the lowlands to the east. These include excavated sites on the valley slopes of the Don at Deepcar (Radley & Mellars 1964) and the Drone at Unstone (Courtney 1978 and 1979), and surface scatters such as those at Woolley Edge overlooking the River Calder south west of Wakefield. Then there are a few valley bottom sites as at Otley in Wharfedale (Cowling & Stickland 1947; Cowling 1973), near the Calder in the Wakefield area (Walker 1935 and 1939, 6), to the east of Sheffield in the Rother valley (Radley & Mellars 1963; Radley 1964), and in the Don valley at Cadeby (*YAJ* 1979, 1). Eastwards again, beyond these 'foothill' sites, Mesolithic material has been recovered from Misterton Carr near the southern end of Hatfield Chase, a site located between the Pennines and Lincoln Edge (Buckland & Dolby 1973) (Fig. 2).

To the west of the Pennines such intermediate and lowland sites are rarer. Mesolithic flints have been found on the sandstone scarp of Alderley Edge (Varley 1932, 51; Varley 1964, 21), and just within our area on the sands and gravels in the Manchester area (Garstang 1906, 215) and in the Irwell valley at Radcliffe (Spencer 1950–1) (Fig. 7).

It has been mentioned already that the most noted area in the uplands proper is that on the Marsden and Saddleworth moors (Fig. 6), which has been scoured for over a century by collectors of flints. Indeed, all the moorland areas of the Central Pennines have been examined in this way. Such continuing interest may have created a bias so far as the occurrence of flints is concerned compared with areas further north or south, but the high gritstone moors of Bleaklow and Kinder Scout to the south have so far produced only a few traces of Mesolithic occupation (Manby 1962, 16; Radley 1963b), while areas to the north are likewise less prolific. Thus there does appear to be a valid and marked concentration of Mesolithic sites in the upland area between Saddleworth and Marsden where the Central Pennines are at their narrowest, the area above 1,200 feet O.D. being little more than half a mile in width on Standedge (SE 020097) where the watershed reaches no more than 1,270 feet above sea level. A subsidiary cluster of sites occurs north west of Sheffield (just outside our area) at one end of the Woodhead crossing of the Pennines, and it is tempting to match these with the Tintwistle Low Moor sites at its western end (Fig. 7).

It is possibly, however, that Mesolithic site records for the uplands might be

Figure 7.

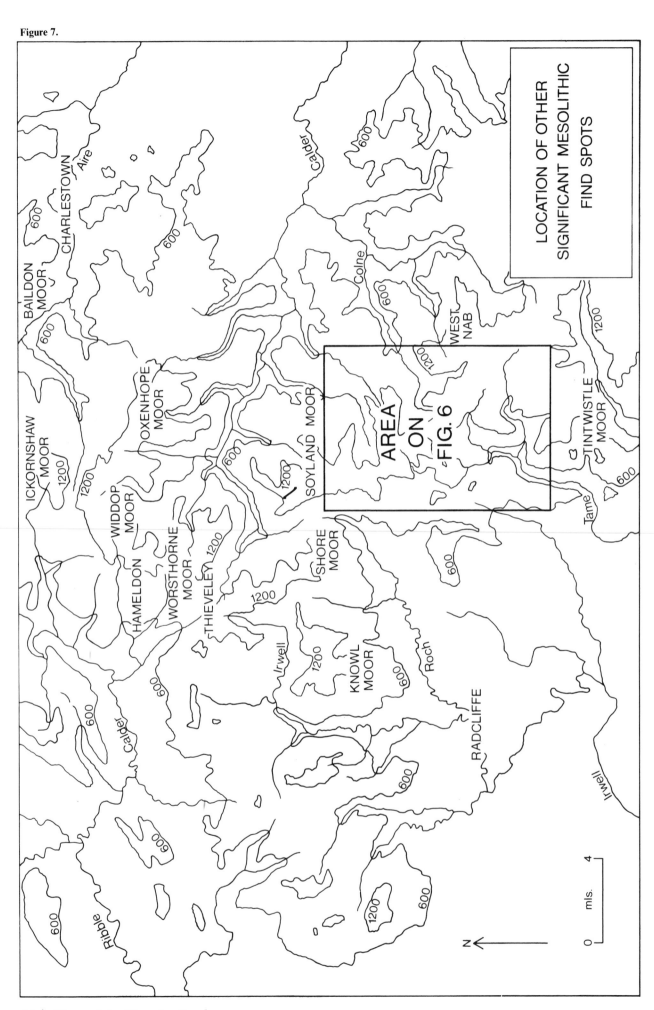

LOCATION OF OTHER SIGNIFICANT MESOLITHIC FIND SPOTS

AREA ON FIG. 6

artificially inflated compared with those for the lowlands. Artefacts in the Central Pennines are invariably found within the mineral soil underlying the peat, and here inevitably their chances of preservation are enhanced compared with lowland sites where disturbance of the soil has occurred. Moreover the chances of finding artefacts are greatly increased wherever erosion has removed the peat cover on the uplands, and peat erosion is widespread in the Central Pennines. There is, however, no simple relationship between the extent of this erosion and the discovery of Mesolithic sites: some moorland areas, such as the south facing side of Dean Clough at 1,400 feet O.D., have flint scatters associated with virtually every erosion patch, while others, like those of the Greenfield area, have very few or none at all. The reasons for this contrast are to be found possibly in differences between their hinterlands (both to the east and west), their altitude and topography. Furthermore, although peat erosion is widespread down to 1,000 feet O.D. on all these Pennine moors, find spots are numerous only above 1,200 feet O.D. At the highest altitudes, where peat erosion is often most severe, few Mesolithic sites have been recorded. Some of the higher spurs projecting westwards from the main watershed (Fig. 6), such as Harrop Edge (SD 9908), Badger Edge (SD 9707) and Wharmton (SD 9805), have proved to have very few flints though they might have been expected to have yielded more, as Crompton Moor (SD 9610) has done, and this may be accounted for by their enclosure and agricultural use. Similarly many lowland sites have probably been destroyed in the past. Thus there is no denying the very considerable number of sites at altitudes over 1,000 feet in the Pennines. Jacobi recorded over 900 find spots above this height, giving an 'overall density of 2.1 per 10 sq. km.' (Jacobi *et al* 1976, 310). Following Simmons (1975) it was calculated that the Central Pennine uplands could only have supported about 25 hunting groups at any one time (Jacobi *et al* 1976, 310).

It is noticeable that in the Central Pennines Mesloithic sites rarely occur singly; they tend to occur in groups, sometimes of more than 50 find spots on a single hillside, as in the Dean Clough/White Hill area (Fig. 6), or sometimes smaller clusters as at Buckley's Warcock Hill North and Badger Slack sites. Elsewhere to the north and south (Davies 1941–3; Radley & Marshall 1963, 95) sites seem to be more widely scattered and few are of any real significance. Their location is similar, however, to those of the Central Pennine sites, off summit hillocks and ridges and sunny slopes between 1,200 and 1,500 feet being favoured; sheltered localities overlooking spring heads or damp hollows which would be attractive to wild animals. Very occasionally 'caves' or shelters between large boulders on rocky hilltops or edges were utilised. On West Nab near Meltham waste flints and blades struck from a single core were found in such a location, while flint implements were found at 1,500 feet O.D. in a cave among large boulders overlooking the Widdop valley, north of Calderdale (Wilkinson 1911a).

As early workers soon realised, these working floors are sharply defined, and there is seldom an indefinite scattering of flint over a wide area (Buckley 1921, 5). This distribution gave rise to the idea of circular emplacements or camping sites, particularly since 'fire pits' and hearths were found on the same spots. On Warcock Hill, for example, Buckley found in one place traces of what seemed to him to indicate a group of four shelters, represented by circular clusters of worked flints, each occupying about four square yards, and in another place a single cluster with a shallow fire pit nearby. At the Badger Slack site he found a litter of burnt birch and ling overlying such a cluster of flints, suggesting the remains of an actual shelter (Buckley 1923; Clark & Rankine 1939, 104). Hearths are recorded regularly on almost all workshop sites, together with burnt flints or with flints focused upon them (eg Radley & Mellars 1964, 6; Radley *et al* 1974, 3–9; Stonehouse 1972, 36; Stonehouse 1976, 15; *LAS* 1976), possibly suggesting the working of flint with the aid of fire. Buckley found three fire pits in a line on Warcock Hill, each about four inches deep, dug into the shale bedrock and containing charcoal (Fig. 8); another example occurred on March Hill Site 2 (Mss. 1924). At the time of writing (1978), a very fine example of hearth is being excavated on the upper slopes of Dan Clough, just to the south of March Hill. Marking its edges are slabs of gritstone which appear to have been deliberately

Figure 8. Francis Buckley's notes on his excavations of Mesolithic Sites on Warcock Hill, near Marsden. (page 18 of Drawing Book 9, reproduced by permission of the Curator, Tolson Memorial Museum, Huddersfield).

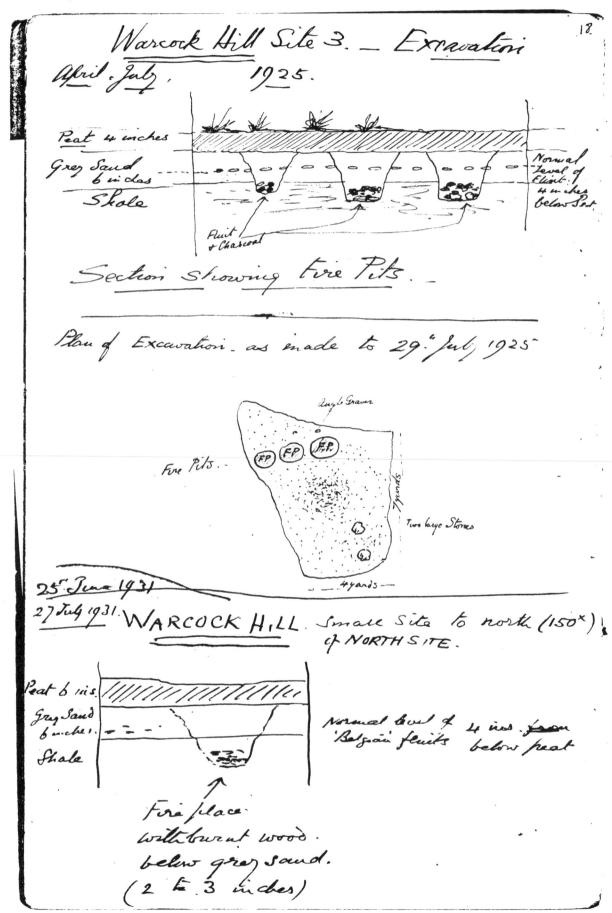

placed there, and again there is a close scatter of flints, some burnt. Although the nature of the peat cover has led to a dearth of obvious structures associated with the hearths, the slight evidence that has been found does suggest that these sites were the temporary shelters where flints were prepared. The comparative lack of 'domestic tools' – in particular scrapers, and also burins – indicates that these were hunting camps rather than true occupation sites where skins might be processed and bone and antler worked. The evidence includes stake holes at Broomhead Moor 5, some with wedging stones and carbonised wood fragments, and at the same site one area had been purposely cleared of stones while another had crude paving – the latter feature also being found at Dunford Bridge A and Sheldon (Radley *et al* 1974, 3; Radley 1968b, 29). No post holes were found at Deepcar, though it is possible that posts were wedged among a roughly circular arrangement of stones, which coincided with the maximum flint density (Radley & Mellars 1964, 5–7). These posts might have supported a wind break. Evidence of similar crude structures is also suggested at Unstone (Courtney 1978). In our area, a stone structure forming an arc with flint assemblages within and a hearth outside has been excavated at Rishworth Drain 2 (*LAS* 1976).

Thus sizes of sites vary considerably; most are small and were occupied perhaps only for a single season; some are larger, possibly having been revisited several times, like the famous sites on March Hill, White Hill, Warcock Hill and other localities on the Saddleworth–Marsden moors, although it is suggested that careful excavation may reveal that these represent the conflation of a number of 'residential units' (Jacobi 1978b, 325), the result of a single occupation by a number of groups. Recent excavations at Unstone in Eastern Derbyshire have demonstrated a multi-phase occupation separated by short periods of abandonment, each lasting possibly only a few years (Courtney 1978).

The stone implements prepared at these upland sites were projectile heads of various forms, evolving into more diverse forms as time progressed. Thus earlier Mesolithic assemblages are characterised by comparatively large, simple forms representing for the most part the tips and barbs of wooden arrows. Some of the smaller, geometric artefacts of the later Mesolithic may represent insets for barbed spearheads of a character similar to those which were manufactured earlier from bone and antler, and which they may well have replaced (Mellars 1976b, 396). In this respect Francis Buckley's excavation of 'a row of 35 flints in a straight line (like the teeth of a saw) and occurring at intervals of 1½ to 2 inches' on the southern slopes of White Hill led to suggestions that they represented the barbs inset into a wooden shaft, the latter having perished in the acidic conditions (Petch 1924, 29; Buckley Mss. 1923). Although doubts have been cast on the validity of this particular find (Davies 1959b), similar discoveries have been reported from at least two further sites in the vicinity, at Warcock Hill North (Radley & Mellars 1964, 18) and White Hassocks (Stonehouse 1978), and elsewhere (Mellars 1976b, 396). Significantly, they are all related to the small, geometric microliths of later Mesolithic times.

At several sites 'anvil stones' have been recorded, as at Broomhead Moor 5, Dunford Bridge A and Sheldon (Radley *et al* 1974, 3–7; Radley 1968b, 29). One at March Hill was found 'with many pieces of waste and cores packed close against a corner . . . and the rest scattered about on the same side' (Buckley Mss. 1939), and this is now exhibited in the Tolson Memorial Museum, Huddersfield. Hammer stones, often quartzite, have sometimes been found in association with these anvil stones, and occur regularly on microlith find spots. Other remains include 'red ruddle' or 'reddle' (red oxides of various kinds), haematite and graphite. 'Ruddle' was found 'in minute particles on all sites at Dean Clough', while at Warlow Pike 'all the flint sites are covered in it' (Buckley Mss. Drawing Book 1, 34); it was also found on the Warcock Hill North and South sites (Buckley 1924a, 5–7), in the Knowl Moor area (Baldwin 1903, 110; Price 1929–31, 48), and elsewhere. Haematite was recorded, for example, at Manshead and Deepcar (Buckley Mss. 1923; Radley & Mellars 1964, 12), Graphite has been discovered on many sites, including Windy Hill 6 and Dean Clough (Buckley Mss. 1922; Wrigley 1911, 31; Davies 1959a), while on Rough Hill near Wardle (SD 9120) 300 pieces were found within a square yard together with 'ruddle', microliths and barbed-and-tanged arrowheads. The graphite and 'ruddle' showed signs of rubbing as if on a piece of sandstone (Sutcliffe 1896–7). It is significant that the graphite could only have originated from Cumbria, and may, therefore, have Neolithic connotations.

Although there are no finds of animal bones in association with the microliths on the moorlands, evidence from elsewhere in England, including Sheldon in the limestone Peak District where numerous bone fragments were associated with Mesolithic tools (Radley 1968b, 29–31), suggests that red deer formed the principal quarry of the hunters.

Palynological Evidence

In late glacial times an open habitat on the uplands with rather sparse tundra vegetation is suggested, with some localised birch. With the amelioration in climate the lowlands became covered in trees, at first alder and birch, the latter then being replaced by hazel which appears very early in north and west Britain (Taylor 1973). Birch continued longer in the uplands, though possibly hazel scrub was the first to replace the early montane grasslands of the Pennines (Radley *et al* 1974, 13).

During the long period of time spanned by the dated Central Pennine Mesolithic sites (Table 2), large scale vegetational changes were occurring. During the early Boreal period oak, elm and lime developed locally among the resident alder and hazel woodlands on the lowlands, and a more or less closed and continuous forest cover existed there by the start of the Atlantic period (Birks 1963–4; Birks 1965).

In the Pennines the sequence of montane grassland and hazel scrub was followed by deciduous woodland, with birch the main constituent accompanied by hazel. A progressive upward extension of the tree line occurred (to around 2,000 feet in parts of the country) by the end of the Boreal period. The widespread tree remains recorded from beneath the peat – notably birch, but also some pine above 1,200 feet – have been regarded as evidence of this former forest cover, though it is now realised that the highest windswept and rocky areas in the Pennines, as in North Yorkshire (Spratt & Simmons 1976, 197; Jones *et al* 1979, 18), retained a tundra or late glacial vegetation and were never wooded (Tallis 1964, 370; Tallis 1975, 483). The soil at these localities may well have experienced wind erosion during the Boreal period and erosion as a result of increasing rainfall later (Tallis 1964, 370). In all likelihood the woodland of the Pennine uplands was not a closed canopy; high percentages of hazel pollen suggest that this scrub was extensive under relatively open stands of birch, pine not being an important component of the Central Pennine vegetation at the time (Appendix 1). The woodland was densest on the steeper, more sheltered slopes. Oak woodland, too, was advancing at this period, again particularly on the lower slopes and sheltered edges of the uplands, but also on some plateau tops as is demonstrated by the occurrence of oak remains beneath the peat in some parts. This oak woodland may well have extended to higher altitudes to the east of the Pennine watershed (Conway 1947, 158). The increased humidity at the end of Boreal times is marked by a sharp rise in alder, especially at lowland sites and on valley slopes, though alder, too, grew on parts of the summit areas as at Warcock Hill and Dean Clough (Appendix 1), where it has been recorded as buried timber, mostly below 1,200 feet.

In the Pennine uplands the increased rainfall at the Boreal/Atlantic transition (B.A.T.) resulted in the podsolisation or gleying of the immature soils, and *Calluna* and *Sphagnum* began to appear. At the highest sites gleying may have developed rapidly with a speedy change to waterlogged conditions (Tallis 1964, 368–70). Elsewhere changes were slower, with a gradual development of *Calluna* vegetation rather than *Sphagnum*. Formerly it was thought that peat formation in the Central Pennines had begun universally at the B.A.T. (*c.* 5000 B.C.) (Conway 1954), but more recently it has become apparent that there was a wide diversity in the time of the initiation of the upland blanket peats in the area. Hence at the highest altitudes (over 1,700 feet) peat formation did begin at the B.A.T. (Tallis 1964, 371; Radley *et al* 1974, 10), and the absence of tree remains below the peat at these altitudes is taken to mean that this was an entirely natural process: again, the area is comparable to North Yorkshire in this respect (Spratt & Simmons 1976,

197). At lower altitudes (*c*. 1,400 feet) where tree remains are common beneath the peat, the initiation of blanket bog has been dated to after the elm decline, *c*. 3,000 b.c. (Radley *et al* 1974, 10; Bartley 1975, 378). On the lower moors, such as large parts of the Rossendale uplands as well as spurs on both sides of the Pennines, tree remains occur within the basal peat layers. At Holcombe Hill (SD 7716, altitude *c*. 1,100 feet) these have been dated to 1,590 b.c. (Tallis & McGuire 1972, 728). Elsewhere on these lower moors peat formation may have been delayed until later – as late possibly as early medieval times (Eyre 1966, 198ff; Hicks 1971, 12ff; Tallis & McGuire 1972, 730ff). Thus on the flatter, ill drained upland plateaux there was probably an inherent tendency for peat to form at any time from the B.A.T. onwards, once the 'inertia' of the existing forest had been overcome. Destruction of this forest cover followed by peat accumulation could have occurred as a result of progressive waterlogging of the soil subsequent to podsolisation and the development of an impermeable pan layer (the latter being well illustrated in Dean Clough), or it could have resulted from deliberate or accidental woodland clearance.

At sites where microliths have been recorded *in situ* below undisturbed peat, (Appendix 1; Broomhead Moor 5 and Dunford Bridge A, Radley *et al* 1974, 14), pollen analysis demonstrates a rise in the total herbaceous pollen levels – mainly *Calluna* in the upper mineral soil layers in association with flints. This is in sharp contrast to pollen diagrams at 'non microlith' sites where *Calluna* pollen levels are not greatly affected by the onset of peat accumulation. Thus the expansion of *Calluna* near Mesolithic sites immediately prior to the onset of peat accumulation is unconnected with its formation and it probably resulted from soil degradation following the destruction of the forest cover as described above. It is tempting to ascribe this removal to burning by Mesolithic peoples, and the occurrence of charcoal in association with microliths at many sites in the Central Pennines supports this idea.

The onset of blanket peat formation in the area had little immediate effect on the extent of the forest cover (Jacobi *et al* 1976, 313) which was by no means continuous over 1,400 feet in any case. The palynological evidence from the Pennines (as well as from North Yorkshire and Dartmoor) suggests, therefore, a sharp disjunction in the vegetation cover of the area during the late Boreal and throughout the Atlantic period between 1,200 and 1,400 feet: while the climatically determined tree line in the uplands in places was around 2,000 feet, in this area the tree line in later Mesolithic times was well below the climatically feasible limit, and an upper level of the forest between 1,000 and 1,200 was more characteristic. The implications of this will be discussed later. The Mesolithic inhabitants at this time, therefore, may have lived in an open forest and scrub environment dominated by hazel and birch with herbaceous communities – perhaps dominated by *Molinia* (Conway 1954, 126) – on the shallow peats of the flatter areas.

Dating and Flint Typology
The microliths invariably occur below the peat, either *in situ* (within the 'grey sand' layer as Buckley consistently notes (eg Fig. 8), and, on occasions, mixed with frequent tree remains), or exposed on the surface after the peat has been eroded away. Thus they predate the formation of the blanket bog, but it is difficult to say by how long since the peat may not rest conformably on the mineral soil. Such would be the case, for example, if wind erosion had occurred, or, more significantly, if the Mesolithic occupation of a site had been accompanied by burning of the vegetation and surface humus layers (Smith 1970, 81). The dating of Mesolithic sites in the Central Pennines from pollen data, therefore, requires consideration of the uppermost soil horizon below the microliths as well as of the overlying peat. Even if the relationship between the microlith-bearing soil and peat is conformable, the time which elapsed between the abandonment of a site and its protection by peat formation is unknown, but it is sufficient for most of the artefacts which might have been dated by radiocarbon methods to have been destroyed (Switsur & Jacobi 1975, 32).

Table 2 summarises the radiocarbon dates for the Central Pennine Mesolithic sites, together with others for comparison. The Central Pennine examples are all from

Table 2 Some Radiocarbon dates for Mesolithic Sites

Site	Characteristics	Lab. No.	Date b.c.
Central Pennines			
Lominot III	Broad Blade	Q1187	7,615 ± 470
Waystone Edge	Broad Blade	Q1300	7,446 ± 210
Warcock Hill S	Broad Blade	Q1185	7,260 ± 340
Warcock Hill III	March Hill Type	Q789	6,660 ± 110
Broomhead Moor V	March Hill Type	Q800	6,620 ± 110
Ickornshaw	(Geometric)	Q707	6,150 ± 150
Dean Clough	March Hill Type	(unpublished)	5,645 ± 140
Rishworth Drain 2	March Hill Type	Q1166	5,600 ± 210
March Hill II	March Hill Type	Q1188	4,070 ± 220
March Hill II	March Hill Type	Q788	3,900 ± 80
Rocher Moss S 2	Rod Dominated	Q1190	3,880 ± 100
Lominot IV	March Hill Type	Q1189	3,660 ± 120
Dunford Bridge B	Rod Dominated	Q799	3,430 ± 80
Others			
Thatcham Site III	Maglemosian	Q659	8,415 ± 170
Star Carr	Maglemosian	Q14	7,607 ± 210
Star Carr	Maglemosian	C353	7,538 ± 350
Thatcham Site V	Maglemosian	Q652	7,530 ± 160
Money Howe Site I	Maglemosian	Q1560	7,480 ± 390
Marsh Benham	Maglemosian	Q1129	7,350 ± 150
Filpoke Beacon	Geometric	Q1474	6,810 ± 140
Stump Cross	Accuracy questioned	Q141	6,500 ± 310
Morton Site A T46	Non-Geometric	NZ1191	6,100 ± 255

charcoal samples from hearths, six of them from Buckley sites, the analysis being on charcoal collected by him in the 1920s and stored until recently in the Tolson Memorial Museum, Huddersfield. The reliability of these dates, based on charcoal collected so long ago, has been questioned recently (Bonsall 1975, 306–7).

Jacobi suggests that the Mesolithic occupation of southern England was earlier by some 500 to 700 years than the earliest dated Mesolithic site in the north, and that this occupation (at Thatcham in Berkshire) was associated with hunting a woodland or woodland margin fauna of *Bos*, red deer and pig. In contrast, evidence from the Creswell and Anston Caves suggests that occupations in the North contemporary with the Thatcham earlier Maglemosian maintained a technology more characteristic of late glacial times, still associated with reindeer hunting (Jacobi 1978b, 298–301). This may be linked with the markedly more open environment of the north, and only later with the establishment of a woodland cover did groups using a Maglemosian technology begin to visit northern England.

The current dating evidence suggests that the British Mesolithic can be divided into two major phases (Mellars 1974, 81ff), with the transition between the 'earlier' and 'later' phases occurring comparatively abruptly around 6,500 b.c. – or perhaps as early as 6,800 b.c. in northern England (Jacobi 1976, 71) – in the middle of the Boreal period (ie when the major components of 'mixed oak forest' were beginning to become conspicuous). The earlier phase was characterised by microliths of non geometric form and comprises industries belonging to the North European 'Maglemosian technocomplex'. The later phase featured the introduction of a greater and more specialised range of smaller geometric microlithic forms, which are briefly described below. In the upland areas of the Central Pennines these two stages are represented by Buckley's 'broad blade' and 'narrow blade' industries respectively (Radley & Mellars 1964, 19ff; Mellars 1973, 15). Although this terminology may be thought of as potentially confusing (Pitts & Jacobi 1979, 166), the descriptions 'broad' and 'narrow' have been so well used with regard to the Pennine industries that they will be used here. From the dates which are available (Table 2) their relative ages can be suggested. A much greater number of narrow blade sites exists, indicating possibly the growth of population during the Mesolithic or, alternatively, internal expansion due to rising sea levels (Jacobi 1976).

The broad blade industry, now recognised from more than 100 locations in the Central Pennines (Jacobi 1978b, 295), was dominated by the manufacture of simple, obliquely blunted points (often retouched on the leading edge) with rarer elongated isosceles triangles and convex-backed blades. Radley and Mellars (1964,

19–20) pointed out the 'Maglemosian affinities' of this group, comparing the content of these upland sites with Deepcar, Thatcham, Colne Valley and Broxbourne, and this is confirmed by the radiocarbon date of 7,615±470 b.c. for Lominot III, as well as by computer cluster analysis (Switsur & Jacobi 1975, 33). The industry is also comparable with Maglemosian sites in the south west (Wainwright 1960).

Of the three early or 'broad blade' sites in the Central Pennines, Lominot III consisted of 'one or two round emplacements' (Petch 1924, 25) on the eastern side of the hill, which were excavated by Buckley in 1924. This excavation produced 34 microliths, end scrapers and awls, 90.9% of the raw material being white flint. Similar material has also been found on other typologically similar sites from both upland and lowland areas (eg Radley & Mellars 1964, 18) and the date agrees closely with determinations from Thatcham and Marsh Benham (Switsur & Jacobi 1975, 33).

The second early site to be dated, Warcock Hill South, differs markedly from the other upland broad blade sites in the shortness and relative width of the microliths, the absence of convex-backed points and points retouched on the leading edge, and in its raw materials (Radley & Mellars 1964, 20–1). Excavated from within an area of four square yards, the industry was based on translucent grey, black or honey-coloured flints which resemble those of Star Carr and Flixton Site I with which it also links statistically, forming a cluster distinct from that which includes the sites mentioned earlier (Switsur & Jacobi 1975, 33; Jacobi 1978b, 304–5). A radiocarbon date of 7,260±340 b.c. agrees with those from Star Carr, and Switsur & Jacobi suggest that Warcock Hill South might be contemporary with Flixton Site I, the occupation of which continued into the early Boreal period.

A third early site on Waystone Edge has been dated to 7,446±210 b.c. Only a preliminary description has yet been published, with no details of the flint assemblages (*LAS* 1976, 8).

The typological diversity of Buckley's narrow blade industries has been discussed by Radley (Radley *et al* 1974, 1). He divided these later Mesolithic sites into three distinct groups, each distinguished both typologically and by the proportions of the raw materials used (see also Switsur & Jacobi 1975, 33). The largest group, dominated by small scalene triangles – Switsur & Jacobi's 'March Hill' type – is represented, for example, by Buckley's assemblages from March Hill (eg Fig. 9) and Windy Hill Site 5, and by the Dunford Bridge A and Broomhead Moor 5 sites. This group is known from both upland and lowland locations in the Pennines, Cleveland Hills and North Lincolnshire, and along the Durham and Cumberland coasts (Switsur & Jacobi 1975, 33). The second group, dominated by straight rod-like microliths, blunted along one or two sides, is known only from high ground in the Pennines and Clevelands. In the Central Pennines it is represented by the assemblages from Buckley's Rocher Moss 1, Dean Clough and Warcock Hill 4 sites, as well as by Dunford Bridge B. The third group, with many trapezoids, is known in northern England only from two or three sites, all undated – at Buckley's White Hill North site, and at Red Ratcher (Stonehouse 1976) both in the Central Pennines, and at Beeley Moor in North Derbyshire (Radley *et al* 1974, 1).

The first two of these narrow blade groups are confined to northern England, and all three lack the 'Horsham' points characteristic of sites in south eastern England. Radiocarbon dates for the March Hill type of industry cover three millennia. One of the earliest, which comes from charcoal from three 'fire pits' excavated by Buckley, is 6,660±110 b.c. from Warcock Hill III, and is connected with a circular concentration of chert chippings including only a small number of triangular microliths. This date is identical to Broomhead Moor 5 and together they represent two of the earliest known dates for later Mesolithic type industries in Britain (Jacobi 1976, 71) agreeing closely with the earliest appearance of small scalene triangles in mainland Europe (Switsur & Jacobi 1975, 33). Some charcoal was excavated from a hearth (Rocher Moss South 2) in an easterly extension of Rocher Moss South I (Stonehouse 1972). The site also yielded 35 rod-like microliths but no scalene triangles of March Hill type. This charcoal gave a date of

Figure 9. Francis Buckley's drawings of flint implements from March Hill, near Marsden. (page 11 of Drawing Book 4, reproduced by permission of the Curator, Tolson Memorial Museum, Huddersfield).

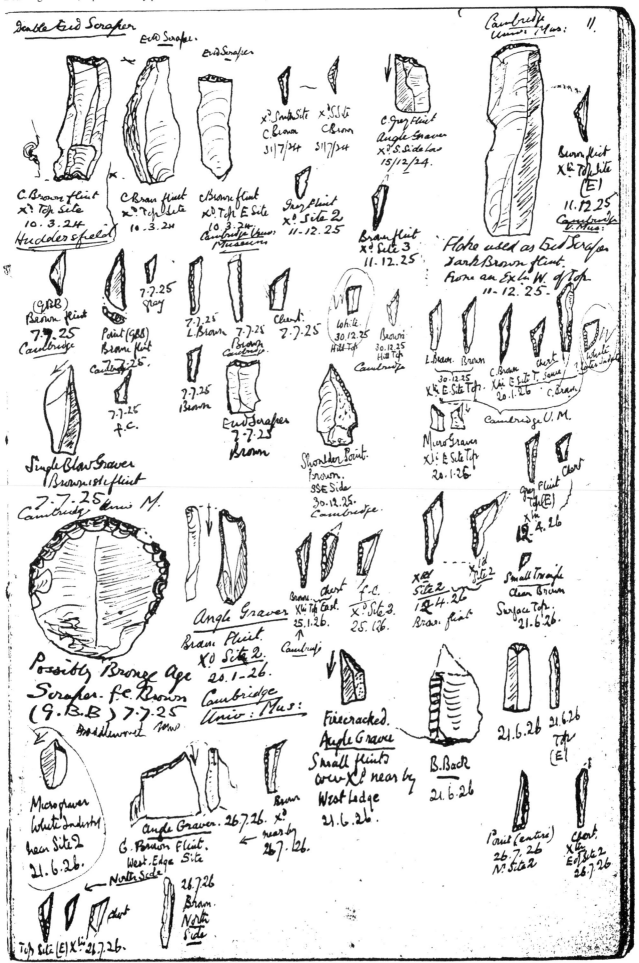

3,880 ± 100 b.c. which along with a date associated with a similar industry at Dunford Bridge B would suggest a date late in the Mesolithic for 'rod microlithic' industries of this type (Switsur & Jacobi 1975, 33).

Thus the radiocarbon evidence from the Pennines indicates that simple broad blade microlithic industries identical to those of Thatcham and Star Carr precede narrow blade industries, which appear before 6,500 b.c., and persist until the end of the Mesolithic. The chronological relationship between these two industries has not yet been established by true stratigraphy in the mineral soil beneath the peat. Woodhead (1929, 15) tried to use the depth of the flints in the soil as an indication of their age, and constructed a composite section to illustrate this, based on the Warcock Hill finds. But, as Manby (1962, 20) points out, this section is meaningless, as it is composed of unassociated finds made some distance apart.

Of particular interest is the fact that the distinction between broad and narrow blade industries is reflected not only in the typology of the microliths but also in the raw materials used. Thus two varieties of flint occur. Broad blade assemblages were manufactured almost entirely from white or grey flint. Radley and Marshall (1963, 92) point out that the white coloration was not produced chemically on the sites and that the peculiar nature of this flint has simplified the search for its origin. White flint occurs in the Middle and Lower Chalk of Flamborough Head, North Lincolnshire and other inland parts of the wolds, and it is also found in boulder clays on Spurn Head and as beach material from the Yorkshire coast. Examination of Maglemosian sites in the Pennines has demonstrated that most of the cortex remains showed a pebble origin and could, therefore, be from the Yorkshire coast (Radley & Marshall 1964, 401). Jacobi points out that the proportions of this white flint on these Pennine sites (between 80% and 99%) are as high as those on sites adjacent to the flint sources (Jacobi 1978b, 304), the implication being that this type of flint was either more highly favoured or more easily acquired by the manufacturers of these broad blade implements.

There is no evidence that this white flint formed an important component of assemblages after this time in the area. The narrow blade industries were generally worked in better quality translucent flint (Buckley 1922; Radley & Mellars 1964, 18), usually brown or deep grey in colour. This flint occurs in drift on the Yorkshire coast, and examples with a pebble origin have been found, for example, at Dunford Bridge Site A – though some at the same site had been quarried, evidence coming from the milky chalk adhering to some pieces (Radley et al 1974, 7). There is much evidence to show that the use of chert increased as time progressed.

Hallan (1960, 52–3) points out that flint sometimes occurs in North Western Drift, presumably originating from Antrim; it is found particularly on the Furness coast, though it may have been available, too, on the 'old' Lancashire coast prior to submergence. But these occurrences are so limited and unreliable that they are unlikely to have compared in importance with such certain sources as those of east Yorkshire, particularly as flint does not occur in the boulders clays in the immediate vicinity of the Central Pennines.

Radley (1968b, 31–3) has examined the use of chert as a raw material on Mesolithic sites in the South Pennines, and discovered that there were at least five varieties of chert available from local Pennine limestones. In many respects chert was inferior to flint, though obviously it had its uses, and the most superior type – a black chert from Derbyshire, found for example, along the north facing slopes of the Wye valley – was at its best almost as good as a good flint. Other varieties of chert came from the Carboniferous limestone areas of the Pennines, the most significant being a brown chert from the Yorkshire Dales (pieces of which were found, for example, at Deepcar), and a shiny grey chert, sometimes translucent enough to be called 'flinty-chert', with a possible source in Upper Wharfedale. Black chert from the Peak District occurs on many sites in the Central Pennines, at least as far north as Rishworth Moor, occasionally making up the entire assemblage or well over 90% of it, as at Rishworth Drain 2 (dated 5,600 ± 210 b.c.), Windy Hill, Brushes Moor, Broomhead Sites 5 and 10, and Arnfield. The 'flinty-chert' was used at Warcock Hill North and Badger Slack (Buckley 1924a; Radley 1968b, 33). In Upper Wharfedale only about 5% of the Mesolithic artifacts were found to be composed of chert, though it was found locally. Thus overall flint was very much preferred, despite having to be brought from a distance. The excess of chert over flint at a site may be due to temporary unavailability of supplies of flint, though it might also reflect different people exploiting different territories. There is another possible reason for the changes in typology and the nature of the material used. The shift in attention from 'broad' to 'narrow' and the increasing use of chert may be seen as being the result of a more careful use of flint, a finite resource if obtained without extensive quarrying, particularly as there was greater pressure on this diminishing resource due to the growth in population. The rising sea level during the earlier part of the Mesolithic would have contributed by submerging many outcrops (Pitts & Jacobi 1979, 174–5).

It has been stated that the distribution of flint types and of specific microlith shapes strongly suggest that the same population inhabited both the Central Pennines and the Lincolnshire lowlands in Mesolithic times, or at least came into contact (Jacobi *et al* 1976, 310). 'Intermediate' sites occur in the area of the Hatfield Marshes (Radley & Marshall 1963, 92; Buckland & Dolby 1973). The distance in a straight line from the early Mesolithic site at Sheffield Hill, north of Scunthorpe on Lincoln Edge (May 1976, 33–5), to the Marsden Moors is 55 miles across what would have been swampy or densely forested tracts in the Thorne and Hatfield Marshes, the Trent lowlands and the Coal Measure foothills (Fig. 2). The distance from the Yorkshire Wolds, on the other hand, across the Vale of York is 60 miles and from the coast near Flamborough Head 80 miles, but an easier routeway – and one much frequented in later prehistoric times – would be provided by the comparatively well drained end moraines of York and Escrick. Thus supplies of flint are just as likely to have come from the Wolds of Yorkshire as they are from Lincolnshire.

The absence of axes on these Maglemosian sites in the Pennines has often been remarked upon, (and comparison might be made with the Bodmin Moor locality of Wainwright (1960, 197)). Isolated finds of tranchet axes in the uplands have, however, been made. One was found in 1936 on the Airedale side of the Pennine watershed on Ickornshaw Moor in the north of our area (341), an unfinished example came from the reservoir on Ringstone Edge in 1923 (287), and a third was located to the north east of the Central Pennine area on Blubberhouses Moor (Davies & Rankine 1960). A further possible tranchet axe has been discovered on the moors at Widdop to the north of Calderdale (339). The presence or at least the use of tranchet axes is also suggested by finds of axe sharpening flakes, and one of these has come from the moorland areas; it was identified in the Buckley Collection at the Tolson Memorial Museum, Huddersfield, and had been picked up on the moors at Tintwistle Knarr in the south of our area (85). Besides these upland examples, tranchet axes and sharpening flakes have also been found in 'intermediate' or valley locations in the Central Pennine area. One such axe was found in 1963 in gravel deposits in the Calder valley near Netherton (411), while another, from just outside our area to the north east, was recovered at Leathley Bridge in the Wharfe valley (Davies 1964). Two axe sharpening flakes have come from valley side sites: one from hill wash deposits in the Calder valley near Mirfield (381) and the other from a possible lake side site at Radcliffe in the Irwell valley (64). None of these finds, however, has any definite relationship to a Mesolithic site, but to the south in the Peak District a probable axe sharpening flake was excavated at Pike Lowe (Radley & Mellars 1964, 20). The absence of axes and some other Maglemosian tools from the uplands may be a reflection of the smallness of the sites or, more likely, the adaptation of the industry to upland habitats.

Discussion

In post glacial times, cultural response to environmental change, although basically a continuation of the Upper Palaeolithic hunting-gathering economy, saw a change in emphasis due to the disappearance of the large herds of late glacial times, changes in equipment as a result of adaptation to forested environments, and a wider ranging food quest (Binford 1968). The restricted range of dates (Table 2) suggests that the Maglemosian occupation of the Central Pennines was restricted to the early post glacial period. Later Mesolithic people must have been present during the period of the maximum extension of the transitional forest communities of pine, birch, hazel and elm which preceded the oak forest of the 'climatic optimum' (Smith 1970). Thus by the late Mesolithic much of the region was covered in mixed deciduous forest. Its carrying capacity for large mammals, however, would not be particularly high because of the relatively low quality of browse except at its edges, either at the altitudinal tree limit or on flooded alluvial plains. In the Pennines, as has been seen, the continuous tree canopy gave way to scrub at around 1,100–1,200 feet, including much hazel, grassland and occasional patches of peat. This set of habitats was doubtless attractive to red deer on account of the browse from the shrubs, and the mixed vegetation types may also have encouraged aurochs and wild pigs. Rivers with steady regimes would be characteristic owing to the tree cover which ensured largely silt free conditions and a lack of flash floods (Simmons 1979, 116). These rivers would have supplied year round supplies of fish, but particularly during the runs of spring and autumn. Surviving glacial lakes peripheral to the uplands, as at Radcliffe and Ashton, would also have been available for fish, wild fowl and some small mammals.

Plant food was scarcest in winter and early spring, so the resources of the forest would have centred round the mammal population during this critical season, helped possibly by stored plant materials such as hazel nuts gathered during the previous autumn. The zone at the upper edge of the forest in the uplands was most attractive to animals in summer. Other spots visited regularly would have been ill-drained hollows and spring heads where the animals came regularly to drink, and as mentioned earlier such localities probably existed on the boulder clay or solifluction deposits in the vicinities of Dean Clough, March Hill, Warcock Hill and elsewhere.

Clark (1972) has pointed out that while a hunting group would choose a well defined and readily available natural shelter as a home base while the resources of a particular area were being exploited, the selection of a location for camping on an open site would be far less influenced by environmental factors. Certain localities, however, would prove more attractive than others and would thus be occupied on more than one occasion, and it has been seen how several of the Mesolithic sites of the Central Pennines may well fall into this category. People dependent on hunting and gathering normally range over a considerable area during the course of a year, exploiting the natural resources from season to season in different parts of their annual territory. The winter period would be the one in which they sheltered longest at one base, especially at a time when annual climatic conditions were more extreme than they are now. Even in today's more equable climate, red deer observe a seasonal rhythm in Northern Britain, sheltering on low ground in winter and moving to higher ground during the summer (Chaplin 1975, 41). Furthermore, there is evidence to suggest that stag and hind groups kept apart and used different sections of the area, often grazing differing sward types (Charles *et al* 1977). The length of movements of individual herds would have varied with the relative gentleness of the transition between the areas of highest and lowest ground, and this may account for the great number of find spots in the Saddleworth–Marsden section of the Central Pennines where the uplands are at their narrowest (Fig. 6).

It has been seen how the occurrence of broad blade industries at sites like Warcock Hill, Windy Hill and Lominot, all over 1,250 feet and comprising no more than small round patches corresponding to tents or other flimsy structures, suggests hunting activities at the peak of the summer when the animals would be grazing the highest parts of their annual territories. The comparative absence of axes may also emphasise the importance of hunting activities on these upland sites, or it may be due to the absence of trees.

The Deepcar site, at an intermediate altitude (about 500 feet O.D.) and with broad blade industries, is very significant, while other local sites in valley situations having flint industries of a comparable age have been described at Radcliffe in the Irwell valley north of Manchester (Spencer 1950–1) (Fig. 7), and to the north of our area at Sandbeds near Otley and elsewhere in the Yorkshire Dales (Cowling & Stickland 1947; Cowling 1973). These lowland riverine sites provide a contrast with the usual upland nature of the Mesolithic occupation of the Central Pennines, a contrast which is also reflected at Sandbeds in the flint assemblages (themselves a reflection of the nature of the activities), and in the frequency of discarded flint and chert cores there (Mellars 1973, 16). These contrasts may be attributed to the different activities undertaken at this and other similar 'lowland' sites. Thus an altitudinal range of seasonal settlement sites is beginning to emerge in the Central Pennines and adjacent areas, and this can be compared to a similar variety of sites that has been distinguished in North Yorkshire (Spratt *et al* 1976).

Mesolithic settlement types of migratory character have recently been discussed in relation to this last area (Simmons 1975; Spratt & Simmons 1976, 199), where three types were distinguished: a light exploitation camp near the coast or estuary occupied in winter and early spring; a 'cuesta' base camp or gathering site occupied in autumn and early summer; and a light exploitation camp in the uplands occupied in summer. All the Pennine sites would fall into the last category, occupied possibly by individual family groups, while sites on the upland fringes like Sandbeds, Deepcar and Radcliffe might be described as 'base' camps, occupied possibly during the rest of the year (see also Mellars 1976b, 377–8). Still awaiting discovery are other foothill or valley sites on the periphery of the Pennines that might shed more light on the annual territories of these Mesolithic hunter-gatherers.

The availability of raw material such as flint and chert would have an important bearing on the size of the annual territory. The location of Deepcar argues that at least some of those who hunted the upper Pennine altitudes during the summer spent the winter somewhere between the Humber and Trent. If this was the case then the annual territories of Pennine groups may have been as much as 50–60 miles, depending on the varying severity of winter conditions from year to year (Jacobi 1978, 301–2). Thus the Lincoln Edge sites were probably winter settlements, and, as mentioned earlier, this lends additional significance to the sites between here and the Pennines, such as the Maglemosian settlement near Hatfield Chase (Buckland & Dolby 1973) (Fig. 2). But it must also be remembered that materials can be transported by mechanisms such as gift exchange, trade or even the dispatching of a small group to collect the material (Woodman 1978, 186–7). Thus in this case smaller annual territories might be envisaged, perhaps less than 30 miles across. There is no reason why Mesolithic groups should not have wintered west of the Pennines, providing the source of raw materials was secure. The discovery of an elk skeleton and of two unilaterally barbed points, resembling group D at Star Carr, at Poulton-le-Fylde is significant (Barnes *et al* 1971). The elk was in the process of shedding its antlers, an event normally occurring in January, and so it can be inferred that a winter settlement is likely to have existed within five or six miles of the finding place. These finds were of pre Mesolithic, Zone II date, but they do illustrate the post glacial exploitation of lowland areas west of the Pennines in winter. The significance of the Radcliffe site is thus enhanced. Lowland areas like the Mersey basin, at the lower end of the mixed forest, became valuable grazing lands for aurochs as well as deer as the rise in sea level submerged large areas of lowland grazing along the west coast (Evans 1975, 45). Some of the early littoral sites may have been inundated by this rising sea level, while industrial and settlement growth west of the Pennines has possibly destroyed many valley or lowland sites. There is, however, the distinct possibility that some Mesolithic sites may await discovery. Ashton Moss (SJ 9299), occupying a hollow in the glacial drift, possibly a former kettle hole occupied by a glacial lake (Tonks *et al* 1931, 187), may have possibilities (Fig. 3).

The above conclusions, based on broad blade sites, can also be applied to the later Mesolithic occupation. Here again a variety of sites is apparent. Besides those in the uplands, others have been found at intermediate altitudes in the foothills: riverine sites occur near the Calder in the Wakefield area, finds have been made on sandy hillocks in the Manchester region (Hallam 1960, 84), and a number of sites have been located to the east of Sheffield in the Rother valley (Radley & Mellars 1963; Radley 1964).

As has been mentioned already, there was certainly a closed canopy forest up to 800 feet and possibly in places to over 1,200 feet, though many local variations existed, while summit areas were probably open heathland. Similarly, the extension of blanket peat from the higher altitudes down to 1,200 feet or lower, together with pollen evidence for forest recession, have been described. The former process was not reversible: once the forest had gone it did not return. In the latter case, the forest limit was either pushed downhill or never attained its climatic potential, with the result that acid grassland or shallow peat formed. There is much evidence to suggest that deciduous forest colonised many such areas after the end of the Mesolithic, so that in these cases the openings were held for hundreds of years (Simmons 1979, 121). The utilisation of the uplands by Mesolithic man might have started when they were still largely unforested, and the subsequent upward extension of trees could have been to some extent prevented by recurrent burning. Widespread evidence of charcoal layers in the blanket bogs suggests firing of the vegetation, and has been recorded in the Central Pennines (Tallis 1975), at Malham (Pigott & Pigott 1959), at Grassington (Walker 1956), in Nidderdale (Tinsley 1975), and further afield on Dartmoor (Dimbleby 1961) and the North Yorkshire Moors (Simmons 1969a). In the Central Pennines these were more than just local or casual disturbances, suggesting purposeful firing of the vegetation, and at least during the later Mesolithic the closed tree cover above 1,200 feet was suppressed by regular burning. Recent studies have described how burning improves both the quantity and quality of browse for ungulates, besides presenting opportunities for easier culling of the herds by imposing a degree of predictability on their movements (Mellars 1976a; Jacobi et al 1976, 315). Mesolithic man may have manipulated the woodland edge habitat in this way, possibly reburning relatively small tracts of forest at 5–15 year intervals on a rotational basis (Jacobi et al 1976, 317). One effect of this burning would have been the encouragement of hazel (amongst other species), thus providing nuts for direct consumption. This sort of phase has been recorded at North Gill on the North Yorkshire Moors, dated around 4,800 b.c. (Simmons 1975, 61), while hazel nuts were also found in association with flints in the Pennines at Stump Cross (Walker 1956) and at Ickornshaw Moor (Mellars 1974, 96).

Although a great range of plant foods was available to Mesolithic communities (eg Clarke 1976, 472–6), the archaeological evidence is largely confined to a single source, hazel nuts. While this reflects the ability of hazel nut shells to survive in archaeological deposits (especially when burnt), there are grounds for thinking that this food resource did in fact play a most important part in the economy of the Mesolithic population, particularly as winter food. The use of hazel nuts in providing valuable combinations of oil and protein, and their relative importance compared to meat have been discussed elsewhere (eg Jacobi 1978a, 82–4). It is very likely that the archaeological record over emphasises certain facets of the seasonal cycle, possibly at the expense of other more important activities (Morrison 1980, 115–16). While artefact evidence is thus biased towards hunting, during the course of the Mesolithic period the balance probably shifted in favour of plant foods, and this change in the economy may have been assisted by the use of fire. Clarke has indicated that a greater emphasis should be placed on this element of subsistence when interpreting tool functions: not all the implements may have been used for hunting, and some economic specialisation may well have been occurring. The greater diversity of microliths in the later Mesolithic may have been a consequence of this change. Indeed, Mesolithic exploitation of the forest for plant food has been described as a variety of horticulture and forest husbandry before the slash-and-burn of later times (Clarke 1976, 476).

Thus there are strong grounds for thinking that the sharp reduction in tree coverage in the uplands between 5,000 and 3,000 b.c. might have been connected with the activities of man. A correlation between the occurrence of fire and vegetation change does not provide proof, however, that man's activities initiated the change: it may have been under way as a result of climatic change and soil deterioration and have been accelerated by man (Smith 1970). The use of fire may have been a resistance to the pressures caused by environmental changes as well as helping to improve food supplies.

All the evidence, therefore, points to a zone of transition between 1,200 and 1,500 feet in the Pennines, precisely the altitudes where most of the Mesolithic sites have been recorded. Here, between the growing peat bogs and the forest, pollen evidence suggests grasslands undergoing acidification, together with scrub or very open woodland with shade intolerant trees and shrubs – the latter, like hazel, being tolerant of the more exacting conditions to be found outside the forest canopy. The importance of this transition zone to fauna would lie in the increased density of browse it would offer to the large herbivores, especially in the summer months, and in providing plant foods for man, and all this could be increased by burning. It seems likely then that Mesolithic man was altering the Pennine environment by causing, or at least hastening, the recession of the forest – on the high ground perhaps permanently, on the slopes only temporarily. The higher and long lived openings would then experience soil leaching which would lead to impoverished conditions on which blanket bog, already encouraged by the prevailing climatic conditions, might spread. It is significant that Tallis has postulated an upward extension of the tree line after Mesolithic times on the gritstone Pennines, and this during a period of deteriorating climate (Tallis 1975); similar evidence is forth-coming from North Yorkshire as well (Simmons & Cundill 1974). Thus it can be demonstrated that alterations of the ecosystem started before the Neolithic period. Pre agricultural hunting and gathering groups were deliberately changing their environment, resulting in ecological changes, some of which were permanent. Environmental manipulation reflected the 'cropping' of natural vegetation resources and the incipient herding of animals, part of the sequence leading from free hunting through manipulative hunting to herding and eventually agriculture. While the way was thus prepared for primitive agriculture, significant changes were taking place in man's tool kit, some almost certainly as a result of these economic advances, others possibly the consequence of changes in the sources of the raw materials.

Chapter Four
Neolithic Evidence

Introduction

Radiocarbon dates, even uncalibrated, now indicate that the British Isles were settled by farmers before 3,000 b.c.: the earliest dates from Ballynagilly in Co. Tyrone set the initial settlement there as early as 3,795 ±90b.c. (UB 305). It is significant, however, that the earliest *landnam* horizon at this site does not seem to appear until around 3,200 b.c., and evidence from clearance horizons in peat bogs in England suggests that here too it was at this period that farming began to make an impact on the environment (Smith 1974, 101). These centuries just prior to 3,000 b.c. also saw the first field monuments being constructed. On the basis of these dates, a division of the period into earlier and later phases is now suggested, with the division around 2,750 b.c. (Smith 1974, 100).

Around 3,500 b.c. the sea level transgressed the modern coast in many parts of Britain, and about this time climatic conditions started to become more continental, as the sub Boreal period began. During this period temperatures were higher than in the Boreal, and there was increased potential for the expansion of settlement and agriculture to maximum elevations, particularly during the later Neolithic and early Bronze Age. This would be the case particularly in well drained areas, such as the Peak District, but on the ill drained gritstone plateau areas of the Pennines the gradual expansion of peat bog from the highest summits downwards which has been described already would militate against settlement there.

Soil now became of fundamental importance. Not only did the type of soil begin to exert an influence on settlement patterns, but man began to affect soil development, often overriding the effects of climate. In the uplands of the Central Pennines there are about 300 mm (and often less) of mineral soil overlying the bedrock. During the Neolithic period there would be developing gley profiles in the wetter areas with podsols in the lower drier areas, particularly where woodland clearances had and were taking place – though for a time the climatic conditions of the sub-Boreal would help in forest regeneration in the more favourable parts. The wooded slopes and foothill areas probably had brown forest soils but drainage conditions would vary enormously between the areas underlain by clayey drift deposits, those underlain by sands and gravels, and those areas unaffected by glacial deposition where soils would be developed from the bedrock, as in the Coal Measure foothills east of the Pennines (Figs 4 and 5).

One of the main features of pollen diagrams at the Atlantic/sub-Boreal transition is the decline of the elm curve. The idea of a marked and maintained climatic change being the cause of this has much less support now (Smith 1970, 90), suggestions being that it is due to cultural influences. While the idea of an elm decline being widespread in Britain (eg Evans 1975, 109) is probably true, it was not found universally throughout the country as will be seen, and less emphasis will be placed on its significance, certainly in this area.

Archaeological Evidence

The pattern of Neolithic activity in the Central Pennine area has to be inferred from the distribution of flints (mainly arrowheads which occur largely in the upland areas), stone axes (with a contrasting distribution on the whole), and, in a negative sense, from the comparative absence of burial monuments and pottery. General surveys of the distribution of Neolithic remains in the Lancashire part of the area have been made by, for example, Garstang (1906, 215–16), Jackson (1934–5, 72–6), and Leach (1951), and on the Yorkshire side of the Pennines by Petch (1924, 35–43), Cowling (1946, 31–60), and Watson (1952, 38–46), though there have been many reinterpretations of the significance of the finds by subsequent writers.

Neolithic artefacts on the uplands of the Central Pennines often occur in conjunction with Mesolithic finds, though they are by no means so widespread or numerous. They consist of flints, mostly leaf-shaped arrowheads and to a lesser degree tranchet types, whose distribution is also comparable with that of the later (and more frequently found) barbed-and-tanged arrowheads of Bronze Age times. An example of the contexts in which they occur is provided by the Saddleworth–Marsden area of the uplands. In 1921 Buckley found several Neolithic artefacts (a leaf-shaped arrowhead, a leaf-shaped 'point' and two flint knives, one of them 'large') on Tintwistle Low Moor (SK 0298) together with Mesolithic artefacts (Buckley, Drawing Book 6, 3–4). On several other occasions whilst excavating Mesolithic sites he came across leaf- and 'lozenge'-shaped arrowheads (eg at Windy Hill Sites 5 and 8, Rishworth Moor and March Hill (Buckley Mss. 1922–32)). At Warcock Hill North he found a 'lozenge'-shaped arrowhead, Mesolithic flints and also a barbed arrowhead 'fairly close together' (Buckley Mss. 1932). Leaf-shaped arrowheads were also found in the lower layers of the peat, for example two inches above the sand layer at Warcock Hill (Mss. 1922) while at Warlow Pike a large flint knife and a scraper were found in peat half an inch above the sand (Buckley Drawing Book 6, 18) though these may well be Early Bronze Age in date. Buckley also recorded four petit-tranchet arrowheads, two being casual finds on Pule Hill and in Dan Clough near March Hill, one in the lower levels of the peat on the north side of March Hill (Buckley Mss. 1938 and Drawing Book 2, 1) and one excavated with Mesolithic flints at Dean Clough Site C (Buckley Drawing Book 1, 29). Similar occurrences of Neolithic arrowheads, barbed-and-tanged arrowheads and other flint implements have been described elsewhere in the area (eg Roose 1894; Anon 1886). Thus the Neolithic flint artefacts occur in the same type of localities as Mesolithic flints, though so far only in unstratified contexts, and have a thin distribution over all the moorland areas, both in the Central Pennines proper and in the Rossendale uplands. A possible concentration, however, might be discerned in the extreme north east of our area on Rombalds Moor (Cowling 1946, 39) and to a lesser extent on the Marsden–Saddleworth moors. If a judgement can be made from the rather ill recorded finds, there does appear to be a predominance of earlier leaf-shaped forms over the later transverse types in the gritstone areas. The latter can be related to later Peterborough ware and, more particularly, to grooved ware, around 2,000 b.c. (Smith 1974, 121).

These petit-tranchet arrowheads occur beyond the distributional range of grooved ware finds in the Pennines which are concentrated on the limestones of the Peak District and north west Yorkshire (Manby 1974, Fig. 1). Some of the other items usually associated with grooved ware, such as polished and flaked flint knives, Seamer axes and Duggleby adzes, also occur spasmodically in the Central Pennines. While the knives are concentrated mainly on the Yorkshire Wolds and in the Peak District, three polished examples have been found in the Pennines north of the latter, one in our area on Slatepit Moor (200) and another just outside to the north on Burley Moor (SE 137458), while flaked examples have been discovered on Shore Moor near Littleborough (178) and Kelbrook Moor just to the north of our area (Manby 1974, 87). Likewise, while Seamer axes and Duggleby adzes both occur mainly in East Yorkshire, isolated examples have been picked up in the Central Pennines: an adze near Bacup (182) and an axe at Keighley in the Aire valley (270) (Manby 1974, Fig. 40). In addition, an edge-polished flint chisel was found at Torside Reservoir in the extreme south of our area (88), while a flint 'axe' from Milnrow (173) has many similarities with the Bacup adze. An interesting later Neolithic adze has recently been discovered in the Medlock valley near Oldham, where it was embedded in fluvial gravels (111). The distribution of all these is shown on Fig. 10.

The polished stone axes may belong to any period between *c.* 3,250 b.c. and *c.* 1,750 b.c., though the third millennium was the period of most intensive manufacture (Smith 1979). Their distribution in the Central Pennine area provides a marked contrast to those of Mesolithic hunting camps and Neolithic leaf-shaped arrowheads, being concentrated around the peripheries of the uplands, often on the flanks of the major valleys (Fig. 10). Over 100 examples are recorded in Appendix 2, and of the 54 whose petrology has been identified, 22 are of Cumbrian origin, four are from Graig Lwyd in North Wales, three from Tievebulliagh in Northern Ireland, two from the Whin Sill, while the south west of England, the south west of

Figure 10.

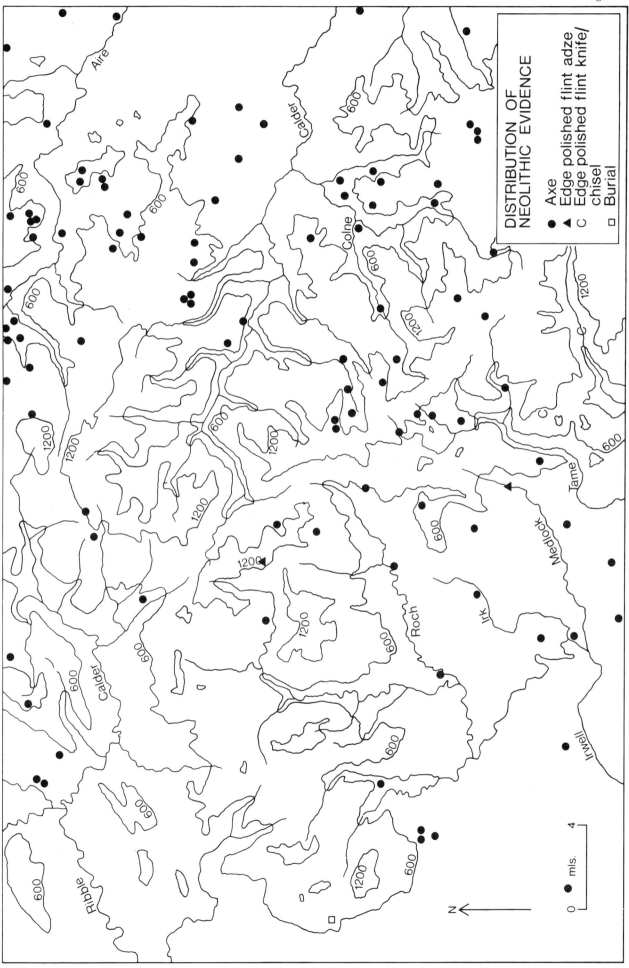

DISTRIBUTION OF
NEOLITHIC EVIDENCE

- Axe
▲ Edge polished flint adze
C Edge polished flint knife/
   chisel
□ Burial

Wales and the Nuneaton area of the Midlands are each represented by a single example; in addition, there are around 20 flint axes. Among these stone axes is a 'rough out' Cumbrian example from Keighley (276) in the Aire valley (where another similar example has been found just to the north of our area), while a Graig Lwyd 'rough out' has been identified at Langsett (SE 2100), north east of the Peak District.

The implications of this lithic evidence so far as settlement is concerned is very tenuous and vague. Late Neolithic occupation sites are reported at Castle Hill, Denby (347), Castle Hill, Almondbury (344) and Holdsworth, near Halifax (295), while to the east of our area a late Neolithic/Early Bronze Age settlement has been attested at Kitchin Farm near Wakefield. In recent years, too, there have been growing indications of possible Neolithic enclosures on Rombalds Moor, part of which impinges on the north eastern section of the area under discussion here. Apart from these examples, however, no other definite indications of Neolithic settlement have yet been identified, the saddle querns and grain rubbers reported, for example, in the Rochdale and Burnley areas (Appendix 2) being just as likely Bronze Age in date. The most promising indications of the location of Neolithic habitation, therefore, would be provided by burial monuments and pottery, but here again the evidence is very slight so far as this area is concerned. No Neolithic pottery has been found, the nearest Peterborough ware occurring in the Peak District, and to the north of our area at Elbolton Cave, Wharfedale (Gilks 1973), and at North Deighton near Harrogate. At the last-named locality, beneath a round barrow, were found the remains of a 'camp' with sherds of Peterborough ware and fragments of polished axes of Langdale and Graig Lwyd origin (Butler 1967, 90). Grooved ware, too, is restricted to the limestone as has been mentioned already (Manby 1974). So far as burial monuments are concerned, only one, a chambered tomb, occurs in the Central Pennine area, while another is located just beyond to the north east: most of the chambered tombs in the Pennines are on the limestone of the Peak District where seven have been identified (Feather & Manby 1970). The megalithic chambered tomb, the Pikestones, is located in the extreme west of our area (Fig. 10), on a lower terrace of the gritstone moorlands 900 feet above sea level near Anglezarke (75). A ruined long cairn is aligned north–south and is of trapezoidal outline, being some 150 feet long, 62 feet wide at the northern end and 45 feet at the southern. The site of the burial chamber at the northern end of the cairn is represented by five slabs, two still standing upright forming the eastern side, and it is at least 15 feet long (Manby 1967, 265). The excavator compared it with Cotswold–Severn type barrows, of which the nearest example is in the Conway valley in North Wales (Bu'Lock 1958, 144), but others disagree with this interpretation, seeing its affinities as lying in the Peak District (Lynch 1966). While nothing further was found associated with the tomb, and the only other fragmentary evidence of Neolithic occupation in the vicinity is related to stray finds of lithic character, it has been pointed out that some of the local Bronze Age monuments, in particular the flat, circular, paved enclosures which on excavation often yielded cremation burials, have superficially Neolithic traits (Bu'Lock 1958, 145). Just outside our area is the other chambered tomb, at Black Hill, Bradley, on the crest of a gritstone hill at about 850 feet O.D. north of the Aire valley (SE 008476). Described as 'frying-pan' in shape – in fact it is basically circular with a 'tail', a characteristic which may shed doubt on its Neolithic origins – and aligned east–west, the burial mound is 218 feet long with a higher, wider mound at the eastern end, 70 feet in diameter and 3 feet high. The lower western part has been badly robbed in the past. A closed chamber was found slightly south of the centre of the eastern part of the cairn, with stone slabs on the north and south sides and drystone walls at the ends: it was just over six feet long, three feet wide and three feet high, was covered by a single capstone and had a paved floor. In a recess in the chamber floor, covered by a large stone, lay a disarticulated skeleton and some cremated bones (Raistrick 1931; Butterfield 1939; Manby 1967, 270). Again, nothing further was found.

Thus the greatest concentration of Neolithic remains in the Pennines occurs on the limestone area of the Peak District, a region more attractive to Neolithic farmers than any other part of the uplands. Even here, however, evidence of

settlement is hard to come by. To the south, on the gravel terraces of the Trent, a
settlement pit at Ashton-on-Trent has been dated to 2,750 ± 150 b.c. (BM 271), the
only such date available for the whole of the Pennine area. A further possible
settlement site has been recorded at Elton, in the heart of the Peak District
(Radley & Cooper 1968). Even in this area there is a marked lack of early Neolithic
remains, and occupation was at a time which is technically Neolithic/Early Bronze
Age, but which has a curious blend of round and oval burial mounds covering
single and multiple burials, with cremation and inhumation traditions. There is a
considerable unity in the cultural remains, probably covering a lengthy period
when grooved ware and beakers overlap (Radley & Cooper 1968, 45). Small
groups practising hunting, herding and farming are seen as part of the initial
flowering of a cultural group which culminated in what has been called the 'Peak
Culture' of the Early Bronze Age (Bu'Lock 1961). The importance of the limestone
plateau for settlement during the Neolithic period and later is indicated by the
henge monuments of Arbor Low (Radley 1968a) and the Bull Ring (Alcock 1950),
together with possibly earlier henges at Standen Low and a proto henge near Arbor
Low (Radley 1968a). The nearest similar monument to our area lies just to the
east at Ferrybridge, where a Class II henge has been identified from air photographs (Manby 1967, 334; Riley 1980, 178). On the other side of the Pennines, the
ritual-burial site at Bleasdale, to the north of the Ribble valley, may have
originated during the Neolithic period (Varley 1938).

Palynological Evidence
The archaeological evidence outlined above points to the inescapable fact that
significant Neolithic remains are sometimes on the fringes of the present moorlands
but frequently are beyond them entirely. Until at least c. 2,400 b.c. there was an
occupational continuum in the Central Pennine uplands in which the ecological
effects of both Mesolithic and Neolithic cultures were quite similar: this is
supported by evidence from pollen analysis. In the gritstone area it consistently
testifies to the lack of widespread forest clearances in the Neolithic. The Pennines
were still forested up to about 1,200 feet or more, and the positions of tree remains
embedded within the basal peat layers (eg Holcombe Hill where birch remains
have been radiocarbon dated to 1,590 ± 120 b.c. (BIRM 147) (Tallis & McGuire
1972), and Moss Moor at 1,200 feet where tree roots one inch up in the peat were
found (Buckley Mss. 1921)) show that pine, birch and willow were all able to
colonise existing shallow peat deposits in the early sub Boreal period and to
maintain themselves during the accumulation of up to 12 inches of peat (Tallis
1975). In the Central Pennines generally, appreciable levels of tree pollens occur in
better drained situations adjacent to the peat margin where peat formation was
delayed until the sub Boreal period at least (Jacobi *et al* 1976, 313). Similarly, in the
Holcombe Hill area, while peat began to form in the valley bottoms in Atlantic
times, relatively unleached soils persisted below fairly open woodlands on the
surrounding slopes, and there is very little evidence of any interference with the
woodlands during Neolithic times (Tallis & McGuire 1972). Indeed, as mentioned
earlier, an upward extension of tree lines at this time probably occurred throughout
the Central and Southern Pennines generally, despite the deteriorating climate
(Tallis 1975). However, it was noted that beneath the Bronze Age burial mounds
at Winter Hill (81) and Wind Hill (165) the soils exhibited a developing podsol
structure, while pollen spectra indicated the local establishment of heathland
communities, suggesting the strong likelihood of local woodland clearance
resulting in the spread of either birch or heather in parts of the Rossendale
uplands prior to the Bronze Age. The suggestion is that these burial mounds and
others of the Bronze Age were possibly constructed in fairly long established
clearings in the forest (Tallis & McGuire 1972, 729). At Rishworth, on the other
hand, pollen evidence suggests only slight clearance of the forest and the possible
establishment of pasturing beginning around 2,060 ± 100 b.c. (GaK 2823), although
not of sufficient intensity to make any significant change in the overall forest cover
(Bartley 1974, 378). Even to the north in the limestone area at Malham, forest
clearance did not occur until the later Neolithic (Pigott & Pigott 1959, 97); in
Nidderdale, though some clearance is suggested around 2,500 b.c., there was only

minor interference with the woodland, probably by semi-nomadic (or transhumant) pastoralists, and major clearances did not begin until after 2,000 b.c. (Tinsley 1975, 20–1; Tinsley 1976, 315). Likewise on the eastern side of the Peak District on East Moor there is a 'hint' of an early Neolithic presence around 3,000 b.c. in the pollen record (Hicks 1972, 8), but small scale clearances – a slight opening of the forest rather than a classic *landnam* – did not occur until later, possibly, as at Malham, associated with the presence of stone axes. Again there is very little evidence of cultivation, the moors being used primarily for pasture: in the early Neolithic in clearings which later regenerated, and around 2,000 b.c. by Neolithic people who began to open the forest more permanently by pastoral activities (Hicks 1972, 17). A similar picture is painted in North Yorkshire (Atherden 1976, 289) where Radley (1969) had noted the archaeological evidence for a late survival of Mesolithic cultures. In one or two places here, small scale and localised agriculture existed, but in small clearings over which the forest later regenerated itself (Spratt & Simmons 1976, 201). A regeneration of woodland following one such opening of the forest has been dated to just before 1,900 b.c. (Simmons 1969a). Dimbleby, too, noted a complete lack of evidence for Neolithic settlement in the Blackamore Forest and continuous forest regeneration (Dimbleby 1961, 127). Dartmoor has many similarities with the Central Pennines at this time for here also Neolithic finds are often associated with Mesolithic material, while 'pure' Neolithic remains generally occur at, or more often beyond, the moorland edge. A similar picture is suggested here of small, temporary clearings, lasting perhaps 50 years, followed by forest regeneration – but only in the early Neolithic because a great increase in settlement occurred later in the period (Simmons 1969, 206–7).

Thus the actual onset of Neolithic clearance is not easy to recognise. The decline in elm pollen as noted above is usually taken as indicative of human interference with the vegetation: it is important, however, to note the time variation which occurs in the elm decline records in Britain (Taylor 1973, 316). Thus at Malham the 'elm shows a temporary lapse' (Pigott & Pigott 1959, 95), while the southern Pennine peats depict a change in the elm horizon lasting between 500 and 600 years (Conway 1954, 143). At Rishworth a slight fall in the values of elm pollen is dated to $3,540 \pm 140$ b.c. (GaK 2822) (Bartley 1974, 378), while in North Yorkshire the elm decline is dated much later at around 2,700 b.c., this later date, it is suggested, possibly reflecting the paucity of Neolithic settlement, the elm decline being part of a general thinning of the tree canopy (Atherden 1976, 289). Finally, on East Moor, just south east of our area, the elm decline is dated to between 3,000 and 2,800 b.c., and is associated there with the appearance of plantain (Hicks 1972, 8).

Discussion

There are contrasts in the distribution of Neolithic finds in the Central Pennine area (Fig. 10), and to account for these we may have to look at environmental considerations to supply the possible answer. The Lancashire (and Cheshire) area would appear to have been less attractive to settlement and exploitation at this time than the eastern fringes of the Pennines. The higher sea level would imply that both the Mersey and Ribble estuaries penetrated further inland, and this, together with the development of a broad belt of lowland peat mosses in many parts of Lancastria, particularly on the flanks of the Mersey valley, would have been at least partly responsible for the extreme poverty of Neolithic (and Bronze Age) settlement over much of the lowland (Freeman *et al* 1966, 27–8), restricting possible exploitation to a belt fringing the Rossendale uplands and the western side of the Pennines. Evidence from Storrs Moss suggests that on the Lancashire lowlands the initial encroachment by pioneer agriculturalists was in the form of small scale openings in marginal woodland, and only later did inroads in the closed forest occur (Powell *et al* 1971, 134). These initial clearings occurred at around 3,000 b.c. at Red Moss on the Lancashire lowlands, where they were still being maintained at $2,765 \pm 80$ b.c. (Q 911) but had ended by $2,420 \pm 80$ b.c. (Q 910) (Hibbert *et al* 1971, Figs. 3 and 4). The wider foothill belt east of the Pennines may have offered more opportunities for settlement, and significantly it is here – particularly in the areas fringing the limestone country – that pollen diagrams indicate the greatest interference with the forest cover.

The difficulty in interpreting the evidence for the Neolithic period in the Central Pennines lies in the fact that whereas for the Mesolithic inhabitants we are dealing with artefacts directly connected with their camps, the distribution of axes and other remains may not necessarily represent the Neolithic pattern of settlement. Taken in isolation they could be misleading, but if coupled with a comparison with the Peak District and with pollen evidence, the likely indications are that prehistoric activity well after 3,000 b.c. comprised pastoralism on the lower ground within the forest area and hunting on higher ground which was partly forested but also had areas of grassland and bog. Only during what is technically very late in the Neolithic period do we find evidence in the gritstone areas of the Central Pennines to indicate agricultural activities: minor clearings are indicated at various places in the uplands and on their peripheries prior to as late as 1,800 b.c., with forest rejuvenation occurring shortly afterwards. The obvious conclusion to be drawn is that small, temporary clearances were made, lasting only about 40–50 years, and the lack of evidence for settlement suggests that pastoral activities may have predominated, on a seasonal or intermittent basis. There is very little evidence of arable cultivation, no cereal pollens having been recorded. There is a strong temptation to conclude that man's contribution to the changing environment in the uplands during the Neolithic period was very similar to that of Mesolithic man, and that the forest clearance, for whatever reason, led to deteriorating soil conditions and therefore to the unsuitability of many parts of the gritstone area for agriculture. Even in the lowland and valley areas flanking the uplands (in common with other parts of Britain) pollen analysis suggests a phase of abandonment with forest regeneration after the initial clearings had been made, and that only in the later Neolithic was agricultural activity renewed. Soil exhaustion due to over grazing or over cultivation – in turn possibly reflecting over population – have been suggested as explanations (Whittle 1978). The picture throughout much of the Neolithic period in this part of the world is one of growing bog on the high ground, especially on ill drained soils, and of forest elsewhere with temporary clearings.

The clear and growing domination of the Peak District is significant, largely the result of soil differences, and all the indications are that the gritstone areas were used only for hunting, and that they remained comparatively neglected until Bronze Age times. In his study of grooved ware in northern England, Manby saw a change in the later Neolithic with intensified activities in the chalk and limestone areas, a change from cyclic cultivation to more stable pastoral farming accompanied by hunting in favoured districts; in fact, hunting activities probably increased at this time, an indication of this being the greater numbers of arrowheads of varying types belonging to this period which have been found, especially in the Peak District (Manby 1974, 101). The scattered finds in the gritstone Central Pennines, which have been described earlier as relating to these later Neolithic times, may also point to the continuing utilisation of the uplands for hunting and gathering activities.

The presence of axes may indicate a certain amount of clearance on the fringes of the uplands, though the possibility of clearance not associated with agriculture must be considered, as the presence of plantain pollen alone is not indicative of anything more than open conditions. Moreover, there is little warrant for linking axe distribution directly with forest clearance (Bradley 1972, 200). Alternatively, the axes may indicate trade routes. As might be expected, the great majority of the Central Pennine axes appear to have originated in Cumbria, and a study of these – and more especially the distribution of 'rough out' Group VI axes – has led to the suggestion of a number of routes through the Central Pennine area: of particular importance may have been one along the western flanks of the uplands between Cumbria and the Peak District, while others are seen as utilising the main gaps through the hills, such as the southern slopes of the Aire Gap and the sides of the glacial meltwater channels at Cliviger and Walsden (Manby 1965, 375–6). The occurrence of a 'rough out' Graig Lwyd axe north west of Sheffield at Langsett may indicate a trade route from North Wales via the Peak District to eastern England. While complete axes might well have been accidental losses, possibly indicating trade routes, it is tempting to follow the suggestion that fragmented axes may have been broken during use, and probably during land clearance. Two of the Neolithic occupation sites in the Central Pennines which were mentioned earlier, at Castle Hill, Denby, and Holdsworth, near Halifax, produced broken polished axes (Gilks 1974, 7). Pursuing this line of thought, it is interesting that five of the 34 axes recorded in Appendix 2 as occurring west of the Pennine watershed (14.7%) were broken, while some 15 of the 70 found to the east of the watershed (21.4%) were in a similar state. Of course, a number of these axes may have been fragmented in more recent times, but the slightly greater proportion on the drier, eastern flanks of the hills may be of some significance so far as land clearance is concerned.

The continuance of Mesolithic cultures into Neolithic times is possibly hinted at by the mingling of artefactual types: hence the 'ending' of the Mesolithic may be impossible to trace. Certainly it would appear that there was a different approach to the Neolithic in this part of the North compared with Southern England. Earlier – and possibly even later – Neolithic activities were not particularly different from Mesolithic practices, especially since pioneer agriculture may have been on too small a scale to register clearly in the pollen record. The possibility that the Mesolithic mode of seasonal movement continued into Neolithic times must be envisaged, though of course any cycle of this type would have been distorted or truncated by early farming on the foothills. In common with the Central Pennines, sites elsewhere in England have yielded Mesolithic flintwork associated with Neolithic artefacts (Ashbee 1978, 66). Neolithic clearings in the uplands may have been made in the course of hunting just as they were in the Mesolithic pattern. It has been pointed out that it is no coincidence that the areas where Neolithic and Mesolithic equipment are found together are marginal agriculturally, areas which in all likelihood were used by farmers for hunting and not for agriculture (Bradley 1978b, 101). Certainly, the distribution of Neolithic arrowheads in the Central Pennines and elsewhere reflects the continuing use and disturbance of forest-edge habitats. Another possible indication of overlapping Mesolithic and Neolithic ways of life may have been provided by recent excavations on the foothill site at Unstone, outside our area between Chesterfield and Sheffield (Courtney 1978), where cultivated barley seeds have been found on a Mesolithic site. While this may suggest contact with the earliest farmers of the area, radiocarbon determinations could demonstrate that worm or root action has been responsible for this phenomenon.

As has been seen, the elm decline was either absent or of less significance in this part of the country compared with the South. In addition, where it does occur it may have been due to other reasons than simply the impact of man on the natural vegetation. In some places it may have been a long, drawn out decline as a consequence of climatic change; in others it may have been hastened by human activities. Furthermore, the principal *landnam* period does not always coincide with the elm decline in this area, where pollen analysis testifies that the main episode of deforestation did not come until later in prehistoric times. Again, the type of forest clearance in the gritstone areas of the Central Pennines differed from that of southern England (and probably also from that of the Peak District) in that small, temporary clearings were the rule compared with the widespread, longer lived deforestation on the Downs. No evidence exists about the techniques used, but it does appear that pastoralism was almost universal in the scattered clearings on the fringes of the uplands, possibly nomadic – or more accurately transhumant – in character, with an emphasis on hunting on the higher ground. Many of these clearings were short lived, and there is widespread evidence of forest regeneration. The elm decline on the moors, where it is present, appears as the culmination of a series of clearances rather than suddenly. With reference to North Yorkshire, where the same picture obtains, it has been pointed out that this might represent the end of Mesolithic occupation or might equally be due to the initial Neolithic incursions (Spratt & Simmons 1976, 201; Jones *et al* 1979, 19). The same applies to the Central Pennines, and here, besides the strong suggestion of some continuity of economy from Mesolithic into Neolithic times, there is also the likelihood of a further continuity into Bronze Age times.

Chapter Five
The Bronze Age

Introduction

Although some might prefer the traditional divisions of 'Late Neolithic' and 'Early Bronze Age', the distinctions between the two are often artificial (Burgess 1976a, i–iii; Whittle 1980). Nevertheless, despite a clear division occurring within the Bronze Age from several viewpoints, there is so much overlapping of various aspects in our area that it was decided to retain the period as a whole, starting with Beaker settlement and continuing to the close of the Late Bronze Age – although even the latter is blurred, as will be seen later.

The use of radiocarbon dating has pushed back the beginnings of the Early Bronze Age in Britain. The early Beaker settlement at Ballynagilly (Co. Tyrone) has been dated at 2,100 ± 50 b.c. (UB 555), while at Newgrange (Co. Meath), people with the first horses in the British Isles and using various kinds of pottery, some of it recognisable as various forms of related beaker ware, began to squat round the decaying edge of the passage grave around 2,100 ± 40 b.c. (GrN 6344) (O'Kelly 1972, 227). Early sites in eastern England are dated at around 1,850 b.c. (Burgess 1974, 223). In our area, however, Early Bronze Age origins are securely dated to around the middle of the second millennium, although on the evidence of Bleasdale and elsewhere the dating of some Early Bronze Age remains may be even earlier (see below). Radiocarbon dating has also brought back into the Bronze Age sites and material traditionally regarded as Iron Age. The transition from the Early to the 'traditional' Middle Bronze Age in the area under study may still fall around 1,400 b.c., and, although the 'traditional' Late Bronze Age began in the tenth century in the lowland zone, it is considered to be in the eighth century or even later in areas like the Central Pennines (Burgess 1974, 169).

Taking Britain as a whole, Burgess points out that pottery has for long been misused as a chronological and cultural indicator for dividing up the period. He emphasises the change from the Early to the Middle Bronze Age as constituting one of the most important watersheds in the period, marked by the disappearance of the last Neolithic survivals, a striking sepulchral/religious hiatus, and the adoption of a new tool kit and weaponry (Burgess 1970). However, while in his terms the Late Bronze Age is customarily divided from the Middle Bronze Age by the adoption of lead bronze and of the three classic Late Bronze Age types, leaf-shaped swords, socketed axes and pegged spearheads, these are by no means universal features. In our area the change is basically between the early traits ceasing in favour of the later massive metalworking techniques, emphasis on metalwork being the dominant feature because of the unavailability of any other features by which to judge this period of the Bronze Age.

Following the ideal conditions in the Early Bronze Age for the spread of upland settlement in Britain, a climatic deterioration occurred during the later part of the period, from the beginning of the first millennium onwards and possibly even earlier. The sub Atlantic climatic phase (Table 1) saw winters in particular becoming more unsettled and raw, while summers too were cooler and cloudier (Taylor 1975, 12). In this way, the uplands became directly exposed to a cooling hill climate which, after 1,000 b.c. in particular, helped to promote the development of non arboreal vegetation, dominantly *Erica* but including moorland grasses, while peat accumulation was renewed extensively (Taylor 1973, 316). In our area the degeneration of the upland habitat, probably initiated by Mesolithic exploitation and continued by Neolithic and Early Bronze Age activities, was intensified and extended by this gradual climatic change.

Attention has justifiably been drawn to the significance of this climatic deterioration during the Bronze Age (Burgess 1974, 166–7). As a result of Britain's latitude, even minor variations in altitude, precipitation and temperature are critical for crop ripening and human habitation, and any climatic change would have been magnified by the more primitive landscape conditions of the time. In

Figure 11. Some Central Pennine Beakers.
II–VI. Sectional reconstructions of Beakers from Saddleworth, Castleshaw Roman Fort (118). (After
Clarke 1970). (Scale 3:11).

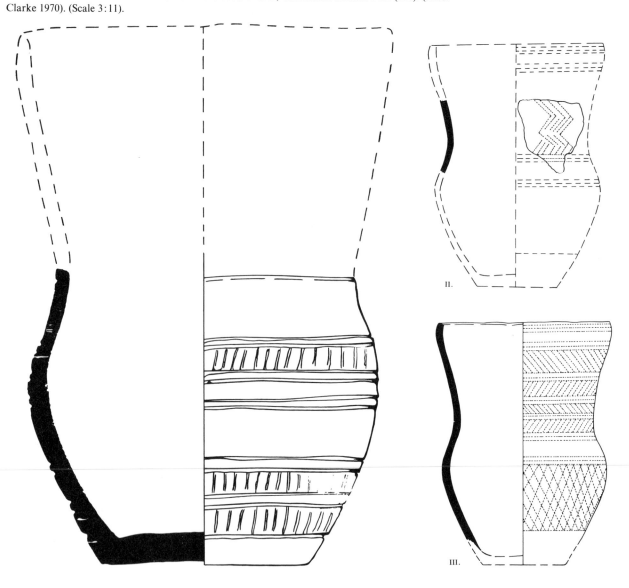

I Sectional reconstruction of Beaker from Burnley, Extwistle Moor (42). (After Manby 1965–6).
Actual size.

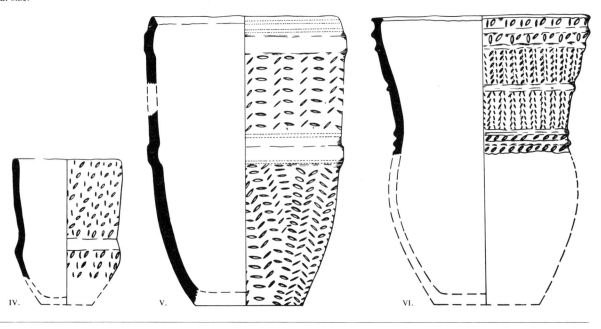

some uplands, Early Bronze Age monuments occur on peaty moorlands, and the peat has clearly formed since the sites were established, the result of both human interference and deteriorating climate. The latter would seriously affect settlement and farming patterns – particularly on the wetter, west facing slopes – combining with human misuse to make the upland tracts marginal or unusable. This, together with waterlogging of land at all levels, including the Vale of York to the east and the lowlands such as Chat Moss to the west, must have resulted in increasing land pressure by the later Bronze Age, which might have made it imperative to defend land and stock by the building of defensive settlements and the occupation of naturally defensive positions such as hilltops (Burgess 1974, 167). These aspects will be discussed in the next chapter.

Thus the climatic deterioration during the Bronze Age may be regarded as being of particular importance, especially considering the fact that it may have begun much earlier than has hitherto been believed, leading to a period of poorer weather certainly during the Middle Bronze Age and possibly late in the Early Bronze Age at higher altitudes. This culminated in a second more serious deterioration more securely fixed around the seventh and sixth centuries B.C.

Archaeological Evidence

1. Ceramic Evidence

Beaker pottery is practically confined to the limestone uplands of the Peak where 35 occurrences have been identified (Lewis 1970, Fig. 18), all associated with burials, mostly of Clarke's developed Southern British types (Clarke 1970, 214–16), or what is postulated as comparatively late in Beaker times, well into the second millennium. These sites are mainly on the headwaters of easterly flowing rivers, the Peak District occupying a strategic position between the Fens and East Yorkshire on the one hand and Northern Ireland on the other (Clarke 1970, 216). In the Central Pennine area, however, only seven possibilities have been cited, mainly on the upland fringes. Five are in our area and these are not all related to burials (Fig. 12).

The most interesting find was that at Castleshaw (118), where beaker sherds were unexpectedly discovered during the excavation of the Roman Fort in 1964 in a 'domestic storage pit' (Thompson 1967). Five distinct beakers were identified (75 of the 122 sherds) which Clarke described as a small but characteristic selection from the Late Southern Beaker domestic array, comprising a giant storage beaker with rusticated decoration and a two tier neck, a small rusticated beaker, two incised and stamped beakers, and a comb impressed beaker (Clarke 1970, 227) (Fig. 11, ii–vi). They were roughly dated to around 1,550 b.c. (Thompson 1967, 15). The Castleshaw pots integrated archaic and proto-typical features for the western flank of Clarke's north-eastern province of Late Southern British Beaker ware. Two of them were characteristic of Late Southern British types, and the other three represented functional variations to be found on domestic ware rarely buried as accessories in Beaker graves, one of them being an everyday domestic pot, and the others variants on larger heavy duty domestic ware. Longworth has pointed out that the linear-incised decoration on one of the vessels (Vessel 1) was of particular significance in the history of Bronze Age ceramics in north western England for it displayed the linear incision that became a technique typical of the collared urn tradition of the area. Furthermore, another of the vessels (Vessel 5) was not far from the general form of the cordoned urn, and the Castleshaw vessel too provides further evidence that cordoned vessels were being made as domestic ware by late Beaker potters (Longworth in Thompson 1967, 16–17). The Neolithic ancestry of such so called 'Beaker domestic ware' has been discussed (Burgess 1976a, ii), and this occurrence may be regarded as yet another link between the Early Bronze Age and earlier periods in this area. Burgess has gone on to argue that while food vessels and urns are entirely associated with burial/ritual purposes, everyday pottery may be represented by these 'Beaker domestic wares' (Burgess 1976b, 320). It is of possible significance that, in the same general area of the gritstone Pennines, flint daggers of the same period have been recorded at Ragstone near Denshaw (126), Rocher Moss (128) and Warlow (199). The discoidal flint knife from Slatepit Moor (200) mentioned already in Neolithic contexts, may be of this age, too, and these flint artefacts together with the numerous barbed-and-tanged arrowheads provide further evidence for not inconsiderable activity along these western slopes of the Pennines.

Less information is available about the other beakers found in the Central Pennines, all apparently in funerary contexts. The lower part of a beaker was found in 1882 on Extwistle Moor near Burnley (42) and contained burnt remnants of bone (Manby 1965–6) (Fig. 11, i). Another beaker, found in the extreme eastern part of our area at Cookridge, Leeds (394), has been described as belonging to Clarke's Developed Southern British Beaker group (Gilks 1973, 176). At Portfield near Whalley (155) a beaker was found beneath Iron Age fortifications, while another beaker has been excavated outside our area to the north on Thornton Moor (King 1969, 46). The four last examples are in close proximity to the Aire–Ribble crossing of the Pennines, as is another beaker found in a barrow at Ferry Fryston to the east of our area (Pacitto 1968). The latter was also described as belonging to the Developed stage of Clarke's Southern Beaker Tradition and was associated with a crouched burial, a bronze awl and evidence of a previous inhumation. Finally, in the extreme south of our area a doubtful example has been described as accompanying an inhumation on Mouse Low near Glossop (82).

Another possible link with Beaker settlement in the area is provided by the assemblage associated with an inhumation in a barrow at Wind Hill, Heywood (165) where a triangular flint knife, a pebble hammer, a V-perforated jet button and a flint scraper were found (Tyson 1980). Just outside our area, a large flint point was found alongside a skeleton at Otley, and this too may represent a Beaker burial (Cowling 1946, 62). Other flint knives have been reported in the Central Pennines, and a flint axe of Beaker date at Cullingworth (256).

There is no evidence anywhere in the Pennines, however, of Beaker settlements. The nearest is south of the Peak District in Derbyshire at Swarkeston, where evidence of a Beaker structure was found beneath a barrow containing a secondary cremation with a collared urn dated 1,395 ± 160 b.c. (NPL 17) (Greenfield 1960). The Beaker pottery belonged to Clarke's Southern Beaker series (Simpson 1971, 136).

The beakers in the Central Pennines, therefore, all belong to the latest periods of the British Beaker tradition, overlapping the span of radiocarbon dates for collared urns (see below), and a distribution which contrasts markedly with that of the flint arrowheads.

Food vessels, too, are concentrated in the Peak District where more than 50 have been identified, mostly on the limestone with very few on the adjoining grit and shale areas (Manby 1957 and 1964a; Lewis 1970, Fig. 21). All of them are of the 'Yorkshire Vase' type, though two may have Irish affinities (Manby 1957). In the Central Pennine area also it is mainly 'Yorkshire Vases' that are represented, but like the beakers they are very restricted in numbers; only eight possibilities have been identified (Fig. 12).

An interesting find of four food vessels together with a pygmy vessel, however, occurred in the centre of the gritstone Pennines – only two miles east of the beaker find at Castleshaw, on the summit of Pule Hill (374), near the watershed between Saddleworth and Marsden, a locality occupied during the Mesolithic period. Excavation in 1899 (Clarke 1902) showed no signs of a mound, where, in 1896, a burial group of two crouched inhumations, at least two cremations with vessels, and two further pots had been found. The site was possibly a flat cemetery, though erosion might have removed the mound. As was the case with the beaker finds in the Central Pennines, this food vessel burial site occurred to the north of the high moors which separate the area from the Peak District to the south, and the affinities of these vessels lie to the east rather than the south, one of them resembling a food vessel found outside our area at Ferry Fryston (Pacitto 1968), another, a footed bowl, belonging to a small group of vessels whose distribution is concentrated in East Yorkshire, while the pygmy cup is described as belonging to the contracted-mouth group concentrated in north east Yorkshire and the Central Pennines (Manby 1969, 275). The food vessel series belongs, by analogy, to a vessel on Harland Edge in North Derbyshire, to the period 1,490 ± 150 b.c. (BM 178), and the pygmy cup to around 1,400 b.c. If the dating is accurate, the

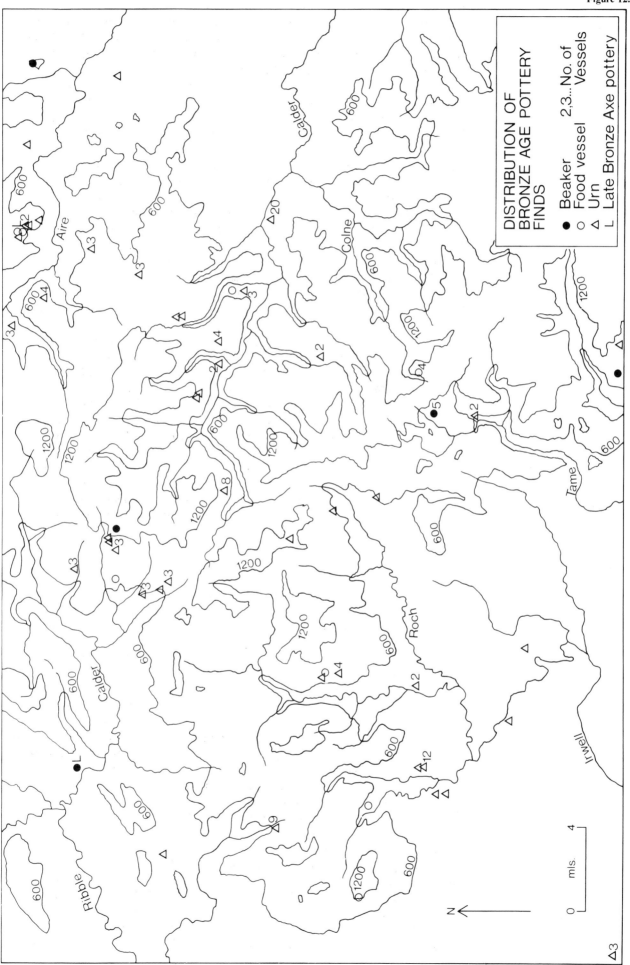

Figure 12.

DISTRIBUTION OF
BRONZE AGE POTTERY
FINDS

2,3... No. of
Vessels

● Beaker
○ Food vessel
△ Urn
∟ Late Bronze Axe pottery

whole assemblage was probably not buried at the same time.

The other food vessels reported in our area are mainly from the fringes of the uplands; at Noon Hill, Rivington (79), Walmsley near Bolton (25), Bank Lane, Ramsbottom (68), Twist Hill, Burnley (54), Halifax (293) (Fig. 13, i), and two possibilities on Baildon Moor to the north east (229 and 230). Another food vessel burial occurred just to the north of our area on Thornton Moor (King 1969, 46). Some of these references are very vague, with little information available about the vessels. The Twist Hill example was found in a stone circle while that at Walmsley (a doubtful example) was in a cairn over an inhumation. The Rivington pot (Fig. 13, ii) was an enlarged food vessel and contained a cremation, and was also associated with a barbed-and-tanged arrowhead. The Bank Lane food vessel was found in a cairn where its sherds were with those of an urn, while both the Baildon Moor examples are said to have been found with urns in cairns.

Collared urns are descended ultimately from Neolithic pottery, and thus from a heritage which included multiple cremation burials within enclosures. The urns appear to be the vessels used by descendants of later Neolithic peoples who adopted the rites and usages of the intrusive Beaker people, and a cremation cemetery mode of burial (Ashbee 1960, 154). About 140 vessels of the collared urn and related traditions have been found in the Peak District (Lewis 1970, Fig. 23), but while the beakers and food vessels have a similar distribution on the limestone, there is a marked difference between them and the urns, the latter being concentrated on the gritstone to the east. Thus, after the Neolithic/Early Bronze Age's rich development in the Peak District, there occurred a break in continuity. The localised development on the limestone appears to end with the beginning of urned cremation, though, of course, this does not imply depopulation: it suggests, rather, a major expansive force with the settlement of previously hinterland areas, in this case the slopes of the Derwent valley and the gritstone moors to the east.

These changes are also reflected in the Central Pennines. Here, as has been seen, colonisation by Beaker and Food Vessel people had comparatively little impact, but urns, on the other hand, are much more widespread (Fig. 12). They occur generally on the fringes of the higher areas or in valleys within the Central Pennines, and it must be remembered that the numbers and distribution of urns have suffered from extensive and unrecorded barrow digging in the past. Primary urns do occur in the area but in small numbers (Longworth 1961, 300–1): they are best represented in East Yorkshire, while 25% of the Peak District urns fall into this category (Lewis 1970, 86). Most of the Central Pennine urns belong to Longworth's secondary series, and range in date from possibly as early as 1800 B.C. to at least 1300 B.C. Burgess is, however, disparaging about the distinction between primary and secondary series vessels, and will not accept Middle Bronze Age associations for any sort of urn (Burgess 1974, 180 and 194). He is supported by radiocarbon evidence (see below) which suggests an overlapping sequence of urn usage from food vessels to primary then secondary series collared urns. This evidence also suggests that even the latest examples were evidently deposited within the Early Bronze Age (Challis & Harding 1975, 31). By the Middle Bronze Age the earlier urn sequence was superseded by bucket and barrel forms of Deverel-Rimbury type and with possibly some globular urns. Very few of these last named types are found in our area, where pottery styles apparently continued to owe much to earlier urn forms. The proportion of collared urns found with dateable associations, however, is small: the possibility of a subsequent phase of urn burial without dateable grave goods cannot be overlooked, maybe continuing into Deverel-Rimbury times, as radiocarbon dates from Deverel-Rimbury urns at Shearplace Hill and Gwithian suggest (Burgess 1974, 228–9). Thus at Harland Edge, east of the Peak District, food vessels of 'Yorkshire vase' type associated with cremation burials were dated 1,490 ± 150 b.c. (BM 178) while a burnt bone in an adjacent pit produced an even earlier date of 1,750 ± 150 b.c. (BM 210) (Riley 1966, 39). Cremation burials in urns at Totley (in the same area) were dated 1,530 ± 150 b.c., 1,250 ± 150 b.c., and 1,050 ± 150 b.c. (BM 212, 211 and 177) (Radley 1966c, 22), and a further date of 1,500 ± 150 b.c. (BM 179) was obtained for a cremation inside a collared urn sealed in an earth circle at Barbrook II (Lewis 1966). Timber from the Bleasdale circle, with its well-developed 'Pennine' urns,

Figure 13. Food vessels and Collared Urns.

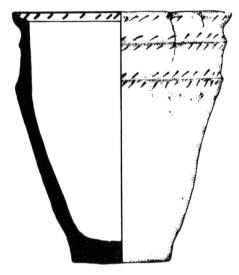

I. Food vessel 'from Halifax' (293). Scale 2:5.

II. Enlarged food vessel from Rivington, Noon Hill (79). (After Cowie 1978). Scale 1:4.

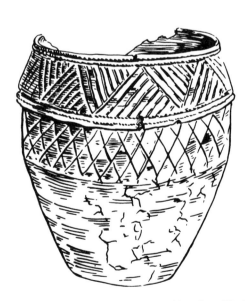

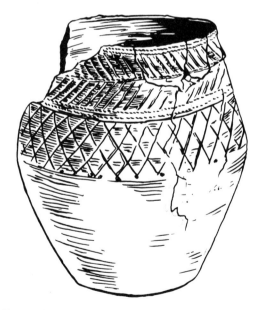

III. Urns from Warley, Tower Hill (338). Scales 1:3, 1:4.

was dated at $1,810 \pm 90$ b.c. (NPL 69) (Radley 1966c, 22). As Radley pointed out, if the date for Bleasdale (which is to the north west of our area) is correct and the cremations there were contemporary, it gives a very early date for these urns.

While all these examples are outside our area, the collared urn from Harland Edge is comparable with the two 'Pennine' urns from Tower Hill, Warley (338) (Fig. 13, iii). Inside one of these urns was a pygmy cup decorated with lines of twisted cord. Two urns, decorated on collar and neck with twisted cord pattern, were found at Brownhill, Saddleworth (114) in 1844, one containing a pebble macehead. Longworth demonstrated that certain traits such as whipped and twisted cord, and grooved decoration found on his primary series of collared urns had their origin in the Neolithic ceramic traditions of Peterborough ware (Longworth 1961). Another interesting group occurs in the burial circle at Mosley Height, Burnley (48) (Fig. 30). There were four pits: the primary burial in the centre had a cremation in a twisted cord decorated collared urn, a second pit contained an inverted collared urn, another contained a badly broken urn, while the fourth contained an unurned cremation. Other remains here included two polished grain rubbers, three fragments of querns, three polished hand hammers and one pestle, together with flint scrapers, arrowheads, knives and pieces of quartz, calcite and Kimmeridge shale. Four pygmy vessels, various kinds of beads, a bronze dagger and awl were found in direct association with at least six cremation burials in 'Pennine' urns at Blackheath, Todmorden (327) near the Long Causeway (like the Mosley Height burials).

Some other interesting associations may be mentioned here. At Whitelow, Ramsbottom (71) urns were associated with a bronze awl, whilst a pygmy vessel and a flat riveted bronze dagger were found with an inhumation burial in a cist at Haulgh, Bolton (20) (Bu'Lock 1961, Fig. III, 1). To the north of our area on Thornton Moor, excavation revealed nine graves, the earliest containing a beaker, another a food vessel, while a large cinerary urn was accompanied by a pygmy vessel and other finds which have been mentioned earlier.

There are some 42 occurrences of urns in our area, some of these with considerable numbers (Fig. 12). Besides those mentioned above, twelve urns were found in a flat cemetery at Breightmet, Bolton (14), nine at Darwen (3), about twenty at Rastrick with cremations (292), three inverted urns at Skircoat (301) and four at Warley with a pygmy vessel (338). At Chellow Heights near Bradford, fragments of three urns and a pygmy cup were found with a cremation (251). Another pygmy cup, this time associated with an inhumation, occurred at Clifton in the Irwell valley north of Manchester (186). The evidence suggests that the pygmy cup was current during the richest phase of urn burial, if the number of grave goods is any criterion.

Thus several examples of continuity involving beakers, food vessels and urns can be suggested. The urns imply a growing population in the Central Pennines during the earlier part of the Bronze Age. However, owing to the difficulties in dating the pottery, and the fact that there are few Deverel-Rimbury forms (if any) in the area, it is possible that the urn tradition lingered on here much later than has hitherto been considered. Later Bronze Age pottery is represented only by sherds that have been excavated at Portfield (155), from below the Iron Age fort, while a bucket urn has been reported from Baildon Moor (229).

2. Earthworks

The surviving Bronze Age earthworks in the Central Pennines are mostly related to earlier Bronze Age burials, and in this respect the area is by no means untypical. The lack of knowledge concerning habitation sites may be due partly to later activities or to natural forces, although the natural vegetation of the moorlands does not lend itself to easy recognition of sites. Most of the settlement evidence occurs on Rombalds Moor, straddling, though mostly outside, the north eastern boundary of the study area. It is interesting to note, however, that in the last decade or so much new information about Bronze Age sites on Big Moor, south west of Sheffield, and on the Beeley and Totley Moors nearby – again outside our area, this time to the south east – has been revealed, and its significance will be discussed later. This section, therefore, is concerned almost entirely with burial monuments.

Though barrows are most numerous on the limestone of the Peak District (Lewis 1970, Fig. 6), about 78 burial sites do occur in the Central Pennines (Appendix 2), and there are marked differences in construction as well as in the burial ritual and the grave goods. The barrows on these gritstone areas, in contrast to the limestone, are invariably cairns, stone for building them never being far away; burials also occur in flat cemeteries and in ring monuments. Cairns generally occur singly in the area, and there are no large clusters of smaller mounds forming cairn groups, such as occur on Stanton Moor on the eastern fringes of the limestone area where there are some 70 cairns on an outlying plateau of gritstone. The nearest equivalent to this can be found in the north east of our area on Baildon Moor, which itself is only part of a larger occurrence on Rombalds Moor generally. The moorland area east of Burnley, however, may represent another, much poorer, example: here in some ten square miles 14 stone circles, ring banks and small barrows have been found, together with other unexplored mounds and enclosures (Fig. 14). The possibility that some of the cairns in these districts had some purpose other than burial must not be overlooked, and the idea that they may represent field clearance heaps will be examined later.

Records concerning barrow excavation are for the most part very vague, and often no details of their construction are available. Bu'Lock (1961, 13) discovered two traditions: single grave burials (with up to five bodies), and cemeteries, the latter being twice as numerous in Lancashire. Single grave burials include simple kerbed or revetted cairns covering inhumations, as at Haulgh and Walmsley, both near Bolton, and Law House, near Burnley, as well as cremations as at Lowhouse (Milnrow), Noon Hill (Rivington), and several near Burnley. Some cairns in the Burnley area may have had free standing peristaliths or this feature may represent the kerb of an outer earthen mound now disappeared (Bu'Lock 1961, 14). The composite cairn of earth and stone is a well defined type: those at Winter Hill (81) and Hades Hill (161), for example, had kerbs round earth and turf mounds over a central cairn, possibly suggesting modification and enlargement after the initial building.

The Wind Hill cairn, near Heywood (165), one of the few completely excavated cairns in our area, was defined by a kerb of horizontal slabs up to three courses high, and on its eastern side the kerb had been heightened and straightened to focus on an opening six feet wide (Fig. 32). A rectangular area outside this opening was defined by inward leaning slabs which were further enclosed by a satellite kerb. Both primary and satellite kerbs were finally concealed to give the cairn a squat pear shape. The excavator considered the burials here to be of Beaker date from the grave goods, and that the structural features of the cairn possessed elements characteristic of a mixed Neolithic ancestry. Generally after 2000 B.C. the people occupied for a time the same areas in the limestone Peak where Neolithic people had built their chambered tombs, and where the diversity of stone axe types indicate the distant contacts of this district in the third millennium. At least 30 Beaker round cairns are known in the Peak District, and the renewed importance and prosperity of the area depended on its connections mentioned earlier.

The distribution of burials of all types is shown on Fig. 14. Twice as many occur west of the Pennine watershed than to the east, though the former does include a greater proportion of the total area. While most of the actual barrows are on false crests, a more interesting feature of the altitudinal distribution of the burials as a whole is provided by another contrast that begins to emerge when the western and eastern flanks of the uplands are compared. To the west, most of the burials occur round the edges of the Pennines proper and the Rossendale Uplands. Bearing in mind the proviso mentioned earlier about the distribution of lower lying land in our area, there is a greater number at lower altitudes on the west, all either on gravel terraces or on fluvio-glacial gravels, as at Bolton. The lowest are at Kenyon and near Stonyhurst respectively: the former (202) is the northern representative of a group on the low sandstone ridge which focuses on the ford at Warrington, while two barrows near Stonyhurst (153) are near a crossing of the Ribble. Both these sites are also in areas with bronze finds. The median altitude of the burials in the western part of our area is 800 feet, with the highest tending to occur on the far western fringes of the Rossendale Uplands. East of the Pennine watershed, however, the median height of the burials is higher, at 1,000 feet, and they occur especially on the south facing flanks of Calderdale and the Aire valley. Only two are at 400 feet or lower, and even these are sited on gritstone terraces, well above the level of the river Calder. Bu'Lock sees the concentrations on the Pennine slopes as representing the western advances of established single grave communities from the east (Bu'Lock 1961, 15).

The flat cemeteries are often, though not invariably, associated with circle monuments. Burl (1976, 62) points out that the further south one goes in the Pennines, the more the stone circle tradition overlaps with that of the enclosed cremation cemeteries and ring cairns – mid second millennium monuments in which several deposits of cremated bones were placed within a penannular bank, as at Blackheath (327) and Mosley Height (48).

The circle monument is a distinctive type of site common to many upland areas of Britain. In the Peak District they are found almost entirely on the gritstone areas flanking the limestone to the east (Lewis 1970, Fig. 10), and Burl (1976, 289) suggests that the antecedents for these cremation cemeteries may be in the Central Pennines where the multiple cremations in the stone-lined enclosures of Blackheath and Mosley Height were accompanied by 'Pennine' urns, pygmy cups, faience beads, etc. A juxtaposition of stone rings, complex ring cairns and earth circles occurs on Big Moor, south east of our area, where a date of $1,500 \pm 150$ b.c. (BM 179) was obtained from Barbrook II, a complex ring cairn, coinciding with the period of major clearance (see below). A ring cairn at Brown Edge to the north of the latter has a series of dates between $1,530 \pm 150$ b.c. and $1,050 \pm 150$ b.c. (BM 212 and 177) (Radley 1966c), the latter date being at a time when the moorland was already being abandoned.

The other circle monuments were described by Radley (1966c, 11) under the general heading of 'ring works'. He defined such a structure as ranging between two extremes: plain, earth-embanked circles with or without an entrance, made from scraping the soil from the outside or from the central area; and, secondly, free standing stone circles. Between these are several variations; earth circles with a central mound, earth circles with standing stone circles inside or on the bank, and stone circles with a central mound (eg Fig. 31). Where stones occur they are seldom more than three feet high, and most stand on low overgrown banks. The circles average about 35 feet in diameter and invariably enclose areas of multiple burials. A possible evolution occurred in these monuments during the second millennium, starting as free circles and concluding as tiny earthen enclosures (Burl 1976, 288). The only true stone circles in the Central and South Pennines are on the limestone of the Peak District, though in our area a 'plain ring', a circle consisting of ten irregular stones, some 35 feet in diameter, with a circular structure in the centre, was recorded at Walshaw Dean in 1902 before the construction of the reservoirs (336). The 'ring works' in the Central Pennines are listed in Table 3 and shown on Fig. 14.

The two most spectacular examples are those at Blackheath (327) and Mosley Height (48). The former is located on the south facing slopes of the Calder valley, and is about 100 feet in diameter (Fig. 36). An earthen circular bank enclosed an area with cairns containing cremations in association with 'Pennine' urns (eg Fig. 15, ii). Sherds of several urns were found together with seven more or less complete urns and four pygmy vessels. The central urn contained one of these pygmy vessels which in turn contained a bronze knife, a bronze pin and a bone pin. Two urns with cremations were probably covered by other vessels, one of them also containing a pygmy vessel and various beads, which will be discussed later. A fourth urn had a cremation and a bone pin. The vessels were all upright and some were surrounded by numerous thin, flat stones placed on edge. One urn was found in the bank. Some parts of the floor were baked by great heat, and the excavator suggested that the pots may have been made here, and where possibly the bodies were cremated. Clay for the urns was seemingly dug from two deep holes found within the circle, and it was tempered with pounded gritstone of which great quantities lay in part of the enclosure. There was the suggestion of at least one

Figure 14.

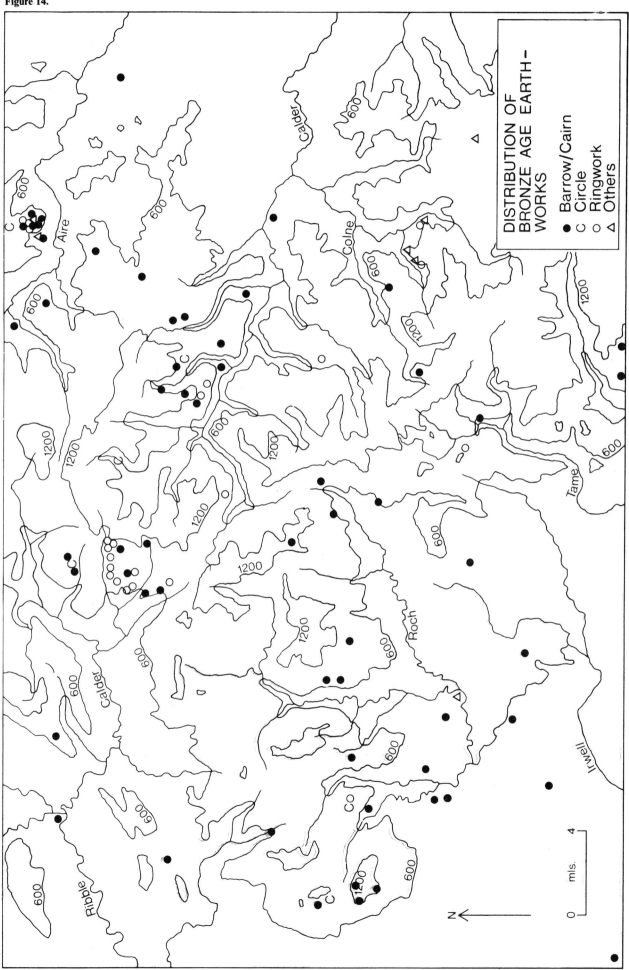

DISTRIBUTION OF BRONZE AGE EARTH-WORKS

● Barrow/Cairn
C Circle
○ Ringwork
△ Others

Table 3 'Ring Works' in the Central Pennines

Bolton, Turton, Chetham's Close	52 feet diameter	stone circle
Bolton, Turton, Chetham's Close	72 feet diameter	ring mound
Burnley, Broadbank	150 feet diameter	earth circle
Burnley, Delf Hill	14 feet diameter	ring mound, 7 stones
Burnley, Hell Clough I	24–30 feet diameter	ring mound
Burnley, Hell Clough II		ring mound, 7 stones
Burnley, Hell Clough III	55–8 feet diameter	ring mound, 7 stones
Burnley, Mosley Height	42 feet diameter	embanked circle
Burnley, Ringstone Hill		ring mound
Burnley, Slipper Hill		ring mound, stone circle
Burnley, Twist Hill	27 feet diameter	earth circle
Burnley, Wasnop Edge II	21 feet diameter	earth circle
Horwich, Anglezarke, Standing Stones Hill	65–70 feet diameter	kerbed mound?
Nelson, Ringstone Hill I		stone circle?
Ramsbottom, Whitelow	68 feet diameter	ring bank
Saddleworth, Hill Top	45 feet diameter	ring mound
Baildon, Birch Close	81 feet diameter	stone circle?
Baildon, Dobrudden I	50 feet diameter	ring barrow
Baildon, Dobrudden III		ring barrow
Baildon, Pennythorn Hill I	50 feet diameter	earth circle?
Barkisland, Ringstone Edge	88 feet diameter	ring work, stone circle?
Bingley, Harden Moor	25 feet diameter	embanked circle
Halifax, Midgley, Han Royd		earth circle?
Halifax, Robin Hood's Penny Stone		stone circle?
Hebden Bridge, Wadsworth, Cockhill II	132 feet diameter	earth circle
Hebden Bridge, Walshaw Dean	36 feet diameter	stone circle
Honley, Hagg Wood	38 feet diameter	ring bank
Honley, Slate Pitts Wood	52 feet diameter	ring bank
Todmorden, Blackheath	100 feet diameter	embanked circle

rudimentary 'furnace', a cist-like structure surrounded by baked soil. Some of the cremations were found in hollows without urns, while other finds scattered about the site included flint scrapers and knives, a burnt leaf-shaped arrowhead near the centre, a whetstone and grain rubbers (Roth 1906, 307–22).

The Mosley Height circle was likewise situated on a hillside, overlooking the northern entrance to the Cliviger gorge. Here a circle of 18 large boulders were irregularly spaced on a stony bank enclosing a paved space 42 feet across (Fig. 30). Three bowl-shaped holes were found in the bank and a fourth just outside. A small central cist contained an inverted collared urn with the cremated remains of an adult female, the urn being crudely decorated with four rows of twisted cord. In pits set haphazardly about this central burial were other cremated burials, one inside an inverted urn, one in a badly broken urn and one unurned (Fig. 15, i). The other remains in the circle have already been described. There is a suggestion here, too, that pottery was made from local clay within the ring bank itself (Hallam 1970, 235). Burl suggests that this site in particular, as its geographical position suggests, has demonstrable affinities with enclosed cremation cemeteries and with stone circles, while there are several other smaller ring works with stone settings in the same neighbourhood, about which far less is known.

Fleming (1971, 23ff) suggests that perhaps the circles were intended not only for burial but also for important ritual activities; certainly some of them contain puzzling 'ritual pits', while others which are larger in diameter than the average barrow suggest that an evolution in their status and function may have occurred. It is possible that the ring work developed from the concentration on an early phase in the ritual which culminated in the erection of a barrow: many old excavation reports mention that barrows, both in this area and further afield, contained internal perimeter pre barrow enclosures which stood while the primary and satellite burials were being made. The reason why their completion was not accomplished may have been due to a declining population, meaning that labour could not be spared for the laborious carting of stone.

It is possible that in some of the cases where urns have been discovered there never was any barrow or other structure, and the idea of flat cemeteries might be invoked. In most of the cases, however, the circumstances surrounding the discovery of the urns is very vague, and invariably they were uncovered during such activities as quarrying, as in the case of the Rastrick, Warley and Brownhill (Saddleworth) urns.

Figure 15. Collared Urns from Burnley and Todmorden.

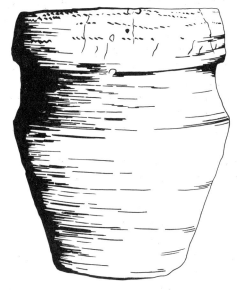

I. Urns from Burnley. Mosley Height (48) Scales 1:3, 2:5.

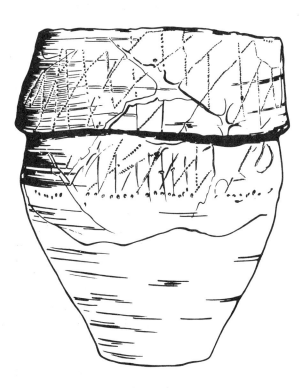

II. Urns from Todmorden, Blackheath (327) Scales 1:2, 1:3.

Grave traditions were in the typical, if devolved, long barrow tradition in both the Southern and Central Pennines prior to the arrival of the single grave element (Manby 1957 and 1967). Some aspects of the grave forms which may be traced back to this tradition will be mentioned below.

Unfortunately, most of the records are very vague when describing grave structures in the Central Pennines, less than one third having sufficient details to help to provide a picture of the whole. Both inhumation and cremation were practised in the area during the Bronze Age, though the latter was far more numerous: only six inhumations have been definitely recorded. A possible continuance of Neolithic traditions is seen in the re-use of barrows for more than one inhumation as at Wind Hill (Heywood) and at Ferry Fryston, just outside the area, though in each case the earlier burial was destroyed in the process. From the scanty records, it is impossible to state whether grave goods were richer in the case of inhumations than with cremated burials, as they are in the Peak District (Lewis 1970, 63). But when the metal artefacts are examined, it emerges that they represent the earlier period only. Later artefacts such as palstaves and socketed implements are not found in graves, and there is an increasing impoverishment of grave furniture.

At only two sites (Pule Hill and Stonyhurst) were the two burial rites found together (two inhumations and at least two cremations at Pule Hill). Multiple burials, however, are common. The Darwen barrow or 'cemetery mound' (Bu'Lock 1961, 17) contained ten cremations, nine in urns which in each case were covered by a flat stone, one being accompanied by a pygmy cup as well (3). The burial mound at Noon Hill, Rivington, contained six or seven groups of cremated bones, one under an inverted food vessel in a stone cist consisting of three individuals, a man, woman and child (79). Both the burial mounds near Ramsbottom (Whitelow and Bank Lane) contained multiple cremations (71 and 68) as did the Cliviger Laithe cairn near Burnley, where the burnt remains of up to five persons were accompanied by three urns (36). At nearby Hell Clough, the urn contained the cremated remains of two persons, an adult and a child (46). As mentioned earlier, some of the ring monuments contained a considerable number of burials: Blackheath, Todmorden (327), at least ten; Ringstone, Barkisland (285), five; and Mosley Height, Burnley (48), four. It has also been described how some sites were possibly flat cemeteries: thus at Rastrick (292) some 20 urns were unearthed; at Breightmet (14) twelve; at Warley (338) at least five; and at Skircoat (301) three. These cremation cemeteries of the Early Bronze Age can be seen to continue Neolithic ideas of multiple burial (Burgess 1970, 210).

Inhumation burials in barrows occur on the natural surface or in a pit, and in the latter case they may be in a cist, roughly enclosed by stones, or laid on a pavement. Cremation burials, too, may be in a pit, cist, below a pavement, or roughly enclosed by stones. The simplest form of grave pit is commonly associated with Beaker folk, and this is abundantly illustrated by Beaker inhumations in the Peak District (Lewis 1970, 52). Beaker burials are poorly recorded in our area, but at Ferry Fryston just to the east a beaker was accompanied by a crouched inhumation in a pit (Pacitto 1968, 297). The possible Beaker burial at Wind Hill, Heywood (165), occurred as a surface inhumation below a barrow (Tyson 1980). The cairn at Walmsley, Bolton, contained an inhumation in a cist accompanied by a possible food vessel (25), while at Noon Hill, Rivington, an enlarged food vessel occurred in a secondary position in the cairn (79). The Pule Hill food vessel burials were in cavities in the rock about 18 inches deep, 36 inches long and 24 inches wide (374), while at Ferry Fryston a crouched inhumation accompanied by a food vessel occurred in a secondary position cist to that of the beaker interment (Pacitto 1968, 297).

In the Peak District, 'shallow' pits were most common, of which five were occupied by food vessel burials. None, however, contained a beaker burial; these were always associated with 'deep' pits (Lewis 1970, 52–3). No such distinction can be drawn in our area. On the other hand, in both areas the cremation pits commonly connected with collared urn burials were usually shallow, though here again the structures varied enormously. Some occurred in cists. At Mount Zion, Ovenden, a square cavity of four upright stones was covered by stone slabs and contained a cremation (309). Inhumations were found in cists at Law House, Burnley (38), and at Walmsley and Haulgh, both near Bolton: in the latter the structure measured 54 inches in length and 12 inches in depth. At Hell Clough, two cremations in an urn were in a cist 18 inches square, built of 'unhewn' stones, which was covered by a triangular slab of grit (March 1886), the whole being enclosed in a circle monument (46). The urned burial at Lowhouse, near Milnrow, was also placed in a rough cist (172), while the burial at Snoddle Hill, Little-borough, had probably been placed in a similar rough structure (170). Finally, at Wasnop Edge, Burnley (56), in a cairn excavated in 1886, no burial was found but the centre was 'arranged like a long sarcophagus' (Bennett 1946, 15). The main grave in the Bank Lane, Ramsbottom, cairn was a stone lined pit seven feet long and two feet wide, and this, too, was empty when opened (68).

Like the Wind Hill (Heywood) cairn, several of the other cairns and circles in the area had no pits or cists, namely Hades Hill, Rochdale (161), Cliviger Laithe, Burnley (36), and possibly Darwen (3). The settings of the urns at Blackheath, Todmorden, have already been described, and they too were on the surface. The urn in the Rose Hill cairn at Bolton was inverted and sunk about six inches into the earth (23).

Thus a mixture of grave traditions obtains, and when these are considered together with the nature of the actual burial structures and the pottery, many survivals from the Neolithic can be discerned. It may be suggested that this is entirely in keeping with the area's geographical situation, largely a backwater and on the fringe of the main developments.

3. *Metalwork*
Though by no means as rich as the Peak District in the occurrence of metalwork, the Central Pennine area does have over 70 find spots, and the objects do exhibit a wider range than the pottery. The difficulty lies in the fact that the great bulk of them are unassociated, occurring as casual finds. To some extent, as with the Peak District (Lewis 1970, 99), the area's location in relation to the rest of the country is reflected at different times by the bronze working traditions of the North and Ireland on the one hand and of southern England on the other, though naturally the former predominate. By no means all the finds are described below, but the distribution can be seen on Fig. 16 and a list is provided in the Index (Appendix 2).

Only ten of the bronze objects (more than 120 in total) have been found in definite association with burials, and from the examples described below it can be seen that all of these have a 'trinket' aspect. In the cairn at Haulgh, Bolton, a dagger with three rivet holes was found with a contracted inhumation in a cist: the dagger was on one side of the head while on the other side was an inverted biconical pygmy vessel (20). It is interesting that these flat riveted knives and daggers are generally broadly contemporary with the sparse, late insular Beaker tradition. At Darwen (Frontispiece), a dagger was found in one of the nine urned cremations which were accompanied by a pygmy vessel beneath a barrow (3). In a barrow at Revidge, Blackburn, a bronze pin head was found associated with a cremation in an urn together with a bone pin (6), while at Whitelow, Ramsbottom, a bronze awl was found with the primary burial (cremation) in a pit (71). At Hell Clough, Burnley, the embanked circle had a cist containing an urn with two cremations and a bronze pin or awl four inches long (46). Finally, the central burial in the embanked circle at Blackheath, Todmorden, contained a bronze knife and awl together with a bone pin and clay beads (327). At Ferry Fryston (outside the area) a small awl occurred with the Beaker burial, possibly belonging to the phase 1,750–1,650/1,600 b.c. (Manby 1964b, 346).

Moulds for Bronze Age metalwork are very thinly distributed in northern England. A notable find of an early date, not far south of our area, at Hope Woodlands in the Dark Peak, consisted of sandstone moulds for bronze ingots and rings. These were attributed to the Migdale/Marnock tradition (Britton 1965, 324–5; Challis & Harding 1975, 15). Just outside our area again, copper 'celts' are said to have been found near Brunthwaite Crag (SE 0546) in the Aire Valley, these being sold by the finder for scrap metal (Keighley Museum). A fragment of an early thick-butted bronze axe from Howden Ridge near Keighley (269) in the

Figure 16.

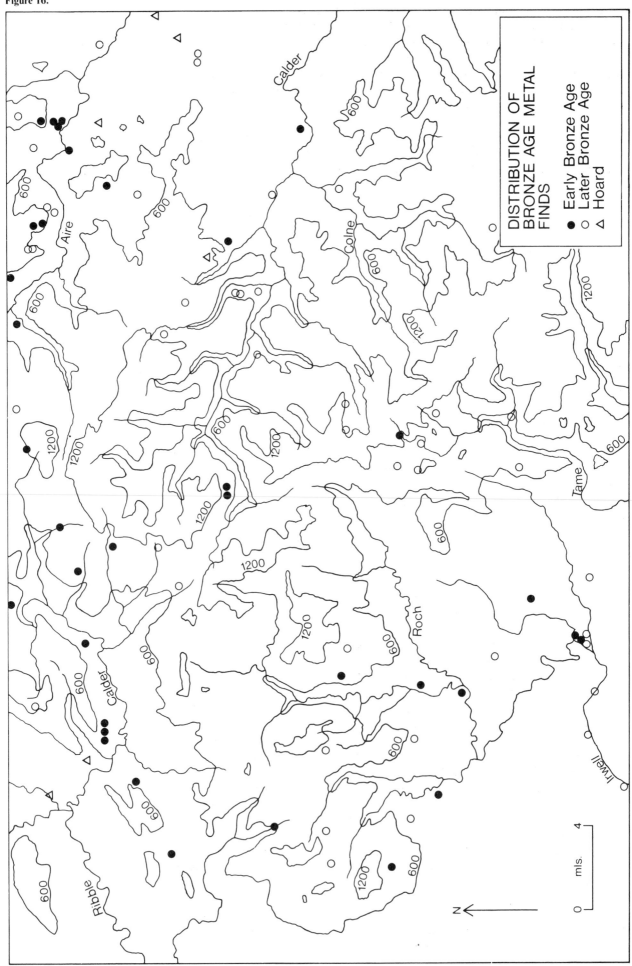

DISTRIBUTION OF
BRONZE AGE METAL
FINDS

● Early Bronze Age
○ Later Bronze Age
△ Hoard

extreme north of our area, belonging to the period 1,750–1,650/1,600 b.c. suggests that the Aire Gap route might already have been in use as a metal implement route (Manby 1964b, 346). The use of this route was discussed by Elgee (1933, 5ff), and likewise by Raistrick (1928) and Watson (1952), discussing the distribution of bronze axes, which showed a concentration extending from East Yorkshire along the terminal moraine via York and Tadcaster (see also Radley 1974, 11) to Leeds, and then through the Aire Gap to the Ribble valley. Another minor concentration of finds occurs along the Yorkshire Calder valley connecting with the Ribble valley via the Cliviger gorge and the Burnley area, or with the Mersey basin to the south west via the Manchester district.

Most of the flat bronze axes in the area probably belong to the Migdale tradition (Britton 1963), and the use of the trans Pennine routes is again reflected in their distribution. They include examples from Blacko Tower (134), Great Harwood (89), three from Read (151) and one from Ickornshaw Moor (342), all on the southern flanks of Ribblesdale. The Migdale industry of around 1650/1600–1550/1500 b.c. continued in its next phase with the flat axe developing into an axe with slight flanges (c. 1550/1500–1400 b.c.), the Arreton industry (Britton 1963). A thin-butted axe from Hipperholme has been related rather generally to the period between 2000–1400 b.c. (289), and on the whole this south east based Arreton industry is even less numerous in our area. Arreton axes from Keighley and Bradford (together with one from Silsden to the north of our area) suggest that the Aire Gap route was still in use. Others include the Rishworth axe (311), probably the flanged axe from Radcliffe (65) (Fig. 17, i) and one just outside the area at Sandal Magna (SE 343184) near Wakefield (Varley 1977). East Yorkshire associations show the Urn people to have been users of Arreton products but the position regarding Food Vessel people in the area is obscure (Manby 1964b, 351). On Mixenden Moor (308), a hoard found before 1816 included a palstave, four barbed-and-tanged arrowheads, a polished stone axe, a stone axe-hammer and a gouge, the contents suggesting a homesteader's possessions with the palstave placing the hoard in an Early-Middle Bronze Age context (Varley 1977, 57). Other probable Early Bronze Age implements include tanged spearheads from Nelson (138), Burnley (26), and Boggart Hole Clough, Manchester (95).

Implements definitely assigned to Burgess's Pickering Phase (c. 1400–1200 b.c.) are rare in our area. A palstave from Edgeworth, to the north of Bolton (4), belongs to this period – perhaps the later part of it in view of the developed state of its form and ornament (Prag 1977). Wing-flanged axes predominate in the Hotham Carr phase (c. 1200–1000 b.c.) (Burgess 1968, 3), and an example was found at Skircoat prior to 1775 (300), which was a close parallel to another found just outside our area near Wakefield (Varley 1974, 174). The assignation of bronzes in the area to these phases and to the subsequent Penard phase (c. 1050–950 b.c.) is very obscure, however, and in this part of England many Penard types continued to provide a major element in the Wallington and associated hoards (Burgess 1968, 5).

The upper limit for the Wallington tradition is around 1000 b.c. The transitional palstave became the characteristic axe form and the straight basal-looped spearhead is one of several Wallington spearhead types. The Shelf hoard (Fig. 35) included a looped palstave, a low-flanged palstave, 4 transitional palstaves, a late palstave, a side-looped spearhead, a basal-looped straight-based spearhead, the point of a large leaf-shaped spearhead blade and a broken spearhead socket (322). This may be a worker's hoard since its series of palstaves includes an unfinished example (the late palstave). Its spearheads are in a very fragmentary state but they were described as 'much decayed' when found (Watson 1952, 88) and this is probably due to the soil conditions and their history since discovery. By virtue of its transitional palstaves and straight-based, basal-looped spearhead, the hoard must have coincided at least in part with the Penard phase of the late eleventh and tenth centuries, yet it includes a late palstave which requires contemporaneity with the Wilburton tradition (Burgess 1968, 28–9). Analysis of the last example showed it to be of ordinary tin-bronze, so that it was presumably a local copy under Wilburton influence. Individual finds in the area of Wallington types include transitional palstaves from Crompton Moor (133), Sowerby (323) and Wall Green,

Figure 17. Bronze Implements. Actual size.

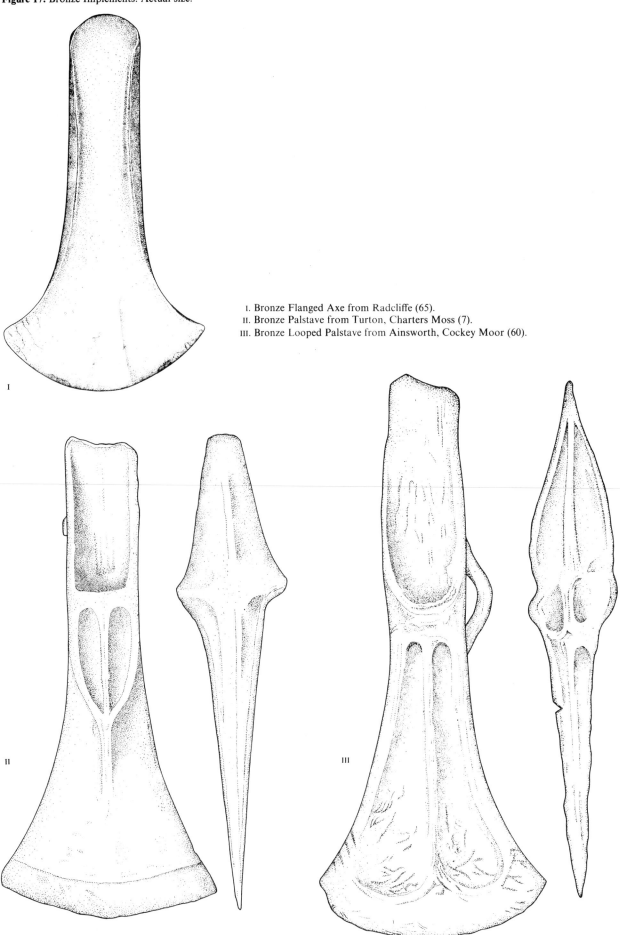

I. Bronze Flanged Axe from Radcliffe (65).
II. Bronze Palstave from Turton, Charters Moss (7).
III. Bronze Looped Palstave from Ainsworth, Cockey Moor (60).

Saddleworth (132), and a spearhead from Brighouse (290), while another Walling-ton hoard has been identified at Farsley (259) (Gilks 1973b, 179).

Only a slight Wilburton penetration occurred in the area, and even this might have arrived late on the scene, probably in the eighth century B.C. (Burgess 1968, 40). A crude leaf-shaped peg-hole spearhead from Milnrow (174) may belong to this phase, while the 'River Ribble' group of implements (of uncertain provenance but probably a genuine hoard) includes some items possessing Wilburton influences (152).

Another hoard from the site of the Iron Age fort at Portfield near Whalley (155) included bronzes which were all damaged in antiquity, and comprises two socketed axes, part of a socketed gouge, parts of the hilt and blade of a tanged knife, part of another knife blade, and a tanged stud, together with some gold objects. The latter which were in a good condition when buried comprised a pennanular lock-ring and a gold bracelet with outwardly expanded terminals with D-section. Thus the association of different designs and types of gold and bronze objects at Portfield gives a firm date within the Heathery Burn phase of the Late Bronze Age. The hoard is considered to reflect contacts with the Irish metal industry and possible trans Pennine routes (Blundell & Longworth 1967–8, 13). Bu'Lock (1965) suggested it was the property of a trader, bartering from a small stock of new gold ornaments for scrap bronze.

Late Bronze Age forms in Britain generally reflect the full adoption, but not the first appearance, of socketed axes, leaf-shaped swords and pegged spearheads. None of the last two named have been found in our area, but socketed axes have been found on eleven sites at least. As was mentioned above, the change to the Late Bronze Age in this area was late, about the eighth century B.C.

The geographical distribution of Bronze Age metalwork in the area (Fig. 16) is restricted largely to the valleys and valley sides, and to the foothills of the Pennines: it is particularly associated with the better drained areas and possibly with the routeways through the hills.

4. *Other Artefacts*

Over 70 stone implements with Bronze Age connections have been identified (Fig. 18), excluding flint artefacts and other small stone objects. The last mentioned, which include shale and clay artefacts, jet and amber ornaments, and galena are invariably associated with burials, as are bone pins together with a number of flint implements. The great majority of the larger stone artefacts, on the other hand, in common with the metalwork, occur as stray finds. Of these, axe-hammers are the most numerous.

Only five, possibly six, of the larger stone implements were found associated with burials. At Lowhouse, Milnrow (172), an axe-hammer was found with an unurned cremation in a composite cairn, while a flint 'battle-axe' is reputed to have been found in a ring mound at Hell Clough II, Burnley (45). A pebble macehead was found inside an urn at Brownhill, Saddleworth, and a second 'celt' is said to have been found later on the same site (114). In the Mosley Height burial circle near Burnley, loosely associated with several urned burials, were a number of stone implements including two polished grain rubbing stones, parts of three querns, three polished 'hand hammers' and a 'pestle', together with numerous flint scrapers, arrowheads and knives and two pieces of Kimmeridge shale (48).

All the other associated finds consist of smaller objects. Flint knives were also found in cairns at Walmsley, Bolton (25) and Wind Hill, Heywood (165), at the latter with a pebble hammer, while flint arrowheads, scrapers and pieces of flint occur widely in burial mounds and circle monuments, such as those at Blackheath, Todmorden (327), Wind Hill, Heywood, Snoddle Hill, Littleborough (170), Pule Hill (374) and Wadsworth (330), and sometimes they are burnt as at Hades Hill, near Rochdale (161). At Whitelow, Ramsbottom (71), a clay stud was found with the flints, and at Noon Hill, Rivington (79), a wide variety of flint implements was found with the several burials, including burnt barbed-and-tanged arrowheads, a transverse arrowhead and scrapers, together with a sandstone 'ball' and a flint knife. A jet stud is said to have been associated with a barrow on Rishworth Moor (313) (Tolson Memorial Museum, Huddersfield). The other occurrences of this

Figure 18.

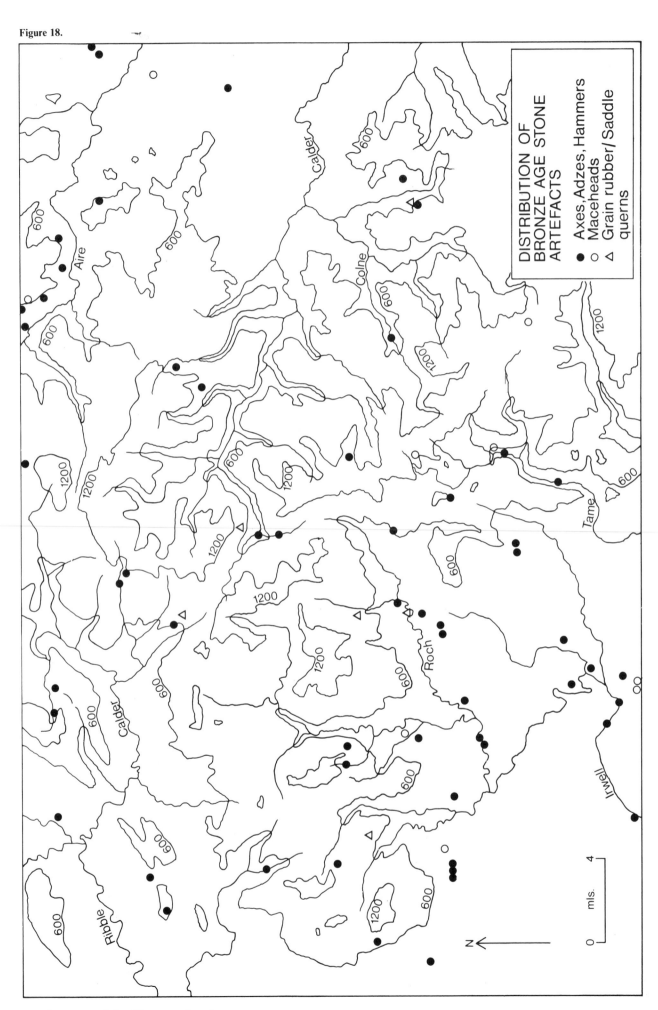

DISTRIBUTION OF
BRONZE AGE STONE
ARTEFACTS

● Axes, Adzes, Hammers
○ Maceheads
△ Grain rubber/Saddle
   querns

material in the Central Pennines are at Blackheath, Todmorden, and Wind Hill, Heywood, while another find of jet was made at Thornton Moor to the north (King 1969, 46). Pieces of galena were found in the cairn at Cliviger Laithe, near Burnley (36). together with a bone pin, and such pins also occurred with the burials at Blackheath, Todmorden, Revidge, Blackburn (6) and Breightmet, Bolton (14).

Besides the flint knives found in the barrows mentioned above, they have also been found widely scattered, though comparatively few in number, on the moors, where they are of rather uncertain age, as at Ragstone and Rocher Moss, both in Saddleworth (126 and 128), West Nab, Meltham (379), two on Rishworth Moor (315) and at least two from Worsthorne, near Burnley (58 and 59).

In one of the urns in the cremation cemetery at Blackheath, Todmorden, were four segmented faience beads, all with eight segments, three spherical beads ornamented with grooves, some large amber beads, nine beads of jet or shale, two bone pins, a pygmy cup, flint flakes and a leaf-shaped arrowhead. The urn was sealed by another inverted over it (Stone & Thomas 1956, 80). Another segmented faience bead has been found in the cairn at Bank Lane, Ramsbottom, where it might have been associated with either a food vessel or an urn (68). It is interesting that only eight faience beads have been found in the Peak District (Lewis 1970, 150), where, with the area's trading connections, one might have expected a greater number.

The casual finds of larger stone artefacts are widely distributed. One interpretation of this spread might relate it to the routeways through the uplands, especially when compared with a similar distribution of the metalwork. There is a notable concentration of these stone artefacts, and in particular of axe-hammers, along the southern flanks of the Rossendale Uplands and in the Manchester area, both in the Mersey–Irwell drainage basin, while another occurs in the Aire valley. Equally significant, however, is the possible relationship of this distribution to the areas of agricultural land on the periphery of the marginal upland areas. Though the functions of many of these artefacts vary, it is very likely that they were all related to clearance and cultivation – although one must beware of treating their concentration or total numbers as any index of the intensity of this clearance (Bradley 1978a, 13). Thus a study of the relative frequency of Neolithic axes and Early Bronze Age axe-hammers indicates much greater activity west of the Pennines than in Neolithic times (Cummins 1980, 50). The smaller flint implements, especially barbed-and-tanged arrowheads, have a different distribution, and are found almost entirely on the moors, a spread compatible with hunting. As stated already, many of them are found in the same localities as Neolithic arrowheads and Mesolithic flints.

Palynological Evidence
Nearly all the pollen diagrams for the Pennine areas indicate forest clearance on the uplands and slopes during the Bronze Age, and likewise on the North Yorkshire Moors (Simmons 1969a; Spratt & Simmons 1976, 203). On Rishworth Moor, in the heart of the Central Pennines, heather and cotton grass spread only gradually at the expense of trees from the late Neolithic/Early Bronze Age to the end of the Bronze Age, slight clearance phases being dated between $2,060 \pm 100$ b.c. (GaK 2823) and 470 ± 100 b.c. (GaK 2824). The pollen diagrams here suggest irregular and spasmodic changes, and the clearances were probably not sufficient to make any great change on the overall intensity of the woodland, the inference being that the uplands in the vicinity were used only for summer pasture (Bartley 1975, 378). A similar picture is suggested for Featherbed Moss on the higher uplands to the south (Tallis & Switsur 1973), and for East Moor on the periphery of the Peak District. Pollen analysis in the latter area suggests a continuance of small scale clearings as in the Neolithic period, possibly connected with a food vessel date at Harland Edge of $1,750 \pm 150$ b.c. (BM 210). A major phase of clearance around 1,500 b.c. may be associated with another food vessel date of $1,490 \pm 150$ b.c. (BM 178) at Harland Edge and a collared urn at Barbrook II of $1,500 \pm 150$ b.c. (BM 179). Subsequent clearances occurred in smaller numbers possibly until after 1000 B.C.; but any opening of the forest during all this time was

due to pastoral activities, there being little evidence of arable farming (Hicks 1972, 9–10).

A reduction in the use of the moors is suggested by a decrease in the amount of burning after Neolithic times, and the fact that trees were able to colonise the shallower peats. The subsequent death of these trees may have been due to natural causes, although since most of them were relatively young it is more probable that deliberate woodland clearance was involved (Tallis 1975, 484). Thus a changing pattern of Bronze Age, and possibly Iron Age, usage of the moors is indicated.

Again, in Rossendale, intermittent local clearances occurred in the uplands from the Neolithic period through to the Iron Age, these clearances differing in character and intensity (Tallis & McGuire 1972, 727). Between about 1170 B.C. and 690 B.C., they occurred mainly on the edges of the uplands, but were followed by upland clearances between 690 and 500 B.C. As in the Neolithic, there is no indication in the pollen diagram of arable farming in this district during the Bronze Age. A similar picture is painted for Nidderdale, to the north of our area, where there were two interference phases after 2000 B.C., one possibly associated with Beaker pastoralists and the other occurring later in the Bronze Age (Tinsley 1975, 21).

At Winter Hill and Wind Hill, at the eastern and western ends of the Rossendale Uplands respectively, the soils beneath the Bronze Age barrows show a developing podsol structure, and the pollen spectra indicate the local establishment of heathland communities with adjoining deciduous woodland, probably with birch and hazel predominant (Tallis & McGuire 1972, 729; Tallis in Tyson (1980, 16)). As mentioned earlier, it is feasible that clearance in Mesolithic times may have started the deterioration in the soil structure. Discussing the Blackamore Forest in North Yorkshire, Dimbleby (1961, 125ff) described the evidence for a similar heathy vegetation under the barrows, and suggested that they were built in these clearings because the land was no longer useful. If this were so, the grazing must have been along the forest margins. He went on to suggest that such openings in the forest were often the undesired result of activities rather than the ultimate aim. This was indicated by the fact that heath colonised them rather than grass or plantain, the fact that barrows were built in them before they were very large itself suggesting that they were made inadvertently rather than deliberately. If grazing was on the forest margins then this would be so because here there would be just sufficient light to allow grass to flourish, but insufficient to allow the invasion of heather. Such conditions can be imagined under hazel in the Bronze Age, and this concurs with the evidence presented, for example, by the pollens from the buried soil beneath the Heywood (Wind Hill) barrow.

Thus, by the end of the Bronze Age, the upland plateaux were dominated by extending peat bog or heath, while the upper slopes below the peat line had an open, discontinuous tree cover. The lower slopes and parts of the lowlands were probably grassland, especially where the better, well drained soils occurred, as is suggested by some lowland pollen diagrams (Birks 1965, 310), with pastoralism dominant. Elsewhere on the lowlands, 'high forest' still predominated, particularly on the heavier glacial boulder clays.

Discussion

As with the Neolithic, restricted aspects of technology and way of death provide much of the archaeological evidence for the Bronze Age. So far as the burial evidence, the pottery and a good deal of the lithic and metal technology is concerned, the early part of the period is highlighted, followed by an hiatus. The Middle Bronze Age sees new metalwork fashions and new attitudes to burial and ritual, and though the survival of urn forms into the Middle Bronze Age has been suggested, it cannot be demonstrated: neither is there much evidence of a Middle Bronze Age Deverel-Rimbury presence in the area. Finds associated with urns (and other pottery) are all consistently Early Bronze Age in date, and, as Bu'Lock (1961) was one of the first to remark, it is difficult to show that these early pottery types were current at a later date. Respectable Late Neolithic ancestries can be found for all of them, and the Neolithic/Bronze Age continuity is easier to demonstrate than that of the Early/Middle Bronze Age. The close relationship of most of the ritual and burial monuments with the Early Bronze Age and with urns in particular has been demonstrated, together with surviving Neolithic traits in some of them.

Pollen evidence suggests irregular and spasmodic forest clearances during the period, generally small scale in character. Evidence of interference with the forests, however, does appear to be widespread, and this, together with the large number of finds, related in particular to the earlier part of the period, shows a widespread activity on both the lower hills and on the higher ground, and it may be inferred that there was a larger population than in Neolithic times. There is little palyno-logical evidence for arable farming, but the scattered querns and rubbing stones which have been found on the peripheries of the uplands do suggest that there must have been some. The main mechanism by which settlement was effected may have been – as in the Neolithic – an economy which favoured woodland grazing in the Central Pennines, possibly on a seasonal basis and carried on from habitations of more lasting status on the lower ground. The presence of many barbed-and-tanged arrowheads on the moors, including the highest ground, presumably means that hunting remained a means of food gathering, reflecting the continuing disturbance of the forest cover (Bradley 1978b, 100). As in the Neolithic, even minor variations in soils and climate were critical for crop ripening, and despite the better climate of the Early Bronze Age, favourable areas even on the foothills must have been individually too small or scattered. The soil also was often too poor to provide the basis for cultivation and settlement. The foothill zones of the Pennines today are classified as being land capable of only medium productivity even under management, and handicapped by unfavourable relief, by shallow soils or by poor drainage (Coppock 1976, Fig. 10), while such conditions must have been magnified by the poorer technology of the Bronze Age inhabitants. Where settlement can be inferred, it may have been partially conditioned by ease of access to the drier uplands, with fishing and fowling near the rivers, though the rise in the water table, a consequence of the deteriorating climate during the later part of the period, may have made conditions more adverse at these lower altitudes. Thus Early Bronze Age penetration of the lowlands to the east of the Pennines in the Vale of York was slight compared with that of east Yorkshire (and even with the Pennines), while later Bronze Age finds on the lowlands are fewer still due to the increasingly adverse physical conditions (Palmer 1966, 105–6). Examination of the pattern and nature of metal finds to the west of the Pennine watershed has led to the suggestion that coastal sites and other lowland areas were occupied during the Early and Middle Bronze Age and that there was increasing colonisation of the upper sections of the valleys as time went on, in part a response to the increasingly wet conditions in the lower valleys (Davey 1976, 12). An exception to this pattern is that exhibited by bronzes from burials, although in this respect it must be remembered that the barrows were probably sited in rather unrepresentative environments.

An interesting feature is the occurrence of abundant remains on the gritstone moors to the east of the Peak District (though not to the west) associated with urn burials, coinciding as has been seen with a break in the continuity of the rich development on the limestone, a cessation of cairn building and poorer grave goods associated with the urns there (Radley 1966c, 13). Most of the cairns in the Central Pennines have also produced collared urns, and the usual view has been that the gritstone uplands were settled as a result of population pressure in the more favourable areas such as the Peak District (eg Childe 1940, 156).

Associated with the spread on to the gritstone uplands is the increasing dominance of the ring work type of cemetery. As mentioned already, the develop-ment of circle monuments reflects the chronological, environmental and cultural changes from open megalithic rings to minute ring banks around burial pits, and this is illustrated best in the sequence from the limestone Peak to the neighbouring gritstone uplands (Burl 1976, 289). A similar variety can be found in the Central Pennines, varying from the one or two small open circles on the one hand to small embanked circles on the other, and ultimately to platform cairns in a few cases, though the chronology here is not as apparent.

These circular monuments rarely occur in isolation but are grouped and often occur in association with cairns. Radley (1966c, 13–19) describes 6 groups on East

Moor to the south east of our area, the furthest north of which is at Broomhead Moor. In our area, further groups can be identified. One overlaps the north eastern boundary from Rombalds Moor to Baildon Moor and Harden Moor. In the Calderdale area, there were formerly three earth circles at Cock Hill, Wadsworth (330); on Midgley Moor are several enclosures, other earthworks and possible barrows (Roth 1906, 306); while at New Laithe, Wadsworth, is a hut circle, 35 feet wide with kerbed rubble walls (331). To the south of the river, a less impressive rubble circle together with other nearby earthworks can be found on Ringstone Moor, Barkisland (285, 286, 288) (Longbotham 1932). The third main concentration is east of Burnley, where there are at least 11 earthen or rubble circles together with other nearby circles not properly identified, while outlying circle monuments occur at Turton to the north of Bolton. These groups of circle monuments and other remains may have significance with regard to Bronze Age settlement (Fig. 14).

The identification of Bronze Age settlement sites in the Central Pennines and elsewhere is difficult because of the lack of clear field monuments and the paucity of material remains which can be placed in a definite context. However, the cairn group or 'extensive settlement' is an important class of field monument, and can broadly be attributed to the early part of the period (Challis & Harding 1975, 125). In northern England these have a severely limited geographical distribution: they are generally on the heather moorlands of grit or sandstone, invariably between 600 and 1,400 feet O.D., and consist of groups of small, stony cairns which are often associated with lengths of rough walling. There are three main concentrations (Challis & Harding 1975, Fig. 84): the North York Moors, the gritstone Pennines, and the peripheral fells of the Lake District. Elgee (1930, 100) considered the cairn had a funerary function, although he also suggested they were possibly associated with habitation in North Yorkshire. Their association with walling together with the evidence of excavation suggests that field clearance was an important and possibly the primary objective. The evidence for North Yorkshire was reconsidered more recently (Fleming 1971), and clearance for agriculture by small groups of shifting cultivators over a period of 200–400 years in the Early Bronze Age was suggested. Similar cairn groups, together with embanked circles, stone-banked enclosures, and probable hut sites have been identified in recent years on either side of the Bar Brook on Big Moor, to the east of the Peak District (eg Lewis 1970, 69 and Fig. 17). A few miles to the north, on Totley Moor, arrowheads occur on the uplands in an area with some evidence of field clearance in the form of linear banks and clearance heaps (Radley 1966c). Birchen Edge further south also exhibits clear evidence, with its extensive cairns and irregular walling, and especially its system of four or five cleared fields defined by lynchet banks (Challis & Harding 1975, 127). Dating evidence of this activity to the south east of our area is provided by collared urns associated with some of the cairnfields and ring banks at Bar Brook II and Totley Moor, accompanying charcoal yielding dates of around 1,500 and 1,600 b.c. (Lewis 1966). Fleming's hypothesis of shifting agriculture and land exhaustion may also be applicable here. Similar occurrences of cairns, old walls and hut sites can be identified in the Green Crag Slack section of Rombalds Moor, to the north east of our area (Cowling 1946, 131). Further evidence from Baildon Moor is illustrated by Fig. 34. This map depicts features which were visible in the mid nineteenth century: at this time there were numerous traces of parallel banks, between 50 and 80 yards apart and intersected by others at right angles, the whole forming a field system (225). The original report described the banks as drystone walls, but, as they had been extensively robbed for road construction and other purposes prior to 1845, it is hardly surprising that there is apparently little or no trace of them at the present day. Comparisons may be drawn with some of the parallel reaves on Dartmoor (Fleming 1978). Stone cairns were dotted within and around these plots on Baildon Moor, and associated with them were also two ring banks of Early/Middle Bronze Age type (Challis & Harding 1975, 127–8). Thus here again, urn peoples probably settled an area which had previously proved unattractive to Bronze Age settlers, and this dispersal may be connected with shifting agriculture, quickly leading to soil exhaustion. Clearance heaps, irregular walling, cairns, small barrows and ring banks may be seen as a type of 'extensive settlement' typical of the earlier part of the Bronze Age, probably beginning substantially earlier in some parts and surviving longer in others.

Although all these examples occur on the drier, rain-shadow fringes of the gritstone Pennines, there are distinct possibilities that a similar pattern of occupation may have been found in areas described earlier, lying to the east of Burnley and in upper Calderdale, both with cairns, ring banks and other evidence of Bronze Age habitation. Near Burnley, however, excavation of a series of mounds in Everage Clough proved inconclusive (40). A recent radiocarbon date of 310 ± 100 b.c. (BIRM 689) from nearby blanket peat on Extwistle Moor, which is described as dating the 'lowest clearance phase of woodland' there (Bartley 1976), does not tie in with the archaeological evidence. Further south, recent work on the slopes of the Holme valley near Huddersfield increasingly suggests the existence of field clearance in this district as well (eg Lunn 1966).

It has been seen how the cairns in the Central Pennines were associated with clearings. Although some of the latter may have been unintentional, many were probably connected with pastoral activities. Fleming (1971) argued against the undertaking of intensive forest clearance for purely pastoral use, but others (eg Spratt & Simmons 1976) disagree with this hypothesis in North Yorkshire. If a cultivation phase is to be inferred in the Central Pennines, it must have been short lived, for no cereal pollen has been identified. Bradley (1972, 201) suggests that there may be a correlation between perforated stone maceheads and areas used for cereals, but again this does not concur with the evidence in our area. Axe-hammers seem to succeed the maceheads chronologically (Roe 1979), and this would be compatible with intensification of land clearance under population pressure. Equally, there is environmental evidence for some local land exhaustion which could have exerted its own pressure.

The climatic deterioration which occurred in the second half of the Bronze Age has been described already. As early as 1500 B.C. areas in the uplands appear to have been abandoned, as on Dartmoor (Simmons 1969b). Soil degradation had been going on for a long time and contributed to the change. The twelfth and eleventh centuries B.C. saw the final great climatic change in the Bronze Age. A total break in settlement types, burial types, pottery and metal technology, indeed every facet of life, had occurred by this time (Burgess 1974, 194). In our area all the deeper hill peats were steadily accumulating in any case, and the change added a fringe of what are now shallow peats around the main core of blanket bog, so that the plateaux above 1,200 feet everywhere in the uplands became peat covered. The consequences of these environmental changes will be discussed later, but it is very apparent how in our area there is very little evidence of settlement in the period succeeding the earlier Bronze Age occupation already described. All the metal and other implements occur as casual finds, and there is very little, if any, later pottery and no burials. However, some of the early hilltop settlements seem to have had their origin in the Late Bronze Age and to have evolved into hillforts, continuing on into the Iron Age: these will be discussed later.

Thus there does appear to be continuity at both ends of the Bronze Age, despite the hiatus in between. The idea of culture contact rather than culture replacement, of a 'static' society, is also strongly supported, particularly by the field systems that are now coming to light.

Chapter Six
The Iron Age

Introduction

The term 'Iron Age' implies a widespread introduction and use of iron during this period. While it is true that a good deal of iron may not have survived due to unfavourable soil conditions in many parts, and the effects of later agricultural techniques in others, there is so little iron ware that can be safely attributed to later prehistoric times in the Central Pennines that the labelling of the period as the 'proto-Iron Age' was considered. The native tradition of bronze working survived throughout the seventh and sixth centuries B.C. (eg Grafton *et al* 1955), while some socketed axes were deposited during 'Halstatt C' (Burgess 1969). It is quite likely, therefore, that some Bronze Age traits survived well into Roman times in this area. Furthermore, many features formerly labelled securely as Iron Age have now been proven to have had their origins in the Bronze Age. This section might on these grounds have included the Later Bronze Age period, under the general title of 'later prehistory'. However, as pollen evidence suggests that environmental changes increased in intensity after 400 B.C., the traditional divisions have been adhered to, though the fact that these changes may have been less the effect of human interference than climatic deterioration must always be borne in mind.

The deterioration in climate during the Later Bronze Age and some of its consequences have already been described. These culminated in the onset of sub Atlantic oceanic conditions, well established by the beginning of the Iron Age. Higher water tables during the first millennium must have led to conditions of waterlogging affecting larger areas to a more serious extent than in more recent times, especially in lowland areas. The Romans found the Vale of York relatively sparsely occupied for these reasons. Further limitations to habitation were set by relief, especially on west facing uplands. Here settlement was depressed below 650 feet, due to exposure, heavier precipitation and deteriorating soils on the upper slopes. Peat bog was found everywhere on the plateaux over 1,200 feet O.D. and was even extending down to lower altitudes on the flatter interfluves; raised peat bogs were also becoming more extensive on parts of the lowlands, especially those bordering the Mersey floodplain. Thus the gentler, more sheltered dip slopes of the eastern flanks of the Pennines were favoured, and settlement was possible here even up to 1,000 feet above sea level.

Archaeological Evidence

Archaeological evidence of Iron Age occupation of the Central Pennine area consists almost entirely of earthworks, both defensive and agricultural in character. Artefacts relating to the period consist on the whole as chance finds, a small number of metal items and equally few artefacts of stone and other materials (Fig. 19). In this respect, the area compares well with the Peak District; indeed, there is a greater number of earthworks in the gritstone Pennines than on the limestone uplands, although subsequent modifications to the landscape may have destroyed some of the evidence in the latter area. Dating of the artefacts found in our area is so insecure that there are no grounds for arguing against a Romano-British origin for many of them.

In the whole of Lancashire, Iron Age metalwork finds are very small in number, only about six or seven items in all (mostly bronze) having been recovered, four of these in our area. At Manchester a small bronze ox-head ornament was found (90), and on the hill slopes north of Littleborough at Mowroad (175) a heavy, beaded torque necklace with iron securing pins was unearthed early in the 19th century. Just inside the Lancashire boundary on Blackstone Edge, to the east of Littleborough, an iron spearhead was found in close proximity to an ox's horn (158). Further north, near the River Ribble at Billington (148), iron spearheads were uncovered in a tumulus in 1836: the only suggestion so far of an Iron Age burial in the Central Pennine area. On the Yorkshire side of the Pennine watershed, a few

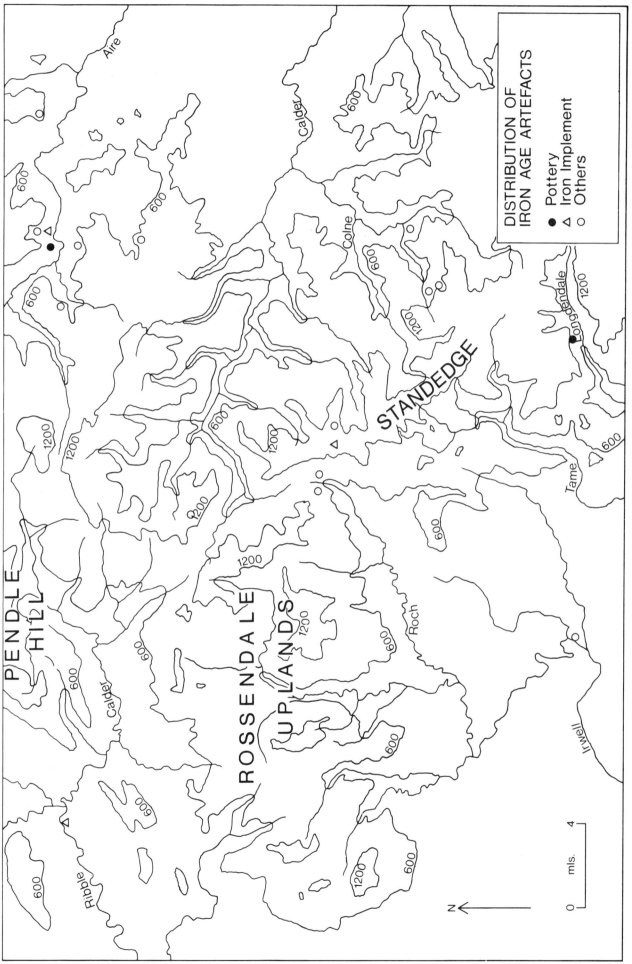

Figure 19.

DISTRIBUTION OF
IRON AGE ARTEFACTS
● Pottery
△ Iron Implement
○ Others

STANDEDGE

PENDLE HILL

ROSSENDALE UPLANDS

Aire

Calder

Colne

Longdendale

Tame

Ribble

Calder

Roch

Irwell

N

0   4
mls.

miles to the north of the Blackstone Edge finds, two bronze harness rings were found on Stansfield Moor (325), while similar rings occurred in a hoard at Honley (361), three miles to the south of Huddersfield on the opposite side of the valley to the hill fort at Almondbury. This hoard also contained Roman coins, and possibly represented the personal wealth of a local tribesman hidden soon after 73 A.D. Another piece of Iron Age metalwork, an iron sickle, has been found in the Aire valley near Baildon (219), while another iron sickle from the eastern slopes of the same valley north of Keighley at Brunthwaite Crag, just outside our area, has been identified.

Among the other items, increasing numbers of rotary querns are being discovered. Despite the impossibility of assigning these precisely to the Iron Age, it is probably of great significance that the vast majority of them have come from the drier eastern slopes of the Central Pennine area, particularly the major river valleys, those of the Calder and its tributaries in the Huddersfield–Wakefield area and the Aire valley between Keighley and Leeds. In the Huddersfield district, two querns were found in association with Iron Age enclosures at Oldfield Hill and Royd Edge near Meltham (377–8). At least three Iron Age mortars, too, have been identified in the Bingley section of the Aire valley (*CAGB* 11, 1966, 89–90). A fine shale armlet was found on Flint Hill just to the east of Blackstone Edge (316), which closely resembles the Kimmeridge shale armlets found at Glastonbury (Bulleid 1968, Plate XIV, 9); fragments of another armlet were found on Snoddle Hill near Littleborough in the same area (169) and these too may be of Iron Age date, while parts of a similar Kimmeridge shale armlet were discovered south of our area in Harborough Cave in the Peak District (Jackson 1929–31). Finally, a limestone loom weight supposedly of Iron Age date has been recovered at Harden, near Bingley (243). Only two Iron Age pottery finds have yet been made in the Central Pennines. One, a late La Tène pot, occurred as a chance find in the Longdendale valley on the southern boundary of our area (84). The other find was made in the course of an excavation of Iron Age earthworks at Crosley Wood, Bingley (238). Just outside our area, only three or four miles from the last named locality, a number of sherds of coarse, dark grey ware have been reported from the Burley Moor area. It is quite possible that the use of barbed flint arrowheads continued well into the Iron Age in the Pennine area (Raistrick 1939, 116), and their widespread occurrence on the upland areas has been described already.

The thinly scattered nature of these Iron Age artefacts bears little relationship to the density of population at this period, but their distribution may have some validity. They show a close relationship to the major river valleys of the eastern flanks of the hills, and there is also a minor cluster in the Littleborough–Blackstone Edge area, a district subsequently traversed by a Roman road. It must be stressed again, however, that many of the items which have been described are probably late Iron Age in date or even of Romano-British origin. Yet in recent years a number of Iron Age settlements have come to light, and these will be mentioned later.

Much more impressive are the Iron Age earthworks in the Central Pennines (Fig. 21). Of the hillforts, the largest in the Pennines and one of the most imposing is a few miles to the south of our area at Mam Tor, overlooking the limestone pastures. This site is significant on account of the evidence it has yielded helping to revise long held theories about hillfort origins and dating. Nearly 1,700 feet above sea level, the fort includes 16 acres and its defences consist of a single stone-revetted box rampart and ditch, with possibly an inner bank and ditch to the south and east. At the southern end of the site near the highest point are two Bronze Age round barrows, and in the 19th century a 'bronze celt' and fragments of urns were found. Recent excavations (Coombs 1976) revealed platforms on which timber huts had been constructed, stake holes and storage pits. Pottery was found in large quantities as a general scatter, together with shale bracelet fragments, a polished stone axe and a fragment of a bronze socketed axe with rib decoration. The pottery was of Late Bronze Age type, relating to the late second and early first millennium. Radiocarbon dates relating to the huts $(1,130 \pm 115$ b.c. (BIRM 192) and $1,180 \pm 132$ b.c. (BIRM 202)) might be appreciably older than the defences, though the first stockaded enclosure may well be of Late Bronze Age origin (Challis and Harding 1975, 103). The socketed axe dates from the eighth century at the earliest, being absent from the Wallington tradition and belonging to Burgess's Ewart Park phase (Burgess 1974, 327 n. 386). Thus the occupation of this hilltop site was not short, and furthermore, it is possible to distinguish three phases in its defences (Coombs 1976, 151). The Mam Tor pottery is significant in that it includes shouldered and bipartite forms, some with relief horseshoe ornament, strongly suggesting a local version of the biconical urn. Early hillfort pottery thus has a long Bronze Age ancestry, stretching back through the Deverel-Rimbury and biconical urns to the Early Bronze Age when shouldered forms were widespread especially amongst enlarged food vessels and domestic pottery (Burgess 1974, 219–20).

The principal hillfort in the Central Pennines is at Castle Hill, Almondbury, near Huddersfield (344) (Fig. 20). It is an eight acre site occupying one of the most impressive landmarks of the east Pennine foothills. The results of the most recent excavations have necessitated a radical reappraisal of its chronology: the earthworks were sited on an earlier 'occupation floor' dated to just before 2,000 b.c. (Varley 1976, 127), but the first establishment of the fort and the sequence of rebuilding and enlargement are still being debated (Varley 1948, 46ff; Challis & Harding 1975, 120; Varley 1976). The first defensive phase, it is argued (Varley 1976), began possibly in the eighth century B.C., with the construction of a simple univallate enclosure on the southern half of the plateau. Subsequently the site fell

Figure 20. Almondbury, Castle Hill (344).

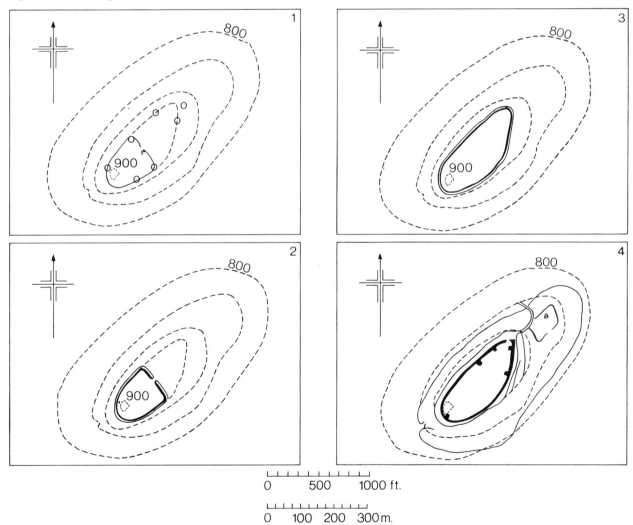

Principal stages in the development of the fortifications: (After Varley 1976).
1. Simple Univallate Enclosure with later stone-kerbed huts.
2. Univallate Fort.
3. Bivallate Fort. (555 ± 100 b.c.).
4. Multivallate structure enclosing parts of lower slopes.

into decay and a land surface developed over the ruins, though later, a series of stone-kerbed huts appear to have been constructed, both on the site of the earlier fort and beyond it on the summit plateau. These huts were roughly circular, about 25 feet in diameter, and within them charcoal spreads were found though no hearths were in evidence. This period of open settlement was followed by several stages of earthworks. This progression of earthworks began with the construction of a univallate fortlet on roughly the same site as the earlier earthwork, followed by a bivallate fort enclosing the whole of the plateau top, an area twice the size of the original. Finally a multivallate structure enclosed parts of the lower slopes. The rampart construction varied in time – though the sequence is arguable – and involved slab-revetted forms with clay core laid between timber and turf rafts, stone-revetted ramparts with timber-laced core, and ramparts with a dump construction (Challis & Harding 1975, 120). The Period Three rampart has been securely dated to 555 ± 100 b.c. (I 4542). The fort was finally destroyed by fire, most likely in the late fifth century, and the site was abandoned until its defensive position commended itself once more in the Medieval period. The significance of the substantial extension or annexe, which was incorporated in the final fort and to which it was connected by a hollow way down the hillside, will be discussed later.

As has been pointed out already, most of the surviving hillforts in the Pennines are in the gritstone areas. To the south of our area, besides Mam Tor, there is a series of small forts flanking the northern parts of the Peak District, from Wincobank and other examples in the Sheffield and Penistone areas in the east, to Combs Moss in the west (Coombs 1976, 414; Ramm 1957; Preston 1954). In the southern part of our area are two earthworks of doubtful age. A three quarter acre site is enclosed by a single bank without a ditch on Harrop Moor on the southern flanks of Longdendale overlooking Torside Reservoir (87), while further north, surmounting the precipitous eastern slopes of the Tame valley is Bucton Castle, a strong promontory position but with few features which compare with the usual Iron Age promontory hillforts (196). Further north, besides Almondbury, there is also Lee Hill (383), not far from the Roman fort at Slack, a possible defensive site, though more likely a defended farmstead (Toomey 1960). It is noticeable how many of these sites, together with the other fortified farmsteads mentioned below, are on the drier eastern side of the Pennine watershed, particularly on the more pliable soils of the Coal Measures (Fig. 21). The idea of a series of small fortified centres is probably more realistic than the picture of a line of forts which, together with Mam Tor and Almondbury, supposedly defended the southern end of the Brigantian territories (Preston 1954, 18).

In the western part of the Central Pennines are two hillforts, both in the northern part of our area flanking the Ribble valley (Fig. 21) at Castercliffe near Nelson (136) and at Portfield, not far from the confluence of the Ribble with the Lancashire Calder (155). The latter is sited on a south facing promontory and for the most part is defined simply by natural scarps; only on the north west and to a lesser extent on the west is there anything of a more artificial nature. To the north west, an inner bank and ditch have a smaller bank and ditch beyond. Earlier sources show additional defences on the east and south east sides, and the outer bank on the north west was shown as continuous around the whole site except where the natural slope made any artificial defences unnecessary (Forde-Johnston 1962). The slab revetment of the inner rampart is interpreted as the earliest rampart on the site (Tyson & Bu'Lock 1957), later replaced by a clay-cored, stone-revetted rampart. The latter is probably of early date (Challis & Harding 1975, 110); indeed, finds made on the site go back to Neolithic times, with Beaker pottery having been found recently, while the coarse biconical pottery and the Late Bronze Age hoard mentioned earlier may indicate the first establishment of the fort. The hilltop site at Castercliffe, with a maximum internal diameter of only 350 feet, has three ramparts: the central one is of timber-framed box construction with evidence of abandonment before completion, while the inner vitrified rampart was probably stone-revetted and timber-laced (comparing with the one at Almondbury). The central rampart has close parallels to Grimthorpe in its construction (Challis & Harding 1975, 106), and demonstrates that despite its comparative remoteness, this part of Lancashire was in step with current trends in

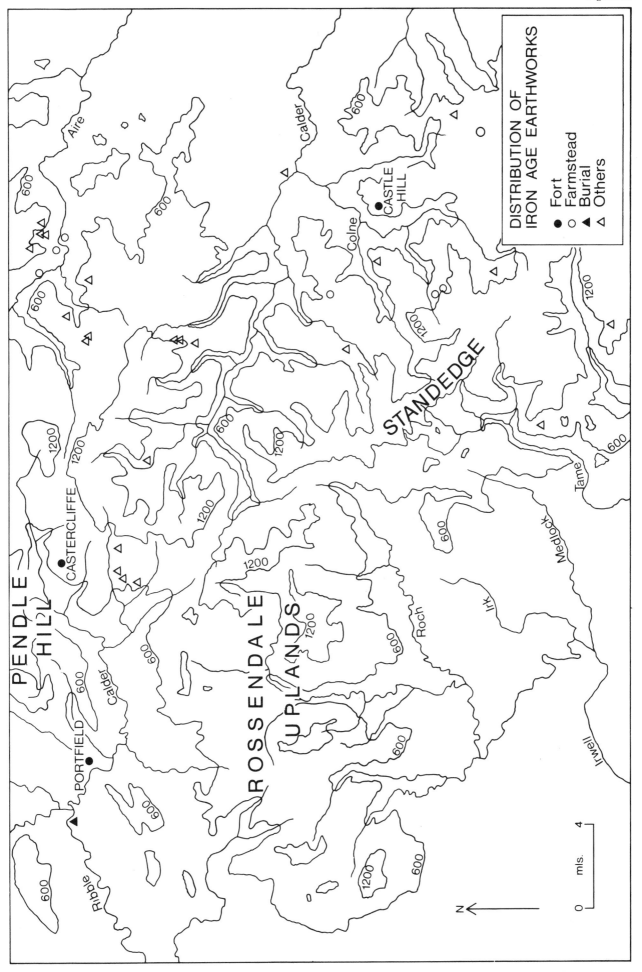

Figure 21.

DISTRIBUTION OF
IRON AGE EARTHWORKS

● Fort
○ Farmstead
▲ Burial
△ Others

CASTLE HILL

STANDEDGE

PENDLE HILL

CASTERCLIFFE

PORTFIELD

ROSSENDALE UPLANDS

Aire

Calder

Colne

Tame

Medlock

Irk

Roch

Irwell

Ribble

600

1200

N

0   4
         mls.

the west European world at least once during the first millennium B.C.

The majority of the excavated hillforts of the Central and South Pennines are of a period earlier than the mature Iron Age, and are mostly between 1000 and 500 B.C. Evidently the role of such structures was not dominant in the social and economic life of the period: even Almondbury, with its several periods of rebuilding, may fit in with this pattern. Evidence of internal occupation has been discovered within many of them. Dump defences such as the latest phase at Almondbury, capping earlier defences, are not common, and seem to mark a diminished concern for the neat appearance of the defences, and possibly a shift in emphasis of social priorities in the later period (Challis & Harding 1975, 124).

So far as Iron Age settlements are concerned, one has been described at Rothwell Haigh on the southern slopes of the Aire valley just outside our area to the east, while further up the same valley at Bingley a possible settlement site is now occupied by school playing fields and a cemetery extension (233 and 234). There are strong possibilities that another settlement site existed in the vicinity of the latter site at Crosley Wood, excavations in the mid 1960s resulting in the finds of pottery mentioned earlier besides demonstrating the survival of remnants of a rectilinear field system and a circular enclosure, probably a cattle pound (238). At Hirst Wood, only half a mile to the south east, similar evidence has been found (278). Numerous other reports have been made over the years of prehistoric walls and enclosures on the lower slopes in these parts of the Aire valley and its tributaries in the Bradford-Keighley area (*CAGB*).

Enclosures are a ubiquitous Iron Age trait. Small sub rectangular enclosures are well known in southern Britain, and a number occur within the Central Pennine area, as, for example, at Barkisland (283) and Kirklees (291), the latter long being interpreted as a Roman camp (Richmond 1925, 24). Their purpose is possibly connected with stock control (Challis & Harding 1975, 131). The strength of some of the structures of some rectilinear enclosures is sometimes such that they warrant the title of 'defensive sites' rather than 'enclosed homesteads'. One such case is the hill slope site at Oldfield Hill near Meltham (377). Here, in the main defensive phase, the one acre D-shaped enclosure had a rampart of rubble and earth seven feet wide, faced with drystone walling, with a presumed original height of over ten feet, a V-shaped rock cut ditch nearly six feet deep and six feet wide, and a counterscarp bank similar to the inner rampart with a drystone revetment surviving to four courses (Toomey 1976). An earlier excavation (Richmond 1924 and 1925, 21–4, Fig. 9) showed that the north east entrance through the rampart had a double timber gateway. A pre rampart palisade trench has been identified on two sides of the enclosure, in which vertical posts had been set about two feet apart. Finds include two stone discs, a rough out beehive quern, iron slag, very small fragments of pottery, pieces of coal and graphite fragments (Toomey 1976). It has been pointed out that the Levisham Moor A site seems to be comparable and is of a late Iron Age date (Challis & Harding 1975, 132).

Another type of small, squarish enclosure defined by inner ditch and outer bank has at least 13 examples in the Pennines and north eastern England (Challis & Harding 1975, 133), nine of these being D-shaped. Two have been excavated, one in our area at Royd Edge, near Melthan (378). A sub rectangular one acre enclosure, it is surrounded by a stone-revetted rubble rampart and inner, rock cut ditch, of dimensions similar to Oldfield Hill, less than half a mile to the north. There are entrances on the eastern and western sides, the latter spanned originally by a double timber gate with a central stop. Deliberately broken stone was thrown down to consolidate the entrance way, and amongst it was a fragment of a beehive quern. Again an earlier occupation is indicated by an inner palisaded enclosure on a rather different alignment which crossed and partly destroyed an earlier circular hut. Later occupation is also shown by a length of palisade running at an angle across the filled in ditch. Finds include flint chips, clinker and baked clay scraps, and a lead spindle whorl, indicating the likelihood of a date in the late pre Roman Iron Age.

Several other earthworks have been identified in the Central Pennines, most, however, of uncertain origin. At Castle Hill, Denby (347), a rectangular enclosure with external ditch has been described, with a suggestion that it may have had an extended life as the Domesday vaccary mentioned in the area. However, recent excavations have shown, firstly, a small Iron Age farmstead and rampart, the latter including beach pebbles of black flint, core trimming flakes and scrapers. Beneath the Iron Age occupation, 2 polished stone axes and a leaf-shaped arrowhead were found in 1970, suggesting a later Neolithic/Early Bronze Age enclosure (see above). On Crosland Moor, west of Huddersfield (365), were one, possibly two, curvi-linear enclosures. Watson (1775, 275) described them as being 77 yards by 64 yards and 98 yards by 87 yards respectively. Three 'ancient millstones' were found in the larger enclosure, each a foot in diameter, together with 11 'hollow places' between two and three yards long and three quarters of a yard deep. At Brackenhall Green, Baildon (217), an earthwork measuring 50 yards by 30 yards had an inner and outer ring of boulders with a packing of smaller stones (Cowling 1946, 71). An increasing number of similar walls together with other circular and rectangular enclosures have also been traced in this part of the Aire valley as mentioned earlier. Some of these may well be related to the Bronze Age enclosures which have been described, while others may date from land enclosures in historic times. Among the more striking examples ascribed to the Iron Age are those on Cullingworth Moor (254–5), Harden Moor (235) and Wilsden (281), all of which are non defensive in character.

Palynological Evidence

Despite the lack of widespread archaeological evidence for settlement during the Iron Age, the pollen record testifies to wide ranging landscape changes. There is at this time, too, the earliest definite evidence of more widespread cereal cultiva-tion, particularly towards the end of the period, often culminating in Roman times. There seems to have been a decline in agriculture accompanied by forest regeneration in post Roman times.

At Rishworth a great increase in the variety and quantity of non-arboreal pollen types and a decrease in tree pollen values are dated at 470±100 b.c. (GaK 2824). These changes culminated around 30±80 a.d. (GaK 2825), while the agriculture which had been pastoral at first included cereal growing just before the Roman conquest (Bartley 1974, 378). The evidence from Featherbed Moss to the south is remarkably similar, though the major clearance phase here extended for a longer period, reaching a maximum around 200 a.d. and declining about 400 a.d., at a later period than at Rishworth (Tallis & Switsur 1973).

West of the Pennine watershed, in Rossendale, pollen analysis indicates a major change in non-arboreal vegetation with *Sphagnum* spore values rising to a peak, followed by *Calluna* as the predominant herbaceous pollen type, suggesting an increase in site moisture possibly due to the climatic deterioration. Peat extended over the spur tops at the same time, though in the later Iron Age there is evidence of cereal cultivation in the vicinity (Tallis & McGuire 1972, 730). While heather moorland and peat were extending on the upper slopes, the persistence of dense woodland on the boulder clay lowlands, at least as late as the early Roman period, is shown by the pollen counts from the soil immediately below the Roman road at Ainsworth, indicating widespread alderwood on the damper lowlands. The buried soil, moreover, contained large amounts of finely comminuted charcoal, presumably resulting from woodland clearance by burning prior to the construc-tion of the road (Tallis & McGuire 1972, 732). Though large parts of the badly drained lowlands and valleys were forested, parts – as in the Bronze Age – were used for pastoral activities with possibly a limited amount of arable, though the first real evidence for cereal cultivation in the Chat Moss pollen diagram is later, in the Romano-British period (Birks 1965, 310).

The same patterns are repeated elsewhere in the Pennines. To the south east of our area on East Moor, Hicks (1972, 10–12) described an opening of the forest canopy on a much larger scale in the Iron Age, commencing around 350 b.c., and here again pastoralism was predominant at first with arable only becoming significant later, particularly in Roman times. Transhumant pastoralism is suggested as the cause of deforestation on the upper slopes, and this might account for the lack of archaeological evidence.

Further north, in the Nidderdale area, open birch-alder woodland survived on the lower slopes until after 300 B.C., and the upper slopes were treeless by then. Further expansion of heath occurred around 250 B.C., accompanied by a prolonged and intensive agricultural phase. Increased grazing pressure led to the reduction of woodland on the one hand and the extension of grassy communities at the expense of heath on the other (Tinsley 1975, 21; Tinsley 1976, 316). The view of the Brigantian people as nomadic pastoralists is not supported in this area, owing to the presence of cereal pollen.

At Carle Moor, north east of our area near Ripon, a Romano-British earthwork was constructed in partly cleared woodland. Here alder and birch were present, hazel and grasses were important, and no cereals were found, a typical later Bronze Age pattern of pastoral activities. These activities probably gave rise to the edaphic deterioration which had resulted in the extension of heath. The pollen evidence suggests that pastoralism continued after the building of the earthwork, with periodic burning of the heath to control it, but there is also a significant occurrence of cereal pollen around A.D. 600 (Tinsley & Smith 1974).

Most sites therefore indicate considerable clearance during the Iron Age, and suggest grasslands and heather were expanding their range at the expense of forest. It is difficult to resist the conclusion that man was involved. Iron technology would mean that forest clearance was more effective, while grazing and associated leaching connected with settlements at lower altitudes would have prevented any regrowth of forest. Thus the moorland slopes would have passed through the stages of woodland – grassland – heathland under the stimulus of human directed activities. It is suggested that the stocking capacity of the uplands would have been affected by the moorland forage being reduced, thus stimulating further grazing in the woodland areas.

Discussion
The evidence for the continuity of occupancy of the region between Bronze Age and Iron Age times is not lacking but it is not firmly supported by stratified association: the hillforts at Portfield and possibly Almondbury, and the farmstead at Denby Dale were apparently built on Late Bronze Age or earlier sites, while some of the enclosures mentioned above may well have had long pedigrees also. Most of the hillforts of the Central and Southern Pennines (with the exceptions of Almondbury and Mam Tor) are of such a size they are more like Later Bronze Age defended homesteads than hillforts. Nevertheless both the Late Bronze Age and Early Iron Age are lacking in artefacts that can be definitely associated with possible settlement sites. Either, as with the Neolithic and Bronze Age, no Early Iron Age dwellings have yet come to light, or the region regained something approaching the popularity of Early Bronze Age times only in the later phase of the Iron Age. There is, of course, the distinct possibility that a good deal of later prehistoric settlement evidence may await location by aerial survey (eg Higham 1979).

If the Iron Age occupation involved cultivation, evidence of 'Celtic' fields might be expected (though, of course, these are not restricted to this period): no examples have been found in the Central Pennines whereas they are common on the limestone areas to the north and south. In this respect the area compares well with North Yorkshire (Spratt & Simmons 1976, 207). Whether preservation is incomplete and they have been destroyed by later field wall construction or other developments, whether the field systems are in an unrecognised form, or whether there was so little cultivation of sufficient persistence to create lynchets, has yet to be determined.

Although the archaeological remains do not strongly indicate the economy of Iron Age folk, they do suggest both arable and pastoral activities. The palaeo-environmental evidence is quite plentiful, though the absolute dating of pollen profiles is rather thin by this time. Cereal pollens occur widely only late in the period, as in North Yorkshire (Atherden 1972), and in both areas, grass and heath extended throughout the Iron Age. Whether the descendants of the Bronze Age peoples continued their pastoral economy within the uplands – as has been suggested for Dartmoor as well (Simmons 1969, 211) – until late in the Iron Age, may never be known. It is interesting to note, however, that remains of aurochs in the form of horn case fragments have been found from time to time within the peat, though unassociated with any archaeological artefacts. One horn in two pieces, each over a foot long, was found between six and eight inches above the grey sand layer at Warcock Hill 4 (Buckley Mss. 1927), while another, over seven inches in length, was found within the lower layers of an eight feet thick layer of blanket peat on Close Moss (Buckley Mss. 1948). Other specimens were found beneath the peat at Cowpe, near Waterfoot in Rossendale (Rochdale Museum), and on the site of the Ashworth Reservoir, north of Heywood (Baldwin 1903, 109). More recently, remains from Holme Clough (SE 0450) have been handed in at the Saddleworth Museum. Most, if not all, of these horn cases are the remains of *Bos longifrons*, the so called 'Celtic shorthorn', which was the familiar ox of later prehistoric Britain; it appeared during the Bronze Age and became entirely dominant during the Iron Age (Jewell 1963, 87). Where cereals have been identified, the clearance phenomena associated with them are usually on a large scale, and again there are also close parallels in North Yorkshire (Atherden 1976, 296). However, differences in agricultural economies, as well as, and possibly resulting in, differences in settlement distribution and density, do begin to emerge when the western and eastern sides of the Central Pennines are compared.

In Lancastria, the archaeological evidence largely consists of hill forts. Late Bronze Age metalwork is comparatively scarce (Burgess 1968, Fig. 23), and in our area notable finds have occurred mainly along the Ribble valley. The two hillforts west of the Pennines are also in the vicinity of the Ribble. It may be in this area that the traditional concept of Iron Age pastoralism is fulfilled, though cultivation, as mentioned earlier, was not absent. Here, and in the Pennine uplands generally, there seems to be an absence of evidence for widespread grain growing in the first millennium B.C., and there are sound environmental reasons for this, reflected in present day land use patterns. Inhibiting factors included the late start to the growing season, wet summers and the likelihood of crops remaining unripe at the onset of winter conditions in November. On the lowlands to the west of the Pennines, the large areas of drift inhibited early agriculture, their surface wetness and high clay content requiring autumn ploughing (Hall & Folland 1970). Population densities would thus be limited by the environmental constraints upon food producing capacity, the northern part of our area in the Ribble valley probably being one of the more favourable areas on this side of the Pennines. Nevertheless, at a time when Iron Age enclosures are being identified in ever increasing numbers on the eastern side of the Pennines, it is difficult to explain the absence of similar sites on the western flanks of the hills. Apart from a few enclosures of doubtful age in the Burnley area (eg 27, 50, 55), nothing has been discovered so far which will help to elucidate Iron Age activities on this side of the Pennines (Fig. 21). It is possible that archaeologists have not recognised the nature of the evidence, but there is a stronger possibility that the evidence has been destroyed by the agricultural activity and the industrial and settlement growth of the last few centuries, particularly if Iron Age farming was less developed here because of adverse physical factors.

To the east of the Pennines, however, better climate and better soils seemingly led to more settled communities. There is more evidence of arable farming, though even here cultivation would only have been really successful below 500 feet, and the more fertile soils of the Magnesian Limestone outcrop to the east of our area would have been particularly favoured. However, the increasing evidence for Iron Age agricultural settlement on the eastern flanks of the Pennines at heights of up to 1,000 feet does show that the gritstone uplands, too, attracted occupation, though material remains are few and the evidence consists largely of small earthwork enclosures, suggesting a pattern of scattered, small homesteads. Possibly the concept of land utility at this time (and earlier in Bronze Age times) centred on a core zone of land of medium altitude; land above and below this zone which had various disadvantages may have been used and settled in a more piecemeal manner, comparing with the 'outfields' of later times (Fleming 1976, 369). The evidence suggests that these settlements subsisted largely upon pastoral activities, although the presence of querns on some of them implies that cultivation was carried on as well.

The increasing volume of evidence of enclosures and walls of one sort or another, which can probably be attributed to at least the later part of the Iron Age, points to the existence of a greater amount of permanent settlement than has been envisaged hitherto. Certainly, the presence of a major hillfort such as Castle Hill, Almondbury, would support such a contention. This is a strong argument against the traditional view that the uplands were simply places visited for summer grazing and spasmodic cultivation by farmers whose permanent settlements were elsewhere (eg Jones 1961). Most of these enclosures seem to have been related to pastoral activities. The greatest numbers are on the slopes of the Aire valley where additional evidence of settlement in the form of possible dwelling sites is also coming to light, as well as indirect evidence such as implements like sickles and querns. Other areas includes the Halifax district in Calderdale and the Holme valley area near the Almondbury hillfort. The vast majority of the physical remains of these Iron Age sites (amongst which are probably unnumbered enclosures of earlier origins) are in parts of the area which had little attraction to later farmers: many are in valley edge woodlands or on higher slopes, sites which were not destroyed by subsequent farming activities. It is therefore highly likely that contemporary enclosures existed on more favourable valley benches and hill slopes, and that these will never be recognised.

In the Central Pennines as a whole the concensus seems to indicate a massive attack on the forest during the Iron Age, often from the beginning with pastoralism as a dominant activity, and, as seen earlier, this conclusion accords with pollen analysis from other upland areas including the Peak District. There remains the interpretation that some or all of the forest recession of the period, particularly the early part, might be the sign of the climatic change towards greater oceanicity. But few other signs of this change have been indicated by the palaeoenvironmental evidence: it does not seem to have been a period of inception of blanket bog, though renewed spreading did occur. There is not enough evidence for the sudden onset of a drastic climatic change to account for the forest recession of the Early Iron Age. Furthermore, virtually all the archaeological and environmental evidence, with the exception of Rishworth, supports the idea that the Iron Age economy continued through the Roman period, to be followed by a rather rapid recolonisation of forest, probably confined to the lower ground, dated in most cases to early post Roman times.

In the case of the Later Bronze Age/Iron Age transition, the environmental and archaeological evidence are at variance, since the latter at present suggests that there was comparatively little Early Iron Age settlement, while pollen analyses indicate forest recession from the beginning, very likely due to human interference, and this is supported by evidence from the Howgill Fells to the north west of our area (Cundill 1976, 308). The general picture in the Central Pennines at the transition period may be one of small communities of herders moving their livestock between summer and winter pastures, and in such a system material culture and settlement archaeology are seldom well represented (Cunliffe 1978, 63). It is likely that it was in the peripheral eastern foothills and on the valley slopes in the central hills that the population and tribal development occurred which led to the creation of the Brigantian heartland; one of the southern centres of this may well have been the hillfort at Almondbury.

The long chronology of the Central Pennine hillforts has been described, but their subsequent history in the Iron Age is obscure. At Almondbury, substantial annexes were added to the main entrance of the fort, and later an outer series of banks and ditches were constructed to enclose the annexes and the original fort, together with a considerable acreage of protected pasture (Fig. 20, 4). Such an arrangement has parallels in the Welsh borderland (Varley 1950), and strongly suggests the increasing importance of livestock which needed protection (Cunliffe 1978, 214–16). Others (eg Challis & Harding 1975, 121) would disagree with this interpretation, regarding these outer circumvallations as essentially of defensive significance. The evidence from north east Wales, however, might be considered in this context. Here there were several hillforts which were not entirely defensive in purpose. The Breidden is one of these, and saw stake-built round houses being constructed during the fifth century B.C. The site has produced carbonised grain and numerous saddle querns, while aerial photography has revealed field boundaries in the vicinity. It is suggested, therefore, that settlement was permanent, and at least partly based on arable farming (Guilbert 1977). While such a situation may also be postulated for Almondbury, it must not be forgotten that the site was abandoned before 400 B.C. There is no reason why, however, the scattered hillside settlements in the vicinity should not have continued to prosper.

General Conclusion

Prehistoric activity had an impact on the Central Pennines from the eighth millennium B.C. Mesolithic hunter-gatherers probably occupied seasonal camps, the population wintering on the lowlands east or west of the Pennines. Although the clearest evidence for this pattern relates probably to the earlier part of the period in our area, there is nothing to suggest that it did not continue throughout Mesolithic times until the fourth millennium and even later. The question yet to be answered – one which has also been posed in relation to North Yorkshire (Spratt & Simmons 1976, 209) – is whether a complete suite of habitation sites has yet been discovered for the Mesolithic anywhere in Britain: there may be significant elements in the yearly pattern yet to be established. Hunting continued on the plateau areas throughout Neolithic and Bronze Age times, and possibly into the Iron Age. Pastoral activities may have begun during the Neolithic period when transhumant pastoralism seemingly took place from the fringes of the uplands to the higher areas. There is little evidence, however, of settlement, permanent or otherwise, in the Central Pennine area until well into the Bronze Age, while cultivation even on the peripheries occurred only in later prehistoric times. Much remains to be discovered about the density of settlement in the Bronze and Iron Ages, but the archaeological evidence does suggest increasing exploitation, particularly of the foothill zones of the area.

The influence of climate and environment on man's activities and distribution during the early phases of technological development was strong, and the study of the changing post glacial climate, flora and fauna as a background to cultural evolution requires the close cooperation of the archaeologist with the geologist, zoologist, botanist and others. Even after man began to acquire the technology to manage and manipulate his surroundings, climate and associated environmental changes meant that the upland habitats of the Central Pennines tended to become more extreme and challenging. Environmental considerations continued in this way to play an influential part in human activities and in the distribution of sites, probably much more so than in other more favoured parts of Britain. Contrasts also begin to emerge within the Central Pennine area, particularly between activities and settlement east and west of the watershed respectively. In any attempt to isolate the factors governing settlement sites, one is obliged to invoke soil quality which must frequently have been decisive. But the order of priorities need not have been constant as between fertility, drainage, water supply, climate, defence and availability of land already cleared and cultivated. The existence of trade routes is often advanced as a reason for settlement growth in the Bronze Age, but it is doubtful whether this can be regarded as a tenable proposition. Other factors among those mentioned above are likely to have played a more important role: drier, rainshadow conditions and the existence of alluvial soils were probably the attractions of the Calder and, more particularly, of the Aire valley rather than their utilisation by traders plying between Ireland and eastern England.

In a given environment, the impact of a group of people depends on numbers, technology and length of occupation. Though the Mesolithic occupants exploited the area over a long period, their population density was low and their ability to affect the environment limited largely to the possession of fire. This was very effective, however, and, especially at the forest edges, they were seemingly responsible for the replacement of forest by scrub, and ultimately by heath and blanket bog. Such activities and changes were continued by later occupants, intensified by more effective technology and the introduction of pastoral activities. The result was a greater efficiency of forest clearance, both in the high forest of the lower slopes and the better drained parts of the lowlands as well as at the upper margins of the forest. In later prehistoric times, as some of the grasslands became heath or bog and population increased, intensified pressure on the forest would in turn have led to clearance at lower altitudes. There is a seeming conflict, however, between the number of Bronze Age monuments and the environmental evidence which suggests that man's impact on the vegetation at this period was less effective than in the Iron Age, which appears to have been the major landscape forming stage. But if some of the changes caused by Bronze Age (and earlier) activities were irreversible, then perhaps the gap between pollen and archaeological evidence for the Iron Age might be resolved: the forest continued to disappear because of encroaching bog and grassland, the soils having become leached by natural processes. It is likely, too, that at this time, during the sub Atlantic phase, climate had its greatest impact on vegetation changes and population distribution. In the area generally, throughout Iron Age times, renewed deforestation and pastoralism kept open the upper terrain, so that the major features of the upland landscape were complete by the end of prehistoric times. On the fringes of the uplands, valley bottom woodlands persisted, and may even have crept up the slopes again after the end of the Roman occupation.

Appendix 1
The Palaeoecology of Three Archaeological Sites in the Central Pennines

By R. Louise Brown

The Sites

The three sites under dicusssion are Rocher Moss South 2 (SE 028087), Warcock Hill South (SE 030095) and Dean Clough I (SD 987125). The two former are within a mile of each other, lying to the south of the Standedge crossing of the Pennines, and they are approximately three miles to the south east of Dean Clough which lies near the source of the River Tame. They are situated in off-summit locations above 1,200 feet. All three sites have yielded radiocarbon dates originating from hearth material (see Table 2):

Warcock Hill South 　　7,260 ± 340 b.c. (Q 1185)
Dean Clough I 　　　　5,645 ± 140 b.c. (Q 1188)
Rocher Moss South 2 　3,880 ± 100 b.c. (Q 1190)

Each of the sites was covered by peat or dark brown peaty soil; peat, of course, being one of the best mediums for the preservation of pollen grains. At these sites samples from the peat or from just below were usually very well preserved. Once into the level of the underlying mineral soil, however, pollen preservation became very much worse, many completely unidentifiable grains being found. The pollen from Rocher Moss was in a much higher state of preservation than that of Warcock Hill which was badly degraded. This reflects the material from which the samples were extracted, that from Rocher Moss being taken from peat for the most part, whilst that from Warcock Hill was wholly from mineral soil.

At Rocher Moss and Dean Clough the peaty layer was approximately 35 cms thick, whilst at Warcock Hill it was at least 10 cms less. At all three sites there was a darkening towards the base of this layer, the material becoming almost black in its colouration. The Rocher Moss site differed from the other sites in not having a clearly defined transitional zone between the peaty horizon and the mineral soil beneath. All three sites had a zone of grey-brown mineral soil with an iron humus 'B' horizon immediately beneath. At Dean Clough there was a noticeably softer humus iron pan, seemingly mainly composed of humus. Beneath the iron pan was a weathered subsoil, either mottled or ochre in colour (Fig. 22).

Methods of Collection and Preparation

At each site a pit was dug down into the weathered subsoil. A face within each pit was cleaned and sampled at approximately 2 cm. intervals. At each stage great care was taken to prevent contamination with material from other levels.

The sediment was transferred straight from the specimen tubes in which it had been collected to boiling tubes; four samples being prepared at any one time. Having treated the samples with sodium hydroxide, the material was washed through fine mesh screens to remove the coarse mineral material. After each treatment with chemicals a sample was centrifuged and decanted to remove the chemical, and this was followed by a washing with distilled water. As much of the material was mineral soil and therefore very gritty, it was necessary to use hydrofluoric acid to remove the mineral matter. Before that was done all calcium carbonate was removed from the samples. The hot hydrofluoric acid treatment was adopted in an effort to speed up the process. Instead of the recommended time of between five and thirty minutes for this process, it was necessary, due to the gritty nature of the material, to heat it for several hours. In the case of the Warcock Hill samples, they were heated for eight hours and then left to stand overnight. To remove the soluble cellulose acetate products of acetolysis glacial acetic acid was added. Finally the samples were washed with distilled water before staining with aqueous safranin. They were then allowed to dry before being mounted in glycerol for expediency.

Because many of the mineral soil samples still contained grit, which had the effect of making it virtually uncountable, the Warcock Hill samples had to be decanted after the above process had been completed. Glycerol being miscible in water meant that the pollen medium could be added to distilled water, allowing the coarse sediments to sink. The mixture was decanted, centrifuged, and remounted in glycerol. How successful this step was is difficult to determine as the material was so badly degraded; it is impossible to say if any pollen was lost via this process.

No absolute counting was carried out. The grains were counted on traverses 2 mm. apart, to ensure that no grains were counted more than once. As far as possible c. 150 tree pollen grains were counted for each sample. This led to varying totals as the amount of tree pollen varied between samples. For Rocher Moss and Dean Clough the total number of pollen grains counted, excluding spores, varied between c. 200 and c. 1,000. The Warcock Hill counts were much smaller, ranging between c. 90 and c. 350; at this site it was virtually impossible to count 150 tree pollens, the material being so badly deteriorated (Figs. 27–9).

Spores were excluded from the total pollen sum and have been represented on the diagrams by their actual numbers. All other grains are presented as percentages of the total pollen sum. Where applicable and possible (if enough grains were counted for it to be valid) pollen has been presented as a percentage of total tree pollen; where these percentages are obviously not really valid they are represented by a pecked line, and have been included for completeness.

Results of the Pollen Analysis

Before looking at the results, there are several points which must be borne in mind as they tend to crop up continually in work on Central Pennine sites. As Tallis has pointed out (Radley et al 1974) the dating of Mesolithic sites in the Pennines requires a consideration of the mineral soil. Microliths invariably occur in it, either in situ beneath the blanket peat or near the surface after the peat cover has been eroded away. This necessarily introduces the possibilities of differential destruction, downwashing, and inwashing of pollen grains into diagrams constructed from mineral soils. It is also recognised that the peat may not rest conformably on the mineral soil, and so, although it is known that the microliths pre date the peat, it is not known by how long. Thus conclusions about date and environment must be somewhat speculative in nature.

It may be useful to consider the results of the three sites under discussion in the light of Godwin's pollen zonation scheme. Generally when speaking of the Mesolithic one is concerned with pollen zones VI and VII. The occupation of sites was almost invariably of short duration, especially in the higher Pennine area. Thus each occupation tends to relate directly to only a short span of any one zone or to a boundary between zones or sub zones. During zone VI pine (Pinus) becomes predominant over birch (Betula), with elm (Ulmus) and oak (Quercus) appearing and increasing. Often hazel (Corylus) is found to exceed tree pollen totals. As this period progresses hazel values begin to fall, as do those of pine, whilst oak and elm maintain their values and are supplemented by the appearance of lime (Tilia) and alder (Alnus). Zone VII, which is divided into two sub zones, is characterised by its high alder values. At the opening of this zone alder increases to between 40 and 50% of total tree pollen, and sometimes its proportion can be even greater. The opening of the zone is taken to be where the alder curve is rising and the pine curve falling. The boundary between sub zones VIIa and VIIb does not at first seem to be based upon a very substantial vegetational change. However, over north western Europe there is a consistent observable decrease in pollen frequencies of elm, pine and lime.

This zonation whilst being a useful guide to changes in pollen is itself subject to wide variations. Thus the time at which the changes take place is not always synchronous; the changes themselves are found to vary in the degree to which they affect any one area. This has been found to be true not only on an inter regional scale but also on an intra regional level. Thus in the Pennines it has been found that on flatter ground there has 'probably been an inherent tendency for peat to form readily after the Boreal-Atlantic transition onwards' (Radley et al 1974, 10); 'onwards' in some places equalling early medieval times. The critical factor in most areas is the overcoming of 'the inertia of the existing forest cover' (Radley et al 1974, 10). In certain areas, such as those above c. 1,500 feet, tree growth may have been inhibited naturally, and the onset of peat accumulation may be synchronous with the onset of wetter conditions. In other areas of peat accumulation the reasons for its development are less certain and may result from anthropogenic influences.

On turning to look at the actual pollen diagrams, the first noticeable point is that total tree pollen levels are relatively low, generally less than or equal to 30% of total pollen (Fig. 23). There is a predominance of either herbaceous or *Corylus* pollen in all three diagrams (Figs. 24–6), with herbaceous pollen tending to be the higher value of the two, reaching values of between 45% and 70%. Each site is definitely post *Alnus* rise in character; values for *Alnus* pollen are typically in the order of around 5% of total pollen in the basal mineral soil and increase to just over 20% in the highest peat sample for Dean Clough and Warcock Hill. At Rocher Moss the percentage varies very little, being between 6% and 7% of the total. Quite consistently at all three sites *Pinus*, *Tilia* and *Ulmus* have low values or are declining. From the reliable parts of the tree pollen diagrams, pollen for these species typically reaches values of up to 7%, but dwindles away to *c.* 1% or becomes totally absent in the peat samples. *Quercus* and *Betula* form the two most plentiful types of tree pollen after *Alnus*, *Quercus* being the more plentiful of the two (Figs. 27–9).

Corylus has values of between 15% and 35% for Warcock Hill and Rocher Moss, while at Dean Clough it tends to vary between around 20% and 50% of total pollen. From the summary pollen diagrams it can be seen that below the mineral soil/peat boundary at Dean Clough tree pollen does not reach 10% of total pollen while at the same levels at the other sites it varies between *c.* 15% and 30%, herbaceous pollen accounting for between 45% and 60% at all three sites. Thus below the soil/peat boundary it seems that in the case of Dean Clough there may be a hazel scrubland. Above the mineral soil/peat boundary (which is only present in the samples for Rocher Moss and Dean Clough, all the samples for Warcock Hill being from below the peat) percentages are typically in the range of 20 to 30. At the boundary the profiles become much more alike in character. An expansion of deciduous tree pollen appears to be accompanied by a contraction of *Corylus* pollen at Dean Clough.

Herbaceous pollen consistently accounts for the largest proportion of the pollen spectra. *Gramineae* and *Ericacea* pollen types form the two major components of the herbaceous pollen spectra. The *Ericacea* pollen is made up almost entirely of *Calluna*. At all three sites the *Gramineae* and *Calluna* pollen seem to be closely linked: when one is decreasing the other is increasing. This link is not proportional, but is nevertheless quite evident. At the Dean Clough and Rocher Moss sites *Gramineae* is dominant below the peat with very little *Calluna* being present. At the mineral soil/ peat boundary, *Calluna* pollen rises to values of between 10% and 20% and continues to rise at each subsequent level until percentages of *c.* 45 are reached. Accompanying this rise is a decline in *Gramineae* to levels of between 2% and 12%. At Warcock Hill, if it were to follow the pattern of the other two sites, one would expect to find either a negligible amount of *Calluna* pollen or its total absence from the spectra. However this is not the case: *Gramineae* pollen declines from *c.* 60% to *c.* 20%, and *Calluna* pollen from being totally absent rises to 20% of total pollen at the top of the profile. Thus it would appear that there has been some development of heath before the onset of peat accumulation.

It must be remembered, however, that the data from Warcock Hill are the least reliable of all. Although this site is definitely both post *Corylus* rise and post *Alnus* rise it is not definitely post elm decline. *Ulmus* and *Pinus* are both present only in the level nearest the boundary, which happens to be the sample which was the least degraded. Rocher Moss can almost certainly be said to belong to the pollen zone VIIa/VIIb boundary. *Pinus*, *Tilia* and *Ulmus* all decrease to a fraction of 1% and *Plantago lanceolata* begins to appear. Dean Clough, the most closely sampled site, also appears to be the most perplexing. It appears to have characteristics from both pre elm decline and post elm decline pollen diagrams. In the basal mineral soil levels, hazel pollen percentages exceed tree pollen totals – indicative of the late zone VI environment. Throughout the same levels, however, *Pinus* is almost absent, *Tilia* and *Ulmus* are found in only small amounts and are completely absent from some levels, and this indicative of the zone VIIa/VIIb boundary. *Plantago lanceolata* is present in only one level and in a small quantity – below 2%. *Calluna* pollen, as in the Rocher Moss diagram, increases at the mineral soil/peat boundary, *Gramineae* decreasing at the same time. Above the transition the proportions of tree pollen to *Corylus* pollen are similar to those of the other sites. It seems that either there has been some soil erosion or clearance of the forest which would allow a hazel scrubland to develop.

Conclusions

Warcock Hill South (Fig. 24) from its radiocarbon date of 7,260 ± 340 b.c. and from its broad blade flint typology should from its pollen results appear significantly older than the other two sites under discussion. Switsur and Jacobi (1975) suggest that the site might be contemporary with Flixton site 1, occupation of which continued into pollen zone V. As has been seen, not only are the levels of birch (*Betula*) and pine (*Pinus*) very low but alder (*Alnus*) forms the major component of tree pollen. Hazel (*Corylus*) pollen is present in quite substantial quantities, often accounting for between around 15% and 20% of total pollen. Unlike the other sites there is some development of heath before the onset of peat accumulation. A similar expansion of *Calluna* has been seen at the sites of Broomhead Moor 5 and Dunford Bridge A (Radley *et al* 1974). In the study of these sites it is concluded that 'since at the "non-microlith" sites peat formation was not associated with increased *Calluna* pollen levels, this expansion of *Calluna* at the microlithic sites was probably largely unconnected with the accumulation of peat'. One explanation for this expansion of *Calluna* is that an increased contribution resulted from the degradation of mineral soils following up on the destruction of forest cover. Under the wetter conditions of zone VII with the forest cover removed the tendency towards leaching and podsolisation would be realised. A possible cause could be the removal of vegetation by mesolithic burning to provide better browse for animals, but at this point it is impossible either to prove or disprove this idea.

What can be said definitely about this site is that it is both post *Corylus* rise and post *Alnus* rise, but it cannot be stated with any degree of certainty whether it is post elm decline. The pollen diagrams would seem to indicate a zone VII environment, an obvious contradiction of both the archaeological and radiocarbon evidence. The reason for this is not clear. It is quite possible that the nature of the material has affected the results. The pollen was very degraded: counts were not large, being in the order of 350, although the basal count was as low as 45. Tree pollen counts were so low that they have been included only for completeness, and it is not valid to discuss them. As pointed out earlier, there may have been problems associated with differential destruction, downwashing and inwashing of pollen grains in a profile wholly constructed with samples from mineral soil. Thus it seems that no firm conclusions can be drawn from the work carried out on this site.

Dean Clough I has a similar industry to the Broomhead Moor 5 site, both having March Hill industries, and it would be appropriate to compare their pollen results to discover any further similarities between them. In the basal parts of the pollen diagrams both sites have low tree pollen percentages, those of Broomhead Moor being consistently slightly higher than those of Dean Clough. Both sites also have *Ulmus* counts of about 5% total tree pollen. In the case of Dean Clough (Fig. 25) both *Ulmus* and *Tilia* decline at the top of the profile and *Plantago lanceolata* is seen for the first time. This would seem to indicate a zone VII date, though a comparable decline is not seen at Broomhead Moor. The expansion of deciduous tree pollen at both sites occurs at the mineral soil/ peat boundary, accompanied by a contraction of *Corylus* pollen. Tallis suggests that this represents a natural vegetational development in response to increasing temperatures as opposed to being the result of anthropogenic influences (Radley *et al* 1974). It is also suggested that the contraction in hazel pollen probably represents a suppression of flowering below a newly developed continuous tree canopy rather than an elimination due to competition. It was pointed out earlier that *Pinus* is barely evident in the Dean Clough diagram, another factor which could be indicative of zone VII. However, on turning to look at other pollen diagrams from the area one can see that *Pinus* made only a small contribution to the total pollen influx during zone VI. The conclusion that may be drawn from this is that pine forest was not an important component of the Central Pennine landscape.

As seen already, hazel pollen percentage totals in the basal mineral soil levels exceed tree pollen totals. Tallis concludes that this is a 'real feature of the late zone VI environment, and not just a result of differential pollen preservation in the mineral soil' (Radley *et al* 1974, 13). Differential pollen preservation is difficult to prove, but the pollen from Dean Clough was generally well preserved. At both sites *Ericaceae* pollen levels (mostly *Calluna*) in association with the *Corylus* maximum are low. At Dean Clough there is not a large increase in herbaceous pollen until the mineral soil/peat boundary. The increase once it occurs is largely attributable to *Calluna* pollen, as at Broomhead Moor. However, the fact that the increase does not take place until the layer of transition is reached may be an indication that at this site it may be connected with the onset of peat formation rather than as a result of anthropogenic influences.

Once the pollen evidence from Dean Clough is seen against the background of other Pennine diagrams a much truer picture can be gained than if it is only compared with Godwin's generalised zonation scheme. It seems that the lower part of the diagram is representing an environment with a late zone VI character. The upper part of the diagram would appear to belong to zone VII, *Alnus* pollen by this point clearly rising. The lack of *Pinus* can be seen as a regional modification to Godwin's scheme.

The time difference of almost a thousand years between the radiocarbon dates for Broomhead Moor 5 and Dean Clough I is to a great extent explained by the fact that the date for the former is early; this in turn has been explained by there being only one centimetre difference between samples of undoubted zone VI and zone VII age. This is thought to represent a stratigraphic nonconformity. Thus Dean Clough would appear to have a late pollen zone VI to early pollen zone VII environment, the exact boundary being impossible to pinpoint due to *Pinus* pollen being almost totally absent in the area. This would agree not only with the typological evidence but also with the radiocarbon date for the site.

The site of Rocher Moss South 2 was the most straight forward of the three sites to interpret, having an obvious zone VIIa pollen spectrum (Fig. 26). It is quite obviously both post *Alnus* rise and post *Corylus* rise; *Ulmus* and *Tilia* are beginning to decline, and *Plantago lanceolata* is becoming apparent at the top of the profile. As in the case of Dean Clough, heath development takes place after the mineral soil/peat boundary, and a gradual increase in herbaceous pollen is seen. The pollen spectrum agrees well, not only with its own radiocarbon date of 3,880 ± 100 b.c., but with the date of 3,430 ± 80 b.c. for Dunford Bridge site B, both sites having rod-dominated industries. The latter date has been fitted into the Dunford Bridge site A diagrams at a level which indicates a late zone VIIa environment. Thus the palaeoecological evidence from Rocher Moss is seen to fit in with the archaeological evidence from its own and other sites.

In conclusion, two points must be made. The Dean Clough, Warcock Hill and Rocher Moss sites have not been as closely sampled as other sites: this may have an important bearing upon the results, as has been seen in the case of Broomhead Moor 5. The sampling of these three sites was carried out after the original excavations, and so it has been impossible to establish the relationship between the material used for the pollen analysis and that used for radiocarbon dating. This may have made some very slight difference to the comparability of results.

Acknowledgements
In the preparation of this work my special thanks are due to Professor Frank Oldfield and to Dr Joan Taylor for their kind help and encouragement. I would also like to thank Dr W. P. B. Stonehouse for introducing me to the three sites examined.

Figure 22.

SOIL PROFILES FROM THE THREE POLLEN SITES

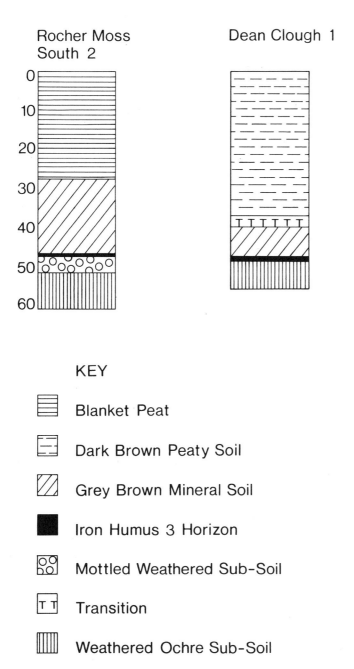

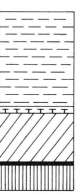

Figure 23.

SUMMARY POLLEN DIAGRAMS

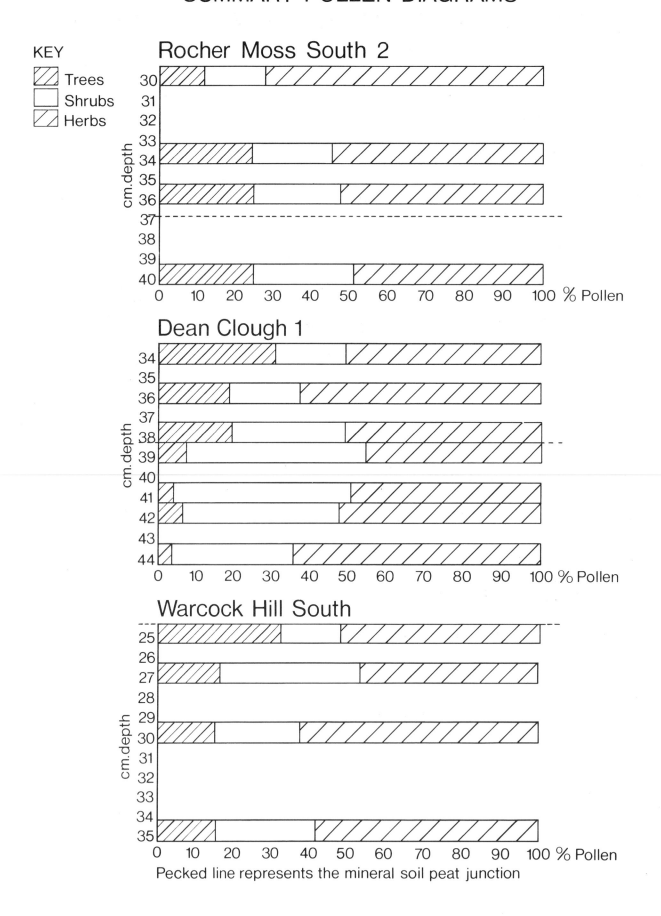

KEY
- Trees
- Shrubs
- Herbs

Rocher Moss South 2

Dean Clough 1

Warcock Hill South

Pecked line represents the mineral soil peat junction

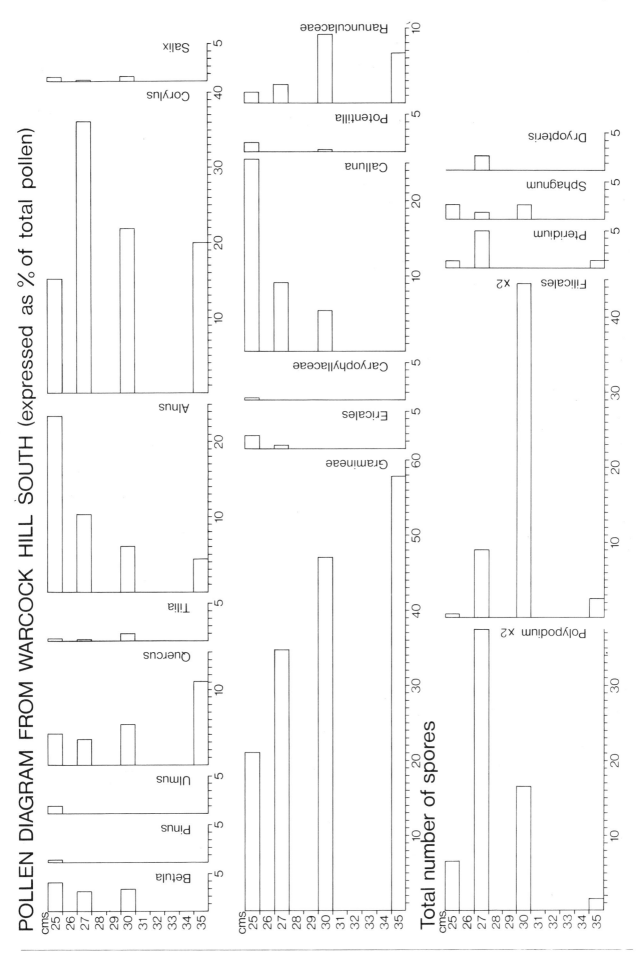

POLLEN DIAGRAM FROM WARCOCK HILL SOUTH (expressed as % of total pollen)

Total number of spores

Figure 24.

Figure 25.

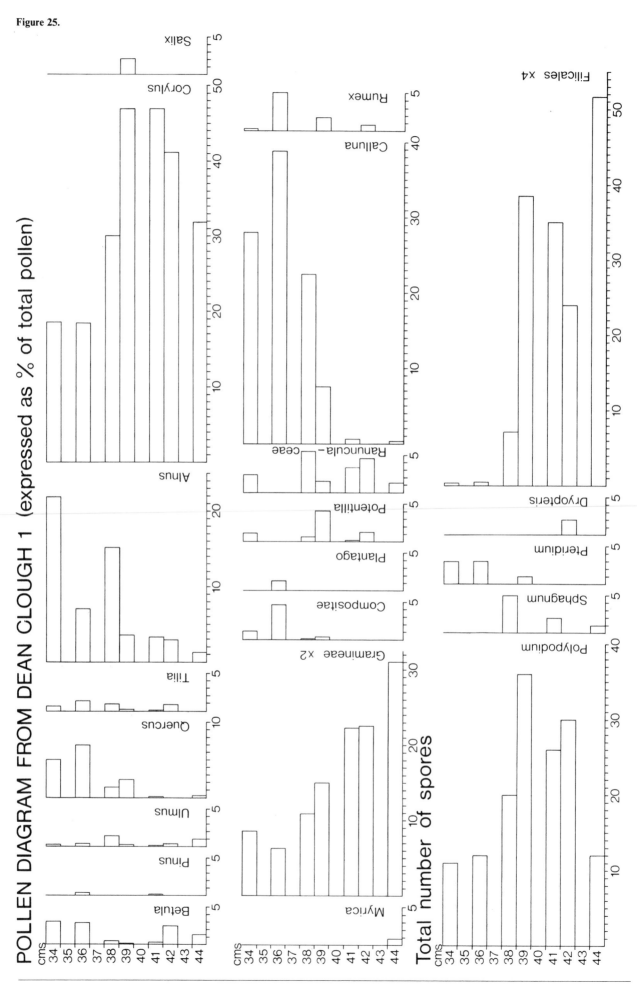

POLLEN DIAGRAM FROM DEAN CLOUGH 1 (expressed as % of total pollen)

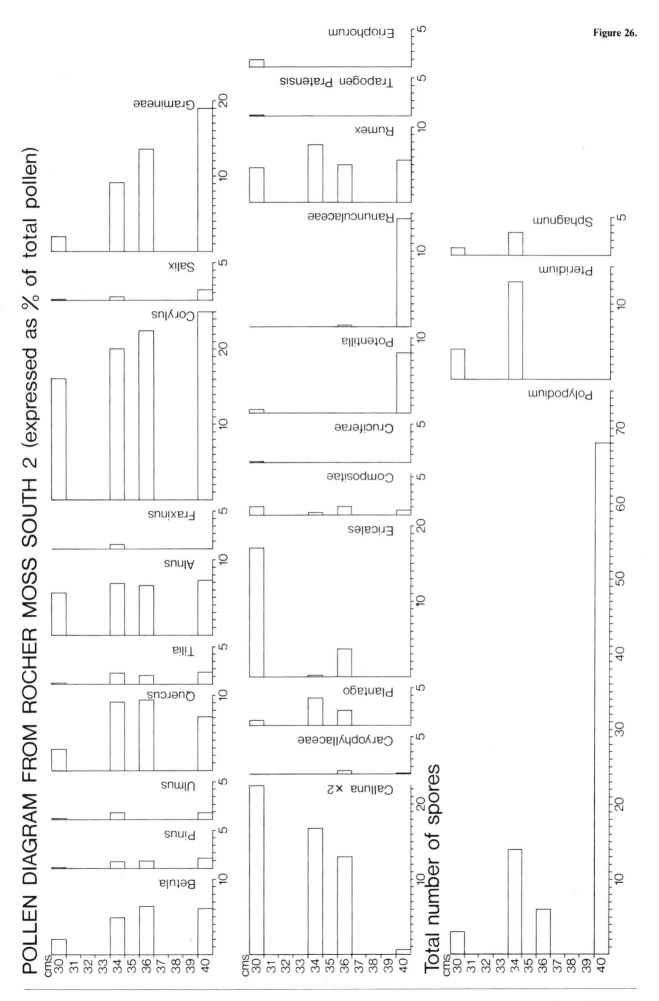

POLLEN DIAGRAM FROM ROCHER MOSS SOUTH 2 (expressed as % of total pollen)

Figure 26.

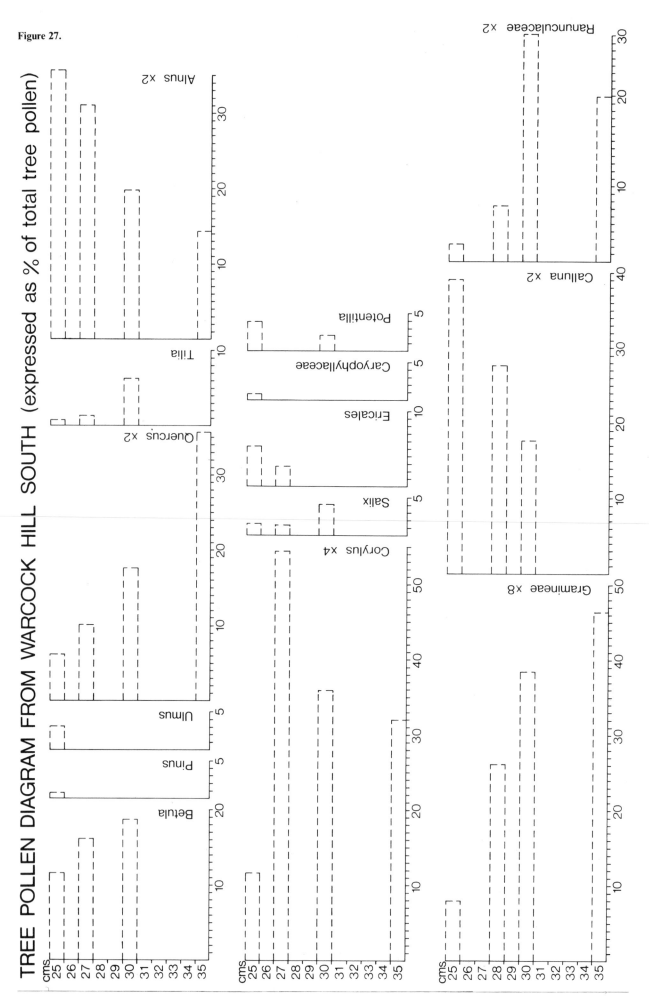

TREE POLLEN DIAGRAM FROM WARCOCK HILL SOUTH (expressed as % of total tree pollen)

Figure 27.

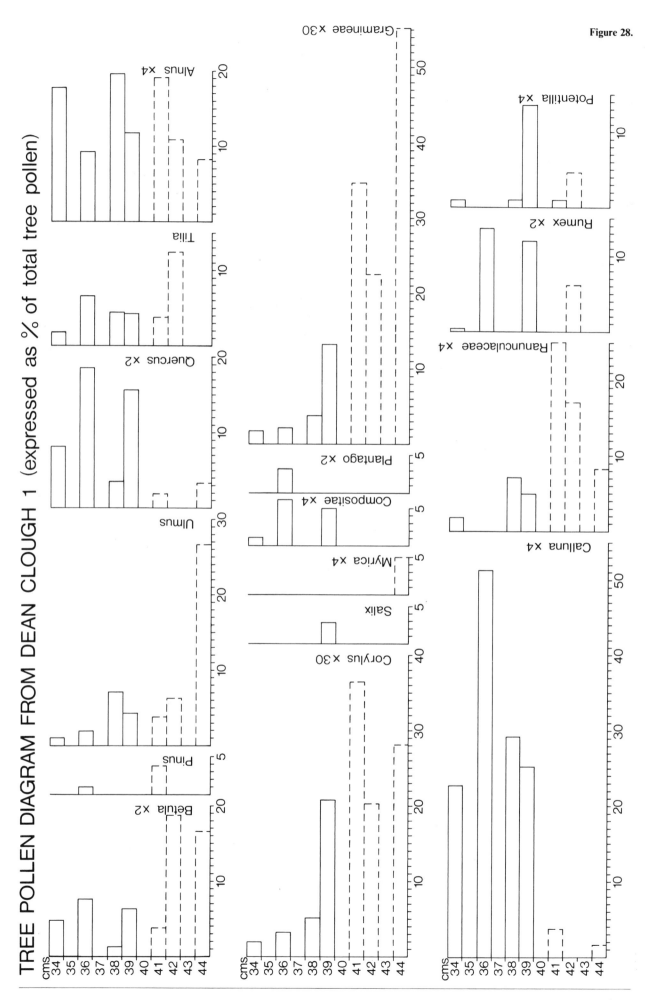

TREE POLLEN DIAGRAM FROM DEAN CLOUGH 1 (expressed as % of total tree pollen)

Figure 28.

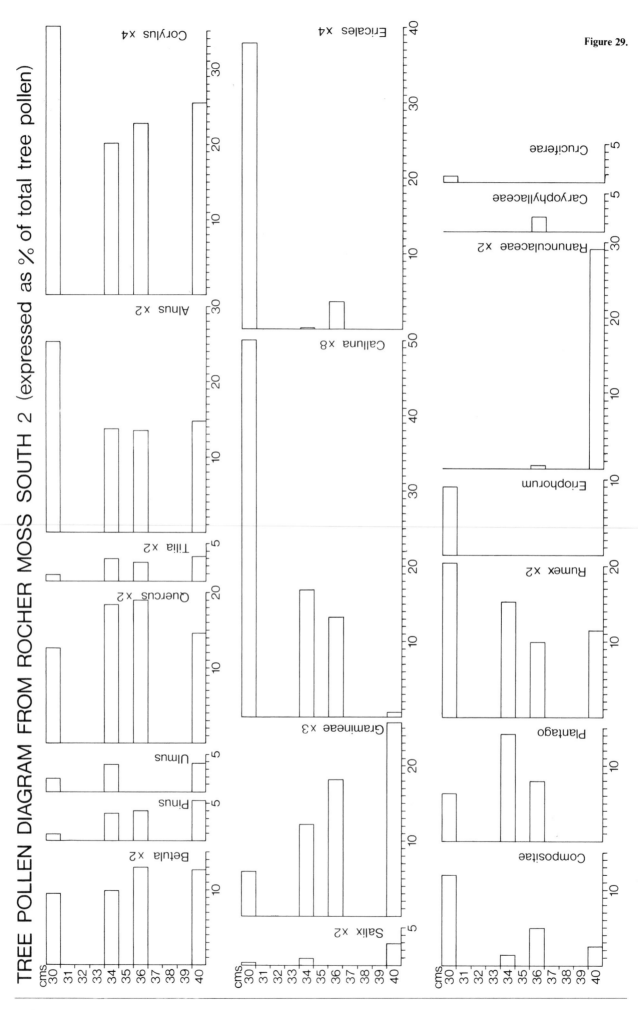

TREE POLLEN DIAGRAM FROM ROCHER MOSS SOUTH 2 (expressed as % of total tree pollen)

Figure 29.

Appendix 2
An Index of Archaeological Discoveries from the Central Pennine Area

The index is in numerical sequence. Within this sequence, the entries are divided into two broad groups geographically, west and east of the Pennine watershed respectively, the dividing line falling between numbers 204 and 205. Each entry has been placed in the context of the present administrative areas, the metropolitan districts. There is no other classification. Where possible each site has been located precisely and given a national grid reference. None of the flint sites, Mesolithic or otherwise, is listed, however, because of the very great numbers: reference to the main Mesolithic find spots can be found elsewhere (Wymer 1977). Neither are beehive querns and so called 'Iron Age' walls included, in both cases for reasons of their doubtful dates. Details of them have been described in other publications (eg *CAGB*; Maxim 1912–13), and they are listed in local museum indexes. Some of the early published details about sites and finds, particularly those in the Burnley and Baildon areas, are very vague and sometimes contradictory. It is hoped that sense has been made of them.

1 Blackburn
Belmont Reservoir   SD 66981701
Middle Bronze Age looped socketed spearhead found in October 1933 on the line of an old road to the north west of an island in the reservoir, 8 feet below high water mark. The spearhead point was projecting 3 inches above the ground. Spearhead has small elongated loops on socket below blade, and part of the original wooden shaft was found in the socket. Bolton Museum (BOLMG 11.34).
a) Jackson 1934–5.
b) Davey & Forster 1975, Fig. 72.
c) O.S. Records SD61NE2.

2 Blackburn
Darwen   SD 6922 ?
'Gritstone hammer found near Darwen.'
a) Plant 1867–8, 73.
b) Yates 1887, 330.

3 Blackburn
Darwen, White Hall   SD 69602080
Round barrow at 675 feet O.D., 90 feet in diameter, 10–12 feet high on eastern side and 2–3 feet on the west, opened in October 1864 during digging of foundations for a house ('Ashleigh') in the grounds of White Hall, Over Darwen. Around 1820 the mound had been planted with trees, and it was during their felling that the discoveries were made. The centre of the barrow was sunk around 6 feet in the centre. 10 burials were found: 'one a heap of burnt bones without a cist or urn; the others were enclosed in urns, only one of which was found in an inverted position. On the top of each of the cinerary urns was a rough flat stone, and they were surrounded and covered by small stones carefully piled up.' 2 of the urns were in a 'tolerably perfect state; the others were very much broken'. 2 pygmy vessels were found in the unbroken urns. Urn A, the most perfect, was 12 inches high and 10 inches diameter at the top, and 'had a deep rim or collar. The ornamentation consisted of a number of dotted indentations produced with the point of a stick'. This urn was filled with burnt bones on the top of which lay the pygmy vessel, also containing human ashes, and measuring 1¾ inches in height, 2½ inches in diameter at the mouth and 4 inches at the middle; it was unornamented. Urn B was 7½ inches high and 7 inches in diameter; 'its middle part and collar were elaborately covered with a reticulated ornament, produced by pressing a twisted cord thong into the pliant clay'. Some of the fragmented urns were 'more ornamented in their reticulations . . . one fragment of the collar of an urn being of the herring-bone pattern'. Some pieces of very corroded bronze were reported, and in one urn a bronze knife/dagger 6½ inches long and 2½ inches wide, much decayed and twisted, was found (Frontispiece).
a) Hardwick 1865–6.
b) Abram 1877, 23–4 and Fig.
c) Garstang 1906, 242 and Figs. 26–7.

4 Blackburn
Edgeworth   SD 74581816
Developed palstave with improved hafting (belonging to Burgess's Pickering phase) found October 1908 whilst cutting trench for a sewer across the road opposite the former Wheat Sheaf Inn, later one of the houses of the National Children's Home. 15.4 cm. long, 5.7 maximum width (originally 6 cm. – one wing damaged). Grimshaw reported bitumen in grooves, used to fix weapon to haft. Prag reports this as a product of corrosion. Manchester Museum 1976.48).
a) Grimshaw 1916.
b) Prag 1977.
c) O.S. Records SD71NW9.

5 Blackburn
Edgeworth, Carve Hill   SD 75491589
Large mound with steep sides, roughly circular, situated on an extensive natural plateau in a wide shallow valley at 700 feet O.D. Height on west 4.2 metres, on east 6.4 metres. No trace of ditch.
a) Hunt 1978.
b) O.S. Records SD71NE8.

6 Blackburn
Revidge   SD 67352940
   On July 26 1879 on upper edge of old quarry, 452 feet above sea level, was found 'sepulchral urn in inverted position, embedded in layer of indurated sand and standing on gritstone, about 4 feet below the surface. The urn was filled with fragments of bones, the remains of a cremated body. Ornamentation consists of zigzag lines on the central part of the urn and of herringbone pattern on the collar' (Abram). The urn was fractured by a pick, but was put together later. The head of a bronze pin was also found and a bone pin 2 inches long. The urn is 10½ inches high, 7 inches diameter at the mouth and 4 inches at the base, and is in Blackburn Museum.
a) Abram 1879 & Fig.
b) March 1887, Plate IV, Fig. 4 (urn).
c) Garstang 1906, 242.

7 Blackburn
Turton, Charters Moss (Fig. 17, ii)   SD 697169
Middle Bronze Age palstave found *c.* 1810 while digging drain, 4 feet below the turf. Nearly 5 inches long, 2⅜ inches at the widest part of the blade, 1¼ inches wide across the ridge. (Probably the same palstave as that recorded by Dawes 1851–2 at Egbert Dean.) Bolton Museum (X.49).
a) Greenhalgh 1871.
b) Harrison 1896.
c) Garstang 1906, 231 and Plate IV, No. 3.
d) Davey & Forster 1975, Fig. 47.
e) O.S. Records SD61NE3.
f) (Egbert Dean) Dawes 1851–2.
g) (Egbert Dean) Garstang 1906, 232.
h) (Egbert Dean) O.S. Records SD61SE17.

8 Blackburn
Turton Charters Moss   SD 697169
Vague references to 'perforated stone hammer' found on Charters Moss (probably the same as that recorded by Dawes 1851–2 at Egbert Dean).
a) Harrison 1896.
b) Garstang 1906, 226.
c) O.S. Records SD61NE4.
d) (Egbert Dean) Dawes 1851–2.
e) (Egbert Dean) O.S. Records SD61SE17.

9 Blackburn
Turton, Chetham's Close   SD 71641589
Stone circle. In 1871 described as 'a stone circle, 7 stones remaining (formerly 11?), diameter 51 feet 6 inches, tallest stone 55 inches high, shortest 8 inches. At a distance of 45 feet south-west from the circle stands a solitary stone 19 inches high, and south-south-east at a distance of 102 feet another stone 35 inches high.' Some

stones were being broken at the time. In 1879 'only 3 stones were left.' O.S. Records described circle as being at 1,075 feet above sea level, 60 metres below the summit of Chetham's Close. Only 6 stones can now be traced and these are either fractured or recumbent. 17.5 metres to the south west is a single upright stone.
a) Dawes 1851–2.
b) Greenhalgh 1871.
c) Greenhalgh 1880.
d) Burl 1976.
e) O.S. Records SD71NW2.

10 Blackburn
Turton, Chetham's Close   SD 71631594
Denuded ring (or kerbed mound), nearer the summit of the hill. Discovered 1893 and excavated 1893–4: 'stone walled, 24 yards in diameter, faced on both sides by large flat stones with the space between them being occupied by smaller stones; 4 feet thick'. O.S. Records describe it as being a circular depression in the ground, 0.4 metres deep. The stones are embedded in the sides of the depression and loose cobbles encircle the lip.
a) French 1894.
b) O.S. Records SD71NW2.

11 Blackburn
Turton Heights   SD 71721590
Late Bronze Age saddle quern found near stone circle (No. 9) in 1954. 20 inches long.
a) O.S. Records SD71NW6.

12 Bolton
Blackrod   SD 61321106
Axe-hammer found 1897 during ploughing at Green Barn, near Blackrod Church. 8½ inches long; 3 inches wide, 2¼–2¾ inches thick; class IIb. Group XV. Bolton Museum (BOLMG 28a.97). Petro No. La36.
a) Garstang 1906, 224.
b) Roe 1979, 44.
c) O.S. Records SD61SW21.

13 Bolton
Breightmet   SD 74170795
Bronze Age stone battle axe found in allotments at Long Lane, June 1948. 4½ inches long, 2¼ inches wide, 1 inch thick with slightly upturned cutting edge. Central perforation is 1 inch in diameter. Group XVIII. Roe's Stage II, truncated butt form. Bolton Museum (BOLMG A.1.1948).
a) O.S. Records SD70NW5.
b) Roe 1966.
c) Roe 1979, 42.

14 Bolton
Breightmet Hill   SD 74300933 ?
'In a field near Breightmet Hill at different times have been found urns containing ashes . . . A few years ago 12 were found . . . which being exposed to the external air soon dwindled away into dust . . . c.9 feet below the surface . . . Every urn contained in the top part of it a small bone pin about 2 inches in length . . .' (Hadfield). A cremation cemetery?
a) Hadfield 1807.
b) Baines 1835, iii, 88.
c) Watkins 1883, 231.
d) Bu'Lock & Rosser 1960.
e) O.S. Records SD70NW14.

15 Bolton
Breightmet Hill   SD 740095
Small unperforated pygmy cup found in 1955 during the building of a new estate at Breightmet Hill. Bolton Museum (1955).
a) Bu'Lock & Rosser 1960.

16 Bolton
Bromley Cross   SD 7213
Stone flat axe/adze, siltstone, a surface find on a building site at Little Brow Estate. Unknown affinities, but has been worked. Bolton Museum (BOLMG. A.1.1961).

17 Bolton
Deane Clough   SD 693083
Three axe-hammers. a) 5 inches by 2 inches, in Warrington

Museum; b) 9¾ inches by 3½ inches, in Warrington Museum; c) 5 inches by 2 inches, in Preston Museum.
a) Yates 1887, 329.
b) Garstang 1906, 224 and Plate II, No. 4 (example b).
c) O.S. Records SD60NE7.

18 Bolton
Deane Clough   SD 693083
Polished stone axe, a surface find on the bank of Deane Clough Brook made in 1962. Bolton Museum (A.2.1960). Petro No. La 70. Camptonite from Nuneaton District.

19 Bolton
Delph Reservoir   SD 6810 ?
Two polished stone axes found 1910, one broad butted the other pointed butted. 'In mint condition' and found 10 feet deep in peat. One is 14.2 inches long, the other 9 inches long. Langdale stone. Bolton Museum (BOLMG.43.10 Pt.1, and BOLMG. 43.10 Pt. 2). Petro Nos. La 35.
a) *CAGB* 1958, 73–4.
b) Manby 1965, 372 and 384.
c) Hallam 1970.

20 Bolton
Haulgh Hall   SD 72420899
Site of three Bronze Age barrows in an area now built upon on Bradford St. just after Dorset St., found 1825 during construction of Bolton–Bury New Road. One, a cairn, prior to excavation was 30 feet in diameter and 4 feet high. In the centre was a cist of 4 stones with a cover, 4 feet 6 inches by 12 inches, lying north–south and containing a contracted burial, head to the north; near the head was a biconical, inverted incense cup 4½ inches by 3 inches, together with a bronze knife/dagger 4⅜ inches long and 1⅜ inches broad, having three rivet holes for hafting. Two other barrows were a few yards to the south. In 1977, during alterations to houses built around 1900 on Bradford St., cracks were noticed in those built on the sites of the three barrows. Finds in Bolton Museum.
a) Dawes 1851–2.
b) Garstang 1906, 231 and 241.
c) Bu'Lock & Rosser 1960.
d) Bu'Lock 1961.
e) Davey & Forster 1975, Fig. 22 (dagger).
f) O.S. Records SD70NW12.

21 Bolton
Horwich, Adam Hill   SD 66321235
At 1,100 feet O.D. a turf-covered cairn (tumulus?), 10 metres east–west, 8.7 metres north–south, near circular and 0.5 metres high at the centre. No ditch.
a) Hunt 1978.
b) O.S. Records SD61SE11.

22 Bolton
Queens Park   SD 70750935
Pebble macehead of quartzite with hour glass perforation, found 1887 in sand at the eastern end of the promenade in the park, 3¾ inches in length, 2¼ inches wide, 1½ inches deep, one end somewhat adze-like, the other hammer-like. Bolton Museum (BOLMG. 14.87). Petro No. La 30.
a) Yates 1887, 329.
b) Garstang 1906, 226 and Fig. 11.
c) Wymer 1977, 163.
d) O.S. Records SD70NW7.

23 Bolton
Rosehill   SD 72460830
Composite cairn found in 1851 at 275 feet O.D. on the western bank of the R. Croal, 60–70 feet above the river. Cairn was 15 feet in diameter and 4 feet high, composed of boulders with c. 2 feet of earth on top. In the centre was a broken 'Pennine' urn, 2 feet high, 1 foot 3 inches wide, inverted and sunk c. 6 inches into the earth. It contained the burnt bones of a young person, together with the bones of 1 or 2 small animals and a small clay bead. Probably little notice should be paid to the alleged piece of Kimmeridge shale found in the mound. Remains of urn in Bolton Museum.
a) Dawes 1851–2, 132 and Fig. 5.
b) Bu'Lock & Rosser 1960.
c) O.S. Records SD70NW6.

24 Bolton
Sharples Hall   SD 7011 ?
Bronze palstave.
a) O.S. Records SD71SW9.

25 Bolton
Walmsley   SD 71071421
Bronze Age cairn found on site of Church on highest part of knoll
to the east of Eagley Brook in 1838. Contained inhumation in cist
with grey, ill-baked 'food vessel' (urn?) and white flint knife 2½
inches long, 1½ inches wide. The urn was broken at the time of
discovery and the sherds lost.
19.5 ems — 8/9 Times 327 —
a) Dawes 1851–2.
b) Garstang 1906, 218 and 241.
c) Jackson 1934–5.
d) Bu'Lock 1961.
e) O.S. Records SD71SW7.

26 Burnley
       SD 8836 ?
Bronze tanged spearhead found 2½ feet below the surface in a field
half way between Burnley and Nelson in 1845. Narrow tang with
rivet hole. 9 inches long, tang 3 inches in length, 1½ inches greatest
width. Found near Nelson, Catlow?
a) Garstang 1906, 234 and Fig. 21.
b) Bennett 1946, 17 and Fig. 2.
c) Davey & Forster 1975, Fig. 15.

27 Burnley
Beadle Hill   SD 890341
'Roman camp' 80 yards square with fosse and vallum recorded
just north of Holden Clough. Possibly an Iron Age earthwork (or
earlier?).
a) Wilkinson 1893.

28 Burnley
Ben Edge   SD 898325
Nine bituminous shale beads found.
a) Leach 1912–13.

29 Burnley
Bonfire Hill I (Pike Low)   SD 89463428
Grassed cairn at 1,060 feet O.D. In 1893 described as 'tumulus or
earth circle, explored in the middle?'.
a) *THSLC* 1891, 34.
b) Harrison 1892.
c) Wilkinson 1893, 160.
d) Clare 1973, Vol. 2.

30 Burnley
Bonfire Hill II (Beadle Hill)   SD 89163411
Almost imperceptible mound at 1,000 feet O.D., described as
tumulus (stone circle).
a) *THSLC* 1891, 34.
b) Bennett 1946, 143.
c) Hunt 1978.

31 Burnley
Bonfire Hill III (Beadle Hill)   SD 89153409
Almost imperceptible mound at 1,000 feet O.D., described as
tumulus (stone circle).
a) *THSLC* 1891, 34.
b) Bennett 1946, 143.
c) Hunt 1978.

32 Burnley
Broadbank   SD 90243522
Earth circle 150 feet diameter, with inner ditch at 1,147 feet O.D.
Excavated 1950: bank composed of boulder clay and consisted of
outthrow from ditch which was c. 1 foot deep when first cut and
c. 10 inches across. Hearth below bank at eastern end, but no
artefacts found. Small number of poor quality flint and chert
flakes found on old ground surface. Site may well have been
abandoned before being brought into use. (NB stone axe found on
bank – see No. 33).
a) Clement 1874.
b) Harrison 1892, 249.
c) Powell 1952.

33 Burnley
Broadbank   SD 90243522
Group VI stone axe found on excavation of earth circle (No. 32) in
1950, on bank below modern turf, ie no association with
monument. 4.05 inches long, 2.25 inches wide, curved cutting
edge; butt thin and rounded. Surface ground smooth but no
evidence of polishing. Liverpool University.
a) Powell 1952.

34 Burnley
Cant Clough   SD 904313
Bronze palstave found 1884.
a) Garstang 1906, 232.
b) Bennett 1946, 17 and Fig. 2.

35 Burnley
Cant Clough   SD 905316
At c. 1,000 feet O.D. a cairn covered two concentric circles of
stones and central pits. One pit, 2 feet in diameter and 1½ feet deep,
contained a 'mixture of fine charcoal and pieces of calcined bone'.
a) Leach 1951, 19.
b) Clare 1973, Vol. 2.

36 Burnley
Cliviger Laithe   SD 8731
Three collared urns found on hill summit near Barcroft Hall. The
first was found in 1886 while digging in a sand fall and was found
to contain cremated bones, of an adult and child according to one
account or of 5 people according to another, the bones being said
to have been enclosed in a kind of sacking, together with a small
bone pin and pieces of galena. Between 1887 and 1889 2 further
urns were found in the same area, each accompanied by a smaller
vessel (all now lost). The first urn is 13.1 inches high, the diameter
of its mouth is 10.8 inches and of the base 4 inches. The decoration
on the collar consists of twisted cord filled triangles enclosed above
by 6 and below by 5 twisted cord lines. On the neck all over
diagonal impressions were made with a blunt round point, while
on the internal bevel of the rim are short diagonal twisted cord
lines. One of the other urns was decorated with a 'fish-bone'
pattern and the other with 'thong ornamentation'. 1886 urn and
contents in Towneley Hall Museum, Burnley (1931.1.1).
a) Wilkinson & Tattersall 1889.
b) Wilkinson 1893, 156.
c) Wilkinson 1903.
d) Bennett 1946, 143.
e) Watson 1952, 92.

37 Burnley
Cliviger Red Lees   SD 8631 ?
Polished stone axe, igneous rock pitted by soil acids. Towneley
Hall Museum, Burnley.

38 Burnley
Cliviger Law House   SD 872302
c. 1763 a 'heap of stones (cairn) was removed as materials for
building a turnpike road' and a cist with an inhumation was found.
In 1766 another tumulus was removed and an urn found. An axe-
hammer is said to have been associated.
a) Whitaker 1872, Vol. 2, 195.
b) Watkin 1883, 232.
c) Jackson 1934–5.
d) Bennett 1946, 143.

39 Burnley
Delf Hill   SD 90063373
At 1,240 feet O.D. six stones, none more than 0.3–0.6 metres long
enclose a small circular area within which is a low mound. The site
was excavated in 1842. One account (Clement) states that from the
'small circle of stones, 7 in number, 14 feet in diameter, Mr.
Spencer of Halifax some years ago exhumed an earthenware urn
(later broken) and another portion of an urn was found not far
away'; other accounts state that 3 urns were found together with
'human remains' and flint arrowheads. One of the urns was later
given to the British Museum.
a) Clement 1874.
b) Wilkinson & Tattersall 1889.
c) Wilkinson 1893, 159.
d) Wilkinson 1903.

40 Burnley

Everage Clough   SD 850301

So called barrows, 8 in number, in Copy Wood were excavated and
yielded nothing. Ditch encircles each mound, but very superficial
in nature. Medieval?

a) Willett & Seddon 1952–3.

41 Burnley

Extwistle   SD 87003368

At 600 feet O.D. a circular entrenchment.

a) Hunt 1978.

42 Burnley

Extwistle Moor (Fig. 11, i)   SD 9133 ?

Beaker, containing burnt remains of bone, found 1882 'just over the
county boundary on Extwistle Moor'. Could this be either the
vessel from Delf Hill (39) or that from Twist Hill (54)? Keighley
Museum.

a) Bennett 1944, 15.
b) Manby 1965–6 and Fig. 54.
c) Clare 1973, Vol. 2.

43 Burnley

Hazel Edge   SD 904314

Flint dagger (beaker type?); 6 inches long, $2\frac{5}{16}$ inches maximum
width, $\frac{3}{8}$ inch maximum thickness (*c.f.* nos. 126 and 199).

a) Jackson 1935, 79.

44 Burnley

Hell Clough I   SD 90203412

At 1,150 feet mound surrounded by a ditch with traces of
external bank. Dug 1887 when described as an earth circle, 24–30
feet in diameter, and about 3 feet below surface 'was a mass of
charcoal, human remains but no urn'.

a) Wilkinson & Tattersall 1889.
b) Wilkinson 1893.
c) Wilkinson 1911.
d) Bennett 1946, 143.
e) Clare 1973.

45 Burnley

Hell Clough II   SD 903343

At 1,100 feet O.D. 'ring mound' or 'circle of 7 stones' (1893
description). Excavation found completely disintegrated urn, large
quantity of bones and a flint battle axe (4 inches by 5 inches).

a) Waddington & Wilkinson 1886.
b) Harrison 1892.
c) Wilkinson 1893.
d) Wilkinson 1903.
e) Bennett 1946, 143.
f) Clare 1973.

46 Burnley

Hell Clough III (Fig. 31)   SD 902341

Well defined circle of stones existed in upper part of Hell Clough.
Trench dug 1887 and a number of loose stones covering a
flagstone were found. Beneath the flagstone (in a cist?) was an urn
(12 inches high, 10 inches diameter at the mouth and 4 inches at
the base) containing bones of two persons, an adult and child,
together with animal bones and a bronze pin or awl, 4 inches long.
The circle was described as being 55 feet in diameter from east to
west, 58 feet from north to south with a ditch inside the mound.
The mound was 6 feet wide and the bottom of the ditch was 2 feet
below its top. There was an entrance 6 feet wide.

a) March 1886.
b) March 1887 and Fig.
c) Wilkinson & Tattersall 1889 and Fig.
d) Wilkinson 1903.
e) Wilkinson 1911.
f) Bennett 1946, 19 and Fig.

47 Burnley

Holme   SD 8728

Gold torc, 130 mm diameter, made from twisted wire of low grade
gold; *c.* 4th–3rd century B.C. Manchester Museum.

a) Whitaker 1872.

48 Burnley

Mosley Height (Fig. 30)   SD 87953005

Platform circle or cairn circle, a low platform surrounded by a
boulder kerb, 975 feet O.D. and 100 yards from the Long
Causeway. Excavated 1950. Within a large circle of 18 irregularly
spaced boulders on a stoney bank was a rough paved area 42 feet
across. In the centre was a small cist, 20 inches deep, containing a
collared urn (complete) inverted over a cremated female. Other
cists (pits) were set haphazardly about the central one: one 10
inches deep to the west contained a cremation burial in an inverted
urn (complete), another 8 inches deep and 8 feet north-north-east
from the centre containing a badly broken urn (only the collar
could be restored), and there was another burial (cremation)
without an urn 4 feet north-east from the centre. Several flint
implements (including scrapers, arrowheads and knives), 2 pieces
of Kimmeridge shale, 2 grain rubbing stones, pieces of quartz and
calcite (from the Furness area?) were also found, and Urn C
contained galena fragments. Urn A is 7.5 inches high, the
diameter of the mouth is 6 inches and the base 4 inches; it is
decorated on the collar by 4 twisted cord lines above short diagonal
twisted cord lines, with attempts to make this into herringbone in
one sector, on the shoulder are 2 rows of quill impression and on
the rim a single twisted cord line (Fig. 15, i). Urn B is 5.4 inches
high, the diameter of the mouth is 4 inches and the base 2.4
inches; it is decorated on the collar by 5 horizontal twisted cord
lines (Fig. 15, i). Urn C has no decoration, the diameter of the
mouth being about 8 inches. There were also 4 'ritual pits' (3 on
the outer circle, one just outside). The flint knives with flaking on
the edges compare with examples from Whitelow (71) and Wind
Hill (165). Among the arrowheads are two transverse examples.
The site has affinities with enclosed cremation cemeteries and stone
circles. Finds in Towneley Hall Museum, Burnley (together with a
plan).

a) Bennett 1950–1.
b) Bu'Lock 1961.
c) Clare 1973, 16 and 51.
d) Burl 1976, 62.

49 Burnley

Ringstone Hill   SD 88583315

Two low mounds at edge of quarry at 890 feet O.D., represent
remains of a ring mound. It is marked as 'earth circle' on 1928
O.S. map.

a) Clare 1973, Vol. 2.
b) Hunt 1978.

50 Burnley

Ringstones   SD 886330

'Roman camp' – oblong enclosure 200 feet by 160 feet with small
enclosure adjoining, 50 feet square. Ditch 20 feet wide with bank.

a) Clement 1874.
b) Watson 1952, 92.

51 Burnley

Roggerham   SD 8833

Flint dagger found near reservoir, 4.5 inches long, 2.2 inches wide.
Towneley Hall Museum, Burnley.

a) Bennett 1946, 15.

52 Burnley

Slipper Hill   SD 88463275

Ring cairn marked as 'stone circle' on O.S. map at 850 feet O.D.
Probably the earth circle in which calcined human bones found
1887. In 1932 the site consisted of 4 stones.

a) Wilkinson 1893, 158.
b) Bennett 1946, 143.
c) Clare 1973, Vol. 2.

53 Burnley

Thursden   SD 8834 ?

Perforated stone implement found in stream in Thursden valley.

a) Watson 1952, 76.

54 Burnley

Twist Hill   SD 88983372

Denuded tumulus at 950 feet O.D., 45 feet in diameter with higher
central area *c.* 27 feet diameter. In 1853 it was over 6 feet high but
the upper part had gone by 1856. Probably the earth circle of 9
yards diameter excavated in 1889 when a 'food vessel' was the only
find. (Is this the beaker No. 42?)

a) Clement 1874.
b) Harrison 1892, 249.
c) Garstang 1906, 239.

d) Bennett 1946, 143.
e) Clare 1973, Vol. 2.

55 Burnley
Twist Castle   SD 889337
'Roman Camp' 150 feet square with smaller enclosure 60 feet
square at its south west corner. External ditch.
a) Clement 1874.

56 Burnley
Wasnop Edge I (Hameldon Hill)   SD 89133262
Barrow (?) dug 1886 30 feet diameter, 4 feet high. 'In the centre of
the mound were a number of large stones placed vertically, 2 at
each side, 1 at each end and the area between was 6 feet long by
3 feet in width, covered by 2 large flags. The grave was empty but
many flint flakes and arrowheads were found.'
a) Waddington & Wilkinson 1886.
b) Harrison 1892, 252.
c) Wilkinson 1893.
d) Wilkinson 1903.
e) Garstang 1906, 239.
f) Bennett 1946, 15.
g) Clare 1973.

57 Burnley
Wasnop Edge II (Hameldon Hill)   SD 89123260
Low and much disturbed tumulus or ring cairn, *c.* 21 feet in
diameter. The site was opened in 1843 by S. Martin of Ormrod
House who dug 'a heap of stones and found an urn containing the
calcined remains of a body'. The vessel may have been in a cist for
it was covered by a stone and round it 'was a sort of wall of stones
filled up with peat or clay'. The urn is undecorated, its mouth is
cracked and damaged and some fragments were found inside. 6.8
inches of its height survive and the diameter of its base is 5 inches.
Towneley Hall Museum, Burnley.
a) Martin 1844.
b) Waddington & Wilkinson 1886.
c) Wilkinson & Tattersall 1889.
d) Bennett 1946, Fig. IV.
e) Clare 1973.

58 Burnley
Worsthorne   SD 8732 ?
Flint dagger (copy in stone of bronze dagger). Towneley Hall
Museum, Burnley.

59 Burnley
Worsthorne Moor   SD 9030 ?
Flint dagger, 6 inches long, $2\frac{5}{16}$ inches wide, $\frac{3}{8}$ inch thick, found.
Towneley Hall Museum, Burnley.
a) Bennett 1946, 15.

60 Bury
Ainsworth, Cockey Moor (Fig. 17, iii)   SD 761105
Bronze looped palstave found in quarry *c.* 1839. Nearly 6 inches
long with splayed cutting edge $2\frac{1}{2}$ inches from tip to tip; blade
ornamented down middle with low rib.
a) Yates 1895.
b) Garstang 1906, 231 and Fig. 14.
c) Davey & Forster 1975, Fig. 48.
d) O.S. Records SD71SE2.

61 Bury
Higher Woodhill   SD79081246
Bronze Age perforated macehead found in garden of 70 Holme
Avenue.
a) *Bury Times* 28 May 1952.
b) O.S. Records SD71SE15.

62 Bury
Hollins   SD 81300796
Stone axe hammer found 1903. No further information.
a) O.S. Records SD80NW3.

63 Bury
Parish Church   SD 805110
Urn found with bronze dagger in the grounds of the old grammar
school at the rear of the Parish Church in August, 1908, while
excavating for a drain. The site is at the top of a bluff overlooking
the river Irwell. Another urn was found 20 yards away, very similar

to the first but in fragments. Both were about 3 feet below the
surface, and both were 16 inches high, $11\frac{1}{2}$ inches diameter. Urn A
was 'decorated', Urn B is undecorated, and when found contained
'a very large number of human remains'. Urn B is in Bury
Museum.
a) *The Bury Historical Review* I, 1909, 15.
b) *Bury Archaeological Society Bulletin*, 1.

64 Bury
Radcliffe   SD 79800720
Possible Mesolithic (lake?) and Bronze Age settlement, within
200 yards of the confluence of the rivers Irwell and Roch, 12 feet
deep in gravel. Quarrying and excavation 1949–50 uncovered
wooden structures, tranchet axe sharpening flake, flint scrapers,
red raddle, hazel nuts, bronze axe, (No. 65) rough red pottery
vessel, several brass hooks, hollowed out tree trunk, 2 spindle
whorls, ox bones etc. Reported wooden structures (7 circles of
posts, 30 feet in diameter, apparently laid out in double rows with
interwoven brushwood) destroyed by quarrying 1949–50. 2 rows of
posts excavated with brushwood interwoven: one row of 14 posts,
other of 3 posts with *c.* 40 inches between the 2 rows. Site is
believed to have been former lake deposit of bluish-grey clay or
mud up to several feet in thickness, overlain by 2 well marked
deposits of gravel derived from the denudation of glacial deposits
further up the valley. These layers are 12–18 inches thick and occur
at a similar depth everywhere within the flood material.
a) Spencer 1950.
b) Spencer 1950–1.
c) Davies 1964 (axe sharpening flake).
d) O.S. Records SD70NE12.

65 Bury
Radcliffe (Fig. 17, i)   SD 79800720
Good example of Early Bronze Age flanged axe found 1950 in
gravel pit below the confluence of the Rivers Irwell and Roch.
Found in top soil (with 'beaker' which has been destroyed) near 7
circles of posts; 4 inches long, $2\frac{1}{2}$ inches across widely curving
cutting edge, and $\frac{3}{4}$ inch across below rounded butt. Weight $6\frac{1}{4}$ oz.
No sign of any stop ridge, but notable in having below centre on
one face only a pattern of 6 small, slightly raised dots, 5 set in an
oblique V, the 6th just below its opening and nearly in the centre.
The flanges rise to nearly $\frac{3}{4}$ inch and are in 3 facets, evidently
created by hammering.
a) *Manchester Guardian*, May 24 1950.
b) Davey & Forster 1975, Fig. 12.
c) O.S. Records SD70NE12.

66 Bury
Radcliffe, Black Lane   SD 784087
Site of alleged disc barrow, *c.* 300 feet O.D. recognised from aerial
photographs.
a) Hunt 1978.
b) O.S. Records SD70NE8.

67 Bury
Radcliffe Bridge   SD 78610694
2 Bronze Age axe-hammers with hour glass perforations. One of
polished quartzite, $8\frac{1}{2}$ inches long, square butted with groove along
sides, found in bank of River Irwell near the bridge in March 1912;
other probably found in same river. In museum attached to
Radcliffe Library.
a) Wilkinson 1912 and Fig.
b) O.S. Records SD70NE4.

68 Bury
Ramsbottom, Bank Lane   SD 805172
Circular cairn at 750 feet O.D., 60 feet diameter, 5 feet high, now
destroyed by quarrying. Retained on north and south sides by
concealed revetment of inward leaning slabs and enclosed by ring
of boulders. Main grave was stone lined pit, 7 feet long, 2 feet wide,
covered by 2 slabs and small cairn at centre, empty when opened.
Cremation found beneath floor of pit. 2nd cremation scattered over
old ground surface outside small central cairn. 3rd found in small
pit covered by a boulder; it was associated with a few plain sherds
of a collared urn. Flint scraper and segmented faience bead found
among basal stones of main cairn. Secondary burial in north
western part of main cairn, associated with a broken food vessel.
Information and finds in Bury Museum.
a) Clare 1973, Vol. 2.

69 Bury
Ramsbottom, Cinder Hill   SD 767169
In bed of stream near Cinder Hill 'battle axe' (?) found 1904.
Naturally formed clay-ironstone nodule, possibly touched up by
man and used as a weapon. Bolton Museum (Reserve Collection).

70 Bury
Ramsbottom, Holcombe   SD 782166
Early Bronze Age axe-hammer (Class Ia) found 1904: $9\frac{1}{2}$ inches
long, 4 inches wide, $1\frac{1}{2}$ inches thick. Group XV. Bolton Museum
(BOLMG.14.32). Petro No. La 33.
a) Roe 1979, 44.
b) O.S. Records SD71NE5.

71 Bury
Ramsbottom, Whitelow   SD 80501626
Single grave cairn and ring bank cemetery, excavated in the early
1960s. Bank of stones 6 feet wide and 18 inches high enclosed a
circular area 68 feet in diameter. Within this enclosure was a
continuous layer of stones and humus, and beneath this was
leached soil. 12 circular pits were found within the bank. Pit A –
cremation, plano-convex tanged flint dagger 3 inches long; Pit B –
charcoal, inverted 'urn' of pebbles and cobbles; Pit C – inurned
cremation, urn inverted, and broken flint knife 4 inches long;
Pit C1 – charcoal covered by slab; Pit E – 'burial' with
triangular flint flake and clay stud; Pit F1 – soot, charcoal,
cremation and calcined flint block $1\frac{1}{2}$ inches long, and broken
bronze awl; Pit F – urn inverted over cremation; Pit G – urn. 2
more pits under bank: Pit D – elongated and sides roughly lined
with grit slabs with inverted urn found at eastern end with other
sherds and scattered bone fragments. Square setting, 5 feet square,
of pebbles and pieces of gritstone beneath sand near centre of site.
Also near centre was a small cairn over Pit F1. Pit F had been dug
through this cairn which had been built on a surface 10 inches
above the old ground level. A standing stone is said to have been
placed in the centre prior to the construction of a continuous stone
layer and an oval setting of small boulders round the stone. Pygmy
vessel found with urn L. Thus 12–13 cremation burials: a primary
and several secondary burials, all the latter being cremations and
mostly in urns while the primary burial was a cremation in a pit.
The flint knife compares with the example found at Wind Hill
(No. 165). Finds in Bury Museum.
a) *Bury Archaeological Society Bulletin*, 1.
b) Bu'Lock 1961.
c) Clare 1973, 16.

72 Bury
River Roch   SD 8108
Polished stone axe found pre 1917 in drift near river Roch, Bury.
$7\frac{1}{2}$ inches long, $2\frac{7}{8}$ inches wide at one end and 2 inches at the other.
a) *TLCAS* 35, 1917, 142.
b) O.S. Records SD80NW1.

73 Bury
Wellington Road   SD 808100
Stone axe-hammer $10\frac{1}{4}$ inches long and $3\frac{1}{2}$ inches wide, weighing
$5\frac{1}{2}$ lbs. found *c.* 1917 on allotment at Wellington Road, the site
now being playing fields and/or modern development. Fine
grained, much weathered sandstone.
a) *TLCAS* 35, 1917, 142.
b) O.S. Records SD81SW3.

74 Bury
Woolfold   SD 7811
Perforated stone hammer found 1905; $8\frac{15}{16}$ inches long, $3\frac{3}{16}$ inches
thick, $4\frac{5}{16}$ inches wide, weight 5 lbs. 6 oz. with hour glass
perforation. Group XV (greywacke from North Wales). No
precise information about find spot. Bury Museum.
a) O.S. Records SD71SE7.

75 Chorley
Anglezarke, The Pikestones   SD 62701720
Megalithic chambered tomb, the only one in Lancashire, on slight
shoulder of gentle south west slope of gritstone moorland at 900
feet O.D. Badly robbed, ruined long cairn, aligned north–south, of
trapezoidal outline, *c.* 150 feet long, 62 feet wide at the northern
end, 45 feet at southern end. No retaining kerb, though some of
the perimeter stones are somewhat larger than the stones of the
cairn. Much of the stone from the cairn has been removed making
it difficult to determine the exact perimeter in places, but sufficient

remains to determine the shape and dimensions: the two ends are
the best defined. The site of the chamber was at the northern end of
the cairn on the main axis, and consists of 5 large stone slabs, 2
representing the eastern side, 1 part of the western side and 2
probably fallen roof slabs: the length of the chamber was at least
15 feet, and it was about 3 feet wide. In the vicinity of the
chamber, especially on the west and south, the stones of the cairn
are much larger than elsewhere. Bu'Lock claimed Severn–Cotswold
affinities; Lynch sees it more closely related to mixed group in
Derbyshire.
a) Bu'Lock 1958.
b) Lynch 1966.
c) Manby 1967.
d) O.S. Records SD61NW6.

76 Chorley
Anglezarke, Standing Stones Hill   SD 64561737
Alleged stone circle, at 1,000 feet O.D. Probably a kerbed mound
or tumulus (possibly with stone retaining circle). Perimeter hard to
define – *c.* 65–70 feet diameter, possibly rising 3 feet above general
level.
a) Harrison 1896.
b) Hunt 1978.
c) O.S. Records SD61NW7.

77 Chorley
Anglezarke, Round Loaf   SD 63791821
Round cairn or bowl barrow at 1,030 feet O.D. Large
conspicuous mound in shallow col, slightly elongated with axes
of about 50 metres north–south and 45 metres east–west. Top of
mound is 6 metres above lower ground to west and 2.8 metres
above ground to east. Small hollow in summit (disturbance). No
trace of ditch. (Clare suggests possible glacial origin).
a) Bu'Lock & Rosser 1960.
b) Clare 1973, Vol. 2.
c) O.S. Records SD61NW2.

78 Chorley
Rivington Barn   SD 6314
Perforated pebble hammer found on surface 1958. Early Bronze
Age? Bolton Museum (BOLMG. A.2.1958).

79 Chorley
Rivington, Noon Hill   SD 64691499
Cairn with kerb on hill crest at 1,260 feet O.D. Excavated partially
in 1958 and 1963. Cairn composed of loose stone core with covering
of earth and turf. Flints numerous in earthen mound. Barrow had
been disturbed in centre, but in the one quadrant that was more or
less fully excavated in 1958 the removal of the stone core revealed
large stones in roughly concentric ring. The basal layer of the
cairn appears to have contained a number of features: a) an
arrangement of stones set on edge in a circle (kerb?), b) a pocket
of cremated bones with a barbed and tanged arrowhead. This
burial may have been put in a rough cist (in the cairn structure?),
c) an inverted 'urn' in a stone cist with a capstone, the 'urn'
associated with 'a charcoal band and bone meal' and a calcined
barbed-and-tanged arrowhead, d) a cremation deposit with a flint
knife/scraper, e) post holes (?) about 2 feet apart, f) a cremation
deposit in a stone lined recess near the centre of the barrow. The
vessel (Fig. 13, ii) was later restored from fragments: light brown
with yellowish tinge, grey-black interior. Coarse ware tempered
with grit; exterior smoothed. Height 262 mm; diameter of rim
225–40 mm; diameter of base 100–10 mm. Vessel described by
Bu'Lock as enlarged food vessel; Bolton Museum. 1963–4
excavation unpublished, but apparently 2/3 more groups of
cremated bones discovered (finds in Manchester Museum).
a) Bu'Lock & Rosser 1960.
b) Bu'Lock 1961.
c) Booth 1963.
d) Cowie 1978.
e) O.S. Records SD61NW 12 and 32.

80 Chorley
Rivington, Two Lads   SD 65501336
Possibly a wrecked cairn at 1,200 feet.
a) Bu'Lock & Rosser 1960.
b) Clare 1973, Vol. 2.

81 Chorley
Rivington, Winter Hill   SD 65581500

Composite, kerbed cairn at 1,200 feet O.D. Primary burial gone. Monument shows late Neolithic traditions in local Early Bronze Age.
a) Bu'Lock & Rosser 1960.
b) Bu'Lock 1961.
c) O.S. Records SD61SE18.

82 High Peak
Glossop, Mouse Low SK 023953
Barrow; reference to inhumation and possible beaker.
a) Addy 1908, 129.
b) Lewis 1970, No. 1625.

83 High Peak
Glossop, Shire Hill SK 052943
Possible grave pit containing inverted collared urn with cremation and charcoal on top of brushwood and some stones. No indications of mound. Urn 13 inches high. Buxton Museum.
a) Jackson 1968 and Plate.
b) Lewis 1970.

84 High Peak
Longdendale SK 055988
Greater part of late La Tène native pot found early in 1958 in natural cavity under large boulders in screes above Longdendale, and further fragments were found later by F. Willett. The pot had stood on a small shelf at the closed end of the cavity. Exterior light brown/grey with some tooling; heavy, coarse, heavily gritted with crystalline stone and perhaps flint. When restored made an almost complete vessel. Manchester Museum.
a) *TLCAS* 68, 1958, 140.
b) Challis & Harding 1975, Fig. 7, No. 10.

85 High Peak
Longdendale, Tintwistle Knarr SK 0399 ?
Mesolithic axe sharpening flake identified in the Buckley collection, Tolson Memorial Museum, Huddersfield.
a) Davies 1964.

86 High Peak
Longdendale, Tintwistle Moor SK 0398 ?
Flint knife (food vessel age?). Tolson Memorial Museum, Huddersfield.

87 High Peak
Longdendale, Torside Castle SK 076965
Single banked enclosure, no ditch; $\frac{3}{4}$ acre. Over 1,500 feet O.D. Iron Age?
a) Preston 1954.

88 High Peak
Longdendale, Torside Reservoir SK 0698
Edge polished flint chisel, grooved ware date.
a) Manby 1974, 117.

89 Hyndburn
Great Harwood SD 727323
Early Bronze Age (Migdale–Marnoch tradition) flat axe, found 1967. 2.7 inches long, 1.6 maximum width, 0.4 inches thick. No decoration; corraded surface. Blackburn Museum (1967–43).
a) Blundell 1965–6, Figs. 52–3.
b) Davey & Forster 1975, Fig. 10.

90 Manchester
Small bronze ox head ornament, Iron Age date.
a) Hallam 1970, 237.

91 Manchester
Late Bronze Age socketed axe, $3\frac{1}{8}$ inches long, decorated with 3 ribs below the moulding of the socket.
a) Whitaker 1771, 13–15, Fig. 2.
b) Jackson 1934–5a, 90–1.
c) Davey & Forster 1975, Fig. 92.
d) O.S. Records SJ89NE3.

92 Manchester
Palstave with 3 ribs found *c.* 1720 in the Manchester area. 'An oddly formed chisel or outlandish wedge . . . from one of our Mancunian Mosses'.
a) Whitaker 1771, 13–14.

b) Davey & Forster 1975, Fig. 60.

93 Manchester
Alexandra Park SJ 8394
2 round perforated hammers/axes/maceheads of fine grained sandstone found in the making of Alexandra Park in the late 19th century. Both badly chipped round the outer edges. One $4\frac{3}{4}$ inches long, 4 inches wide and $\frac{3}{4}$ inch thick; the other $4\frac{1}{4}$ inches diameter and 1 inch thick. Manchester Museum.
a) Yates 1887, 330.
b) Garstang 1906, 227.
c) Jackson 1936.
d) O.S. Records SJ89SW6.

94 Manchester
Alexandra Park SJ 83469435
Mesolithic perforated stone macehead (oval pebble of sandstone) found 1937 in garden of 18 Waltham Road, Alexandra Park, 6 feet down. 3 inches wide, 4 inches long, hour glass perforation; very well preserved. Manchester Museum.
a) Thomson 1947 and Fig.
b) O.S. Records SJ89SW2.

95 Manchester
Boggart Hole Clough SD 865025
Early Bronze Age tanged spearhead found 1959. Manchester Museum (0.9227).
a) Bu'Lock 1961, Fig. IV No. 1.
b) Davey & Forster 1975, Fig. 14.

96 Manchester
Cheetham Hill SD 840008
Neolithic flint axe stated to have been found in 'Braddock's Field', probably near Brideoak Street, Cheetham Hill. Described as a square butted axe of Scandinavian type; poor condition, cutting edge very blunted. Black, good quality flint; no signs of polishing. Seemingly well used until no longer serviceable. Manchester City Art Gallery (1909.57).
a) *TLCAS* 27, 1909.
b) Willett 1952–3.
c) O.S. Records SD80SW22.

97 Manchester
Cheetwood SD 841001
Neolithic flint dagger found 1908 in clay of brick croft at Cheetwood Brick Works.
a) *TLCAS* 27, 1909.
b) O.S. Records SD80SW23.

98 Manchester
Cheetwood SD 8399 ?
Bronze Age perforated stone adze (broken) found 13 feet down in clay; fine gritstone. Manchester Museum.
a) Garstang 1906, 220 and Fig. 5.
b) Jackson 1936.
c) O.S. Records SD80SW24.

99 Manchester
Corporation Street SJ 841999
Bronze Age perforated and polished stone hammer found in 1870 under foundations of Borough Buildings, Corporation Street, 20 feet below the surface. 5 inches long, $2\frac{7}{8}$ inches wide, $1\frac{1}{2}$ inches thick.
a) Yates 1887, 327.
b) Garstang 1906, 219 and Fig. 4.
c) Jackson 1936.
d) O.S. Records SJ89NW27.

100 Manchester
Fallowfield SJ 8594 ?
Neolithic polished flint axe found in allotment, 2 feet 6 inches deep in yellow clay. $4\frac{3}{4}$ inches long, $2\frac{1}{4}$ inches wide at cutting edge, $1\frac{1}{4}$ inches wide at butt, $1\frac{1}{8}$ inches thick; flattened sides; evidence of re-sharpening.
a) Jackson 1936, Plate 7:5.
b) O.S. Records SJ89SE7.

101 Manchester
Greenheys SJ 844955
Perforated stone adze/hammer of white quartzite found in 1885 in

brick yard, Upper Lloyd Street. $4\frac{3}{8}$ inches long, $2\frac{3}{4}$ inches wide, $1\frac{1}{4}$ inches thick. It was found 'with other stone implements'.
a) Yates 1887, 328.
b) Garstang 1906, 219 and Fig. 3.
c) Jackson 1936.
d) O.S. Records SJ89NW38.

102 Manchester
Hanging Bridge   SJ 83859870
Bronze dagger and fragment of flat bronze axe found in 1880 during excavations at the north east corner of Hanging Bridge in an old ditch under the foundations of a building. The dagger was later in private ownership, but the axe is lost. The dagger (or notched butt rapier) is $5\frac{1}{2}$ inches long, narrow with traces of two rivet holes in the base. Cast Manchester Museum.
a) *TLCAS* 24, 1906, 179.
b) Jackson 1934–5a.
c) Davey & Forster 1975, Fig. 62 (Dagger/rapier).
d) O.S. Records SJ89NW18.

103 Manchester
Hanging Ditch   SJ 839987
Polished stone axe (Langdale stone?). Manchester Museum.

104 Manchester
Heaton Park Reservoir   SD 826050
Late Bronze Age socketed bronze axe found during construction of reservoir. Square socket, $3\frac{1}{8}$ inches long, cutting edge 2 inches wide (damaged at points). Faces ornamented by 3 ribs, centre one longer than other 2. Loop broken off. Lost.
a) Jackson 1936, Fig. 4.
b) Davey & Forster 1975, Fig. 87.
c) O.S. Records SD80SW7.

105 Manchester
Hyde Road   SJ 89229591
Polished stone axe found 1892 at the site of Hyde Road Station during the construction of the Fallowfield–Fairfield branch of the Great Central Railway lying embedded in clay. Dark green, fine grained rock (volcanic ash), highly polished with flattened sides. 7 inches long, $2\frac{3}{8}$ inches wide near the cutting edge and $1\frac{1}{2}$ inches wide at the butt; $1\frac{1}{4}$ inches thick. In 1913 in private ownership.
a) *TLCAS* 31, 1913, 152.
b) Jackson 1936, Plate 7:2.
c) O.S. Records SJ89NE22.

106 Manchester
Long Millgate   SJ 8398
Bronze Age bone implement found in 1899 during excavations by the railway company on the south bank of the River Irk.
a) *TLCAS* 27, 1909.
b) O.S. Records SJ89NW4.

107 Manchester
Openshaw   SJ 878974
Very fine loopless bronze palstave found in 1908 near the new Whitworth Works, 18 inches deep in the gravelly soil of a watercourse. $6\frac{5}{8}$ inches long, greatest width $2\frac{7}{8}$ inches.
a) Bowman 1909 and Fig.
b) Jackson 1936.
c) Davey & Forster 1975, Fig. 36.
d) O.S. Records SJ89NE21.

108 Manchester
Queens Park   SD 860008
Bronze Age perforated stone axe-hammer found in February 1868 3 feet below the surface in the blue clay of glacial deposits at a brickyard near Turkey Lane. Gritstone; $6\frac{3}{4}$ inches long, $2\frac{3}{4}$ inches wide, 3 inches thick. (In some reports described as clay ironstone.) Roe's Stage III.
a) Devis 1867–8.
b) Plant 1867–8.
c) Yates 1887, 331.
d) Garstang 1906, 221 and Fig. 6.
e) Roe 1966.
f) O.S. Records SD80SE10 and 11.

109 Oldham
     SD 9205 ?
Vague reference to 2 stone hammers (exhibited in 1860s) in private

ownership.
a) Yates 1887, 331.

110 Oldham
Chadderton Hall   SD 89790647
Probable barrow site at 350 feet O.D. near Chadderton Hall: it 'yielded several relics of antiquity'.
a) Aikin 1795, 241.
b) O.S. Records SD80NE17.

111 Oldham
Medlock Valley   SD 94850335
Late Neolithic flint adze found May 1980 in right bank of River Medlock. Weight 171.8 gms; 141 mm long, 48 mm wide, 44 mm wide at 'waist', narrows to thin butt 10 mm wide. Somewhat clumsy in appearance, flaked rather coarsely on both sides. Small residual polished area near cutting edge – possibly once extended across whole breadth, and present condition may be due to its use as a working implement. Flint is very attractive golden brown in colour with 2 darker bands.
a) Stonehouse & Barnes 1980.

112 Oldham
Royton Park   SD 920080
Polished stone axe (greenstone), 8.8 inches long, 2.6 inches wide found pre 1890. Apparently used subsequently as a whetstone. Cast in Rochdale Museum.
a) Garstang 1906, 218.
b) O.S. Records SD90NW4.

113 Oldham
Saddleworth, Badger Slack   SD 998121
Small quartzite pebble hammer with hour glass perforation, $2\frac{5}{8}$ inches long, $1\frac{1}{2}$ inches wide. Found by C. March, late 19th century. Flint knife also found later in vicinity. Both lost.
a) Wrigley 1911, Plate K (hammer) and Plate M No. 16 (knife).
b) Jackson 1936 (hammer).
c) Watson 1952, 76 (hammer).
d) Roe & Radley 1968 (hammer).

114 Oldham
Saddleworth, Brownhill   SD 99570642
Barrow at top of quarry near Saddleworth Station opened by quarrymen in May 1844, and 2 urns and a pebble macehead were found. The opening was noted by G. Shaw in 2 letters, the first written the day after the discovery and the second on 17th June. His drawings of the sherds and other finds are in the Raines Mss. 24, 287 (Chetham's Library, Manchester). The urns, which were dug up without damage but then thrown away by the workmen and fragmented, were 'deposited in a small circular hollow' (a primitive cist?), and apparently the site was marked 'with a pile of stones'. The vessels were 4 feet apart and *c.* 4 feet 6 inches down from the top of the barrow in a layer of burnt wood. They had their mouths uppermost, were covered with stones and were decorated 'with cord ornamentation'. One of them contained a quartzite pebble macehead, 3.7 inches long and 2 inches wide, with hour glass perforation, which was broken into 3 pieces possibly as a result of being burnt. A 'second celt' is said to have been found later on the same site. Macehead is in Tolson Memorial Museum, Huddersfield (A.24.58).
a) Shaw 1889 and Fig. (sherds and macehead).
b) Wrigley 1911, 44 and Plate K (sherds and macehead).
c) Petch 1924, 50 and 59.
d) Roe & Radley 1968 (macehead).
e) Gilks 1977 (has incorrect grid reference).

115 Oldham
Saddleworth, Castleshaw Higher Reservoir   SD 998100
Polished greenstone axe found 6 feet below ground level at 820 feet O.D. while excavating the bed of the reservoir in 1891. $4\frac{1}{2}$ inches long. $2\frac{1}{2}$ inches wide at the cutting edge.
a) Roth 1906, 299 and Fig. 207.
b) Wrigley 1911, 36 and Plate J.
c) Watson 1952, 70.

116 Oldham
Saddleworth, Castleshaw   SE 000097 ?
Socketed bronze axe 4 inches long and ornamented with 3 ribs found pre 1771. Round socket, side loop, and when found contained remains of original wooden haft.

a) Whitaker 1771.
b) Wrigley 1911, 16–17 and Plate A.
c) Petch 1924, 53 and Fig. 22.5.
d) Jackson 1936.

117 Oldham
Saddleworth, Castleshaw SE 000097 ?
Spindle whorl found near Roman Fort by T. Thompson of Delph.
a) Kendall & Roth 1912.

118 Oldham
Saddleworth, Castleshaw Roman Fort SE 99830967
Prehistoric pit found beneath floor of Roman Fort during 1964 excavations: it had been cut into the closely packed, flaggy gritstone to a depth of *c.* 15 inches and was 21 inches in diameter. Its fill was a clean orange-brown soil with occasional charcoal fragments and closely packed Beaker sherds – 122 in all, all but 47 of which could be assigned to 5 vessels. A few sherds were found scattered on the clayey surface of the gritstone, together with occasional worked flints. The vessels consisted of a) a late Southern British Beaker; b) a rusticated beaker; c) a late Southern British Beaker; d) a rusticated beaker; e) a cordoned biconical vessel. Clarke suggested that the site was a 'late Southern British (S3) Beaker domestic site, *c.* 1,550 ± 50 b.c.' (Fig. 11, ii–vi).
a) Thompson 1967, 8, 13–17 and Fig. 23.
b) Clarke 1970, 1, 227; and 2, Figs. 973–5.

119 Oldham
Saddleworth, Castleshaw Roman Fort SE 998096
Stone spindle whorl found by A. Wrigley 3 feet below the 'Roman floor' in 1907.
a) Wrigley 1911, Plate N.
b) Kendall & Roth, 1912.
c) Petch 1924, 37.

120 Oldham
Saddleworth, Cudworth Quarry SE 000110
Polished stone axe found in rock cleft at 1,220 feet O.D. in 1887; 7 inches long, 3 inches wide, end broken off. Diorite; 'Cumbrian type'.
a) Roth 1906, 298–9 and Fig. 205.
b) Wrigley 1911, 35–6 and Plate I.
c) Petch 1924, 50.
d) Jackson 1936.
e) Manby 1965.

121 Oldham
Saddleworth, Dean Clough SD 9812
Bronze dagger reported as being in 'Oldham Museum' in 1924.
a) Petch 1924, 55.

122 Oldham
Saddleworth, Dean Clough SD 9812
Butt fragment of flint axe, 4⅝ inches long, with its cutting edge broken in antiquity. Greyish patina. Tolson Memorial Museum, Huddersfield (23.1.66).
a) Tolson Memorial Museum Index.

123 Oldham
Saddleworth, Greenfield Brook SE 0204 ?
Stone axe, 3⅝ inches long, 1⅜ inches wide at cutting edge, 5½ oz. weight, found by Fred Allen in brook. Pecked surfaces with polished cutting edge; chip broken out of cutting edge. Greenstone or possibly porcellanite of Irish origin. Tolson Memorial Museum, Huddersfield (A.19.58).
a) Petch 1924, 50.
b) Davies 1963a.
c) Keen & Radley 1971.
d) Tolson Memorial Museum Index.

124 Oldham
Saddleworth, Hill Top SD 98010745
Well defined ring mound, 45 feet diameter, 1 foot 6 inches high. Excavation of part of it produced pieces of charcoal and fragments of burnt stone. Situated at 1,000 feet O.D.
a) Wrigley 1911, 46.
b) Clare 1973, Vol. 2.

125 Oldham
Saddleworth, Lark Hill SD 99430749
Complete polished stone axe found 1959. Faceted sides; cutting edge well abraded. Greenstone (Group VI). Saddleworth Museum.
a) Keen & Radley 1971.
b) Tolson Memorial Museum Index.

126 Oldham
Saddleworth, Ragstone SD 99331190
Flint dagger found 1924 in 3 pieces. Tolson Memorial Museum, Huddersfield.
a) Petch 1924, 46 and Fig. 19.

127 Oldham
Saddleworth, Ramsclough SD 968089
Axe-hammer with socket incompletely bored.
a) Petch 1924, 46 and Fig. 21.

128 Oldham
Saddleworth, Rocher Moss SE 027087 ?
Flint knife (food vessel age?) – 'one of the finest specimens found in the area'. Tolson Memorial Museum, Huddersfield.
a) Wrigley 1911, 26 and Plate A.

129 Oldham
Saddleworth, Spring Grove SD 99900417
Bronze palstave found 1860–1 on site of Co-Operative Stores. 6¾ inches long, 2¾ inches wide at maximum; plain blade and convex flanges. Cast in Rochdale Museum.
a) Wrigley 1911, 18 and Plate B.
b) Davey & Forster 1975, Fig. 41.

130 Oldham
Saddleworth, Thornlee SD 967037
Fragment of bronze spearhead/rapier found during drainage operations Nov. 19th, 1900, in a valley meadow between Quick Edge and Brown Edge, 'near the old track coming over Quick Edge'. 14 inches long, tapering from 1¾ inches in width to a point; a rib or half round fillet runs along middle of blade.
a) Andrew 1901, 240.
b) Wrigley 1911, 18.
c) Petch 1924, 55.
d) O.S. Records SE90SE2.

131 Oldham
Saddleworth, Uppermill SD 997056
Small, dark grey stone hammer found by Mr Shaw in gravel alongside River Tame near Uppermill Station. Exhibited in 1868.
a) Plant 1867–8, 74.
b) Yates 1887, 331.
c) O.S. Records SD90SE5 (wrongly placed in Mossley).

132 Oldham
Saddleworth, Wallgreen SD 97821045
Transitional looped bronze palstave (Wallington type) found April 1932 18 inches below surface during digging of pipe trench on north bank of River Tame. 6½ inches long, 1½ inches wide at cutting edge; stop ridge is 3½ inches from anterior end; weight 11 oz. Dark green patina, pitted in places. 3 blow holes in the septum. Private possession; casts in Saddleworth Museum and Tolson Memorial Museum, Huddersfield.
a) Jackson 1936, Fig. 3.
b) Burgess 1968.
c) Davey & Forster 1975, Fig. 56.
d) Tolson Memorial Museum Index.

133 Oldham
Shaw, Crompton Moor SD 9610 ?
Transitional bronze palstave (Wallington type); 5⅜ inches long, 1⅞ inches wide; weight 11¾ oz. Private possession. Cast in Rochdale Museum.
a) Petch 1924, 55.
b) Burgess 1968.
c) Davey & Forster 1975, Fig. 51.

134 Pendle
Blacko Tower SD 859422
Early Bronze Age flat axe (Migdale industry) found by scouts while gathering stones to renovate top part of tower, 1952. Narrow butt, expanding towards cutting edge. 14% tin, 85.4% copper, 0.3% zinc. Private possession; cast in Keighley Museum.
a) *CAGB* 5, 1960, 40.

b) Manby 1964.
c) Davey & Forster 1975, Fig. 5.
d) Ilkley Museum Index.

135 Pendle
Boulsworth SD 9235 ?
Stone axe; broken tip only. Towneley Hall Museum, Burnley.

136 Pendle
Nelson, Castercliffe Fort SD 885383
Iron Age fort in good defensive position on spur at 800 feet O.D. Commands good views of several routes through Pennines (Aire Gap, and the Wycoller, Widdop and Cliviger cols). 3 ramparts enclose a small oval site. Central one timber frame box rampart – evidence of abandonment before completion. Inner rampart probably stone revetted, timber laced; vitrified.
a) Challis & Harding 1975.

137 Pendle
Nelson, Catlow SD 885368
2–3 urns found *c.* 1854 (exhibited in 1886), possibly containing cremations.
a) Waddington & Wilkinson 1886.
b) Clare 1973, Vol. 2.

138 Pendle
Nelson, Old Laund Booth SD 8337 ?
Tanged bronze spearhead; uncertain provenance. Bennett Collection, Towneley Hall Museum, Burnley.
a) Davey & Forster 1975, Fig. 166.

139 Pendle
Nelson, Ringstone Hill I SD 891367
Large circle of stones said to have existed at 900 feet O.D. All gone by 1856.
a) Clare 1973, Vol. 2.

140 Pendle
Nelson, Ringstone Hill II SD 89263693
Small mound, 3 m diameter, on shoulder of hill, 975 feet O.D.
a) Clare 1973, Vol. 2.

141 Pendle
Newchurch SD 8239 ?
'In the neighbourhood of Newchurch in Pendle was found several years ago (ie between 1810 and 1818) a stone mallet with a perforation for the handle.'
a) Whitaker 1872, Vol. 1, 299.

142 Pendle
Pendle Hill SD 7840 ?
Polished stone axe/adze, dark green in colour with light mottling (jadeite?). Bennett Collection, Towneley Hall Museum, Burnley (1950.1.4).

143 Pendle
Pendle Hill SD 7840 ?
Late Bronze Age socketed axe. Towneley Hall Museum, Burnley.

144 Pendle
Pendle Hill, Ogden Clough SD 8039 ?
Axe-hammer, gritstone with polished surface, found 1903. $10\frac{1}{2}$ inches long, $4\frac{1}{8}$ inches wide, $2\frac{3}{4}$ inches thick; weight 6 lbs 10 oz. Towneley Hall Museum, Burnley.
a) Garstang 1906, 224.

145 Pendle
Trawden, Combe Hill SD 957390
Neolithic saddle quern found October 1955 on peat at Onion Bank, Combe Hill at 1,300 feet O.D. $21\frac{1}{2}$ inches long, 14 inches wide at widest, $5\frac{1}{4}$–$1\frac{1}{2}$ inches thick. Coarse gritstone, Hollowed area 14 inches by 10 inches and about 2 inches deep at centre.
a) *CAGB* 2, 1957, 87 and Fig.

146 Pendle
Trawden, Lumb Spout SD 9236
Bronze spearhead found by metal detector in 1978 in field near Lumb Spout, 8 inches down.
a) Towneley Hall Museum Index, Burnley.

147 Pendle
Windy Harbour SD 819415
Polished stone axe of mottled greenstone found in turf pit; 10 inches long, 2 inches wide, flattened sides. British Museum; cast in Towneley Hall Museum, Burnley.
a) Garstang 1906, 217, Fig. 1.
b) Jackson 1936.

148 Ribble Valley
Billington, Brockhall SD 699375
'A Tumulus existed on the south bank of the River Ribble near Bullasey Ford until 1836 when the farmer at Brockhall removed it. It was about 500 yards from the river on the left of the road leading from the house. In the cist the farmer discovered some human bones and the rusty remains of some spearheads of iron. The whole crumbled to dust on exposure to air.' The cist was 'formed of rude stones'. The whole possibly represents a 1st millennium B.C. burial.
a) Luck 1894, 32.
b) Challis & Harding 1975.

149 Ribble Valley
Clitheroe SD 7441 ?
Vague references to 2 stone axes and 1 stone hammer from Clitheroe. In Blackburn Museum is an axe head from Up Brook Farm, Clitheroe, of Langdale stone.
a) Plant 1867–8.
b) Yates 1887, 331.
c) Garstang 1906, 226.

150 Ribble Valley
Mellor SD 6531
Axe-hammer found 1855; 8 inches long, 3 inches wide. 'Igneous rock'. Blackburn Museum.
a) Garstang 1906, 223 and Plate III No. 2.

151 Ribble Valley
Read SD 7634 ?
3 Early Bronze Age flat bronze axes found *c.* 1780. 9–12 inches in length. One now in British Museum (cast in Towneley Hall Museum, Burnley), others lost.
a) Whitaker 1872, Vol. 1, Plate II and Vol. 2, 39.
b) Yates 1895.
c) Garstang 1906, 229 and Fig. 13.
d) Davey & Forster 1975, Fig. 3.

152 Ribble Valley
River Ribble
8 bronze implements were reported found in the river Ribble in 1800, and they may represent a genuine hoard. They include a looped 'late' palstave, 2 indented socketed axes, a socketed axe with a square socket and a socketed gouge. The palstave and indented socketed axes have been described as being under Wilburton influence. Manchester Museum (0.7875A–G).
a) Barrit 1800 and Fig.
b) Burgess 1968, 64–5 and Fig. 21.2.
c) Davey & Forster 1975, Figs. 156–64.

153 Ribble Valley
Stonyhurst, Winckley Lowes SD 70673748
A bowl-shaped tumulus, 11 feet high and 115 feet in diameter, was excavated by Rev. J. R. Luck, S.J. in 1894. Below the turf covering was a cairn and in the stones 5 feet from the top many bones (including a skull) and a small flint knife were found. Lower down, 5 feet south of the centre, bones and parts of another skull were recovered. In the centre a dome of stones 4 feet thick covered a cremation lying on charcoal; no pottery was found. Another skull was found '4 feet below the centre' together with pottery sherds and animal bones. The pottery was later identified as medieval but as the flint knife (which was 3.9 cm long, 2 cm wide and 1 cm thick) is Bronze Age, this suggests that the barrow was robbed in medieval times. Nearby is another steep sided mound (at SD 70853731), *c.* 5.4 m high; it is flat topped, elliptical in shape with its long axis 35 m in length.
a) Luck 1894.
b) Garstang 1906, 218.
c) Edwards 1969 and Fig. 14.2.
d) Clare 1973, Vol. 2.

154 Ribble Valley
Whalley, Jeppe Knave Grave   SD 75993782
Denuded tumulus at 950 feet O.D., illustrated in 1872 as having 2
standing stones at the head and the foot of the grave.
a) Whitaker 1872, Vol. 2, 34.

155 Ribble Valley
Whalley, Portfield (Planeswood)   SD 745355
Hill fort on shallow, south facing promontary, 400 feet O.D.
overlooking River Calder not far from its confluence with the
Ribble. Mainly defined by natural scarps: only on the north west
and to a lesser extent on the west is there anything of a more
artificial nature. To the north west an inner bank and ditch have a
smaller bank and ditch beyond. Earlier sources show additional
defences on the eastern and south eastern sides, and the outer bank
on the north west was shown as continuous around the whole site,
except where the natural slope made artificial defences
unnecessary. The slab revetment of the inner rampart is
interpreted as the earliest rampart on the site, later replaced by a
clay cored, stone revetted rampart, probably of early date. Finds
date back to the Neolithic; Beaker pottery has been found recently,
while the coarse biconical pottery also found and the Late Bronze
Age hoard may indicate the first establishment of the site. The Late
Bronze Age hoard was found by workmen laying a pipeline through
the site during the summer of 1966 and consisted of 2 gold and 7
bronze objects together with a piece of rough metal resembling a
splash. The gold objects consisted of a penannular tress ring of
hollow triangular section, decorated with fine concentric incised
lines made with a tracer, and plain penannular bracelet of flattened,
slightly hollow D-section, with externally expanded terminals. The
bronze objects included a single looped, socketed axe with
expanded curved cutting edge, 8.3 cm long and 4.8 cm wide at
cutting edge; another single looped socketed axe with expanded
curved cutting edge (broken), 8 cm long; 2 pieces forming a tanged
knife, the lower part of the blade missing, 10.7 cm long; part of the
blade of another knife, 6 cm long; and the lower half of a socketed
gouge, lacking the mouth and cutting edge, 6.1 cm long. All were
damaged in antiquity. Considered by Longworth to be the
property of a bronze smith together with a personal decorative
element; the objects have an all over similarity with elements of the
Heathery Burn Cave assemblage, and therefore a date not later
than the 7th century B.C., and possibly represent evidence of an
active trade link along a trans-Pennine route, the tress ring being an
Irish import. Finds in British Museum; casts of metal hoard in
Blackburn Museum.
a) Tyson and Bu'Lock 1957 (fort).
b) Forde-Johnston 1962 (fort).
c) Bu'Lock 1965–6 (hoard).
d) Blundell & Longworth 1967–8 and Fig. (hoard).
e) Challis & Harding 1975 (pottery and hoard).
f) Davey & Forster 1975, Figs. 142–8 (hoard).

156 Ribble Valley
Wilpshire   SD 6832
Axe-hammer with one end 'rounded'.
a) Garstang 1906, 222 and Fig. 7.

157 Ribble Valley
Wiswell   SD 7437
Polished stone axe of felspathic porphyry found in 1835; $11\frac{3}{4}$
inches long, $3\frac{1}{4}$ inches wide, $1\frac{1}{4}$ inches thick. Graig Lwyd origin.
Blackburn Museum (1835.1).
a) Garstang 1906, 217.
b) Jackson 1936.

158 Rochdale
Blackstone Edge   SD 973168
Iron spearhead found 300 yards south of the Roman road, just
inside the Lancashire boundary. 9 inches long; socketed with blade
$4\frac{1}{2}$ inches long and $1\frac{1}{2}$ inches at widest bearing a rib for strength.
Very corroded when found. Trace of wooden shaft in socket.
Fragment of ox's horn found alongside. Rochdale Museum.
a) Price 1932–4.
b) O.S. Records SD91NE10.

159 Rochdale
Blackstone Edge   SD 9716 ?
Neolithic (?) wooden spear tip found in peat; 82 mm long, 15 mm
wide. Rochdale Museum (9101 03–04/142).

160 Rochdale
Castle Hill   SD 891128
Late Neolithic polished stone adze/axe with bevelled cutting edge
found in 1905 at the foot of Castle Hill. Greenstone, flat on one
side, convex on other: $6\frac{3}{4}$ inches long, $2\frac{1}{2}$ inches wide, $1\frac{1}{4}$ inches
thick; weight 1 lb $3\frac{1}{4}$ oz. Rochdale Museum.
a) Platt 1909–11.
b) Jackson 1934–5.
c) O.S. Records SD81SE20.

161 Rochdale
Hades Hill   SD 90802020
Composite barrow at 1,380 feet O.D. in depression between Hades
Hill and Rough Hill, originally measuring 52 feet north–south and
45 feet east–west, 3 feet high. Consisted of stone cairn covered by
sandy clay mound with a kerb or circle of rough sandstone blocks
set on the ground surface. It was 'excavated' in 1898 after an urn
and human bones had been found. The urn was near the centre,
mouth upwards, and was covered by the cairn. It was described as
being of the 'two tier variety', marked by carelessly impressed rope
imprints placed chevron-wise. The same imprints ornamented the
apex of the urn, which was about $16\frac{1}{2}$ inches high and had an
'inside diameter' of $16\frac{1}{2}$ inches. It was full of imperfectly cremated
bones and burnt flint implements. Bu'Lock (1961) considered the
vessel to be a food vessel urn but it could just have well have been
a large collared urn. In the barrow were further flint implements
(including a 'broken Jasper flint nodule') one of which was
possibly a plano-convex flaked knife of food vessel age, a burnt
ox tooth, animal bones, charcoal, a piece of coal and a quartz
pebble. Sherds, bones and other finds in Rochdale Museum
(901020.40/272).
a) Sutcliffe 1898–1900.
b) Sutcliffe 1899.
c) Sutcliffe & Parker 1899.
d) Garstang 1906, 238–9.
e) Bu'Lock 1961.
f) Clare 1973, 16.
g) Cowie 1978.

162 Rochdale
Half Acre   SD 88101270
Saddle quern and grain rubber (for use on saddle quern) found
1913. Rochdale Museum.
a) Maxim 1912–13.

163 Rochdale
Heywood, Ashworth Moor   SD 828154
Middle Bronze Age (Acton Park phase or Pickering phase of
Northern England) palstave found 1905 during construction of
reservoir below 9 inches of soil. 5.8 inches long, 2 inches wide
across blade; no loop; shield shaped panel below stop ridge and
narrow cutting edge. Private possession; cast in Rochdale
Museum.
a) Garstang 1906, 232 and Fig. 16.
b) Davey & Forster 1975, Fig. 37.
c) Tyson 1980, 36 and Fig.

164 Rochdale
Heywood, Knowl Hill   SD 8416
'Polished shale bead' and 'jet button' found.
a) Baldwin 1903.

165 Rochdale
Heywood, Wind Hill (Fig. 32)   SD 833149
At 980 feet O.D. two contiguous walled structures beneath cairn.
The remains of the ruined cairn 34 feet in diameter, 2 feet high,
were excavated in 1968–72 by the Bury Archaeological Group. The
cairn was defined by an almost circular kerb of horizontal slabs up
to 3 courses high. On the east side the kerb was heightened and
straightened to focus on an opening 6 feet wide. A rectangular area
outside this opening was defined by inward leaning slabs, which
were further enclosed by a satellite kerb. Both primary and satellite
kerbs were finally concealed to give the cairn a squat, pear shape.
No grave pits were discovered, but among the basal stones at the
centre a triangular flint knife, a V-perforated jet button and a
'pebble hammer' were found. Only a few small chips of unworked
flint came from the satellite, but the rectangular enclosed area was
lined with vegetation and leached soil. The burials were evidently
surface inhumations, and the excavator maintains that the grave
goods 'formed a typical Beaker assemblage'. The flint knife with

flaking on the edge compares with the example from White Low (No. 71). Various aspects of the monument suggest a mixed Neolithic ancestry. Finds in Bury Museum.
a) Tyson 1980.

166 Rochdale
Hollingworth   SD 943149 ?
Neolithic polished stone axe (made of hard, black stone), 5 inches long, $2\frac{3}{4}$ inches wide.
a) Garstang 1906, 218.
b) Jackson 1934–5.
c) O.S. Records SD91NW4 and SD91SW22.

167 Rochdale
Hollingworth Lake   SD 936148 ?
Stone spindle whorl (alternatively interpreted as small perforated hammer or fishing net weight) found together with Neolithic scrapers and a hammerstone.
a) Garstang 1906, 215 and 227.
b) Kendall & Roth 1912.
c) Petch 1924, 37.
d) O.S. Records SD91SW6.

168 Rochdale
Hopwood   SD 8708 ?
2 (?) stone axe-hammers found pre 1854.
a) Harrison 1896.
b) Platt 1898–1900.
c) Garstang 1906, 226.
d) O.S. Records SD80NE3.

169 Rochdale
Littleborough, Snoddle Hill   SD 95061837
c. 1905 part of shale armlet found near barrow, 64 mm in length. Possibly broken in the process of making a much smaller ring than the Flint Hill example (No. 316). Manchester Museum.
a) Jackson 1929–31, Fig. 2.
b) Rochdale Museum Index.

170 Rochdale
Littleborough, Snoddle Hill   SD 95061837
Alleged Neolithic barrow, probably remains of Bronze Age round barrow, mutilated and robbed of stones, but originally a kerbed cairn. Now consists of circle of flat stones and when investigated *c*. 1900 a cist was found (now consisting of 3 large stones haphazardly set into ground, and not identifiable as a cist). A number of flints were also found and a 'circular perforated ornament'. The interior of the ring is hummocky with small depressions suggesting minor excavations. (The circular ornament was the shale armlet, No. 169.)
a) Garstang 1906, 218, 239.
b) Jackson 1934–5a, 100.
c) O.S. Records SD91NE1.

171 Rochdale
Middleton   SD 8706 ?
Small, highly polished stone hammer (Neolithic) found in gravel at Middleton, and in 1868 it was in the possession of Mr Shaw of Saddleworth.
a) Plant 1867–8, 74.
b) Yates 1887, 331.
c) O.S. Records SD80NE14.

172 Rochdale
Milnrow, Lowhouse   SD 93311322
At 600 feet O.D. a barrow 24 yards in diameter and made of earth and stones was found under outbuildings at Low House Farm in 1899. In the centre, $3\frac{1}{2}$ feet below the surface, was a rough cist where an urn containing a cremation and a stone axe-hammer (or battle axe) were found. The urn was plain, 8 inches high and 8 inches in diameter, and was destroyed together with its contents. The axe-hammer is 6.4 inches long, 3.6 inches wide and 2.5 inches thick, and weighs 2 lbs $5\frac{1}{4}$ ozs; it has an hour glass perforation, diameter 1.6 inches. Rochdale Museum (901020–40/27).
a) Platt 1898–1900.
b) Garstang 1906, 223.
c) Watson 1952, 76.
d) Bu'Lock 1961.
e) Roe 1966.
f) O.S. Records SD91SW17.

173 Rochdale
Milnrow, Newhey   SD 9310
Flint axe with polished cutting edge found 1923 on Whitfield Moor, Newhey. Butt end chipped; 135 mm in length, 70 mm wide. Rochdale Museum (901030–30/269).
a) *Maxim Mss.*

174 Rochdale
Milnrow, Piethorn   SD 9612
Crude Late Bronze Age leaf-shaped spearhead, $6\frac{3}{8}$ inches long with small lunate openings in the blade. Found by the late G. Radford and in private possession. Casts in Tolson Memorial Museum and Rochdale Museum.
a) Garstang 1906, 235 and Fig. 24.
b) Jackson 1934–5.
c) Burgess 1968, 65.
d) Davey & Forster 1975, Fig. 51.

175 Rochdale
Mowroad   SD 945184
Iron Age bronze torque found in 1823 beneath flagstone at Mowroad Farm, Calderbrook. 4 inches in diameter, weight 5 oz. Rather more than half the collar consists of bronze beads of 2 different shapes strung alternately on a piece of iron of square cross section. The remaining segment consists of a bronze tube of rectangular cross section. The 2 halves are dowelled together with iron pins, fixing an iron tooth at each end which fits into an appropriate socket in the other half. Richmond describes it as a beaded native collar, comparing with others in Northern England and Southern Scotland, ie typical of the Brigantian area, and very late Iron Age or Romano-British in date. Rochdale Museum (901030/50/278).
a) Whatton 1833–4.
b) Kirkmann 1843.
c) Fishwick 1889 and Fig.
d) Garstang 1906, 247–8 and Fig. 32.
e) Simpson & Richmond 1941.
f) O.S. Records SD91NW2.

176 Rochdale
Oakenrod   SD 887130
Axe-hammer/battle axe found *c*. 1870 in old bed of River Roch. 4 inches long, 2 inches wide, straight perforation nearly 1 inch in diameter. Clearly marked ridge on two sides thought to indicate that the implement was made in imitation of a cast metal one. Gritstone; weight 1 lb. Roe's Stage IV (?). Rochdale Museum (901040.40/136).
a) Fishwick 1889, 13 and Fig.
b) Garstang 1906, 221.
c) *Maxim Mss.*
d) Roe 1966.
e) O.S. Records SD81SE21.

177 Rochdale
Shore   SD 9317 ?
Barrow with urn, calcined bones and small pieces of flint.
a) Garstang 1906, 218 and 239.
b) Clare 1973, Vol. 2.
c) O.S. Records SD91NW5.

178 Rochdale
Shore Moor   SD 9218 ?
Flaked flint knife of Grooved Ware date. Manchester Museum.
a) Manby 1974, Fig. 37.

179 Rochdale
Sudden   SD 885118
Small stone axe-hammer found 1908. Tapered at striking end, with hour glass perforation; fine grained sandstone, $3\frac{7}{8}$ inches long, 2 inches wide, $1\frac{3}{8}$ inches thick. Rochdale Museum (901040.40/135).
a) Platt 1909–11.

180 Rochdale
Wardle   SD 908178 ?
Edge ground, polished flint axe found in bed of gravel on bank of stream during excavation of reservoir; $4\frac{3}{4}$ inches long. Cast in Rochdale Museum.
a) March 1887.
b) Fishwick 1889, 4 and Fig.
c) Jackson 1934–5.

d) O.S. Records SD91NW3.

181 Rossendale
Bacup, Stocksteads   SD 8521 ?
Polished stone axe found 1978, 13 feet down beneath the site of the
Western Board School. On the same site a spinning whorl (loom
weight?) was found recently 5 feet below the surface.
a) Bacup Museum.

182 Rossendale
Bacup, Tooter Hill   SD 888237
Edge polished Neolithic flint adze found at 1,450 feet. Grooved
ware date (Duggleby adze). 172 mm long, 54 mm wide at cutting
edge, 39 mm at butt end, 37 mm at waist. Maximum thickness 20
mm. Weight 194.9 grams. Both sides of cutting edge finely polished
up to one third of long axis, remainder being carefully chipped.
Creamy white flint with bluish-tinted patina. Bacup Museum; cast
in Tolson Memorial Museum, Huddersfield.
a) *Maxim Mss.*
b) Jackson 1928.
c) Manby 1974.

183 Rossendale
Whitworth   SD 8717 or 8818
Saddle quern and grain rubber found in either Cowm or Spring
Mill Reservoir. Rochdale Museum.

184 Salford
Barton   SJ 7697
Socketed bronze spearhead found during excavations for
Manchester Ship Canal near Barton. 7½ inches long, blade 6½
inches long and just over 2 inches wide, tapering to a point. Very
short socket; rivet holes on each side below blade. Blade has mid
rib along centre. Small fragments of wood at tip of socket.
a) Jackson 1936, Plate 8, 3.
b) O.S. Records SJ79NE18.

185 Salford
Broughton Park   SD 832021
Possible barrow ('evidence of trench and mound') found 1873 in
the grounds of Broughton Old Hall *c.* 150 yards from the end of
the lake, on the site of the Congregational Church. In the centre at
a depth of 5 feet was found an inverted urn, burnt bones and ashes.
The urn was 5 inches in height, 6 inches diameter at the widest, 5
inches diameter at the mouth and 3½ inches at the base. It was
ornamented 'by diagonally running impressions in 6 rows over the
broad rim'. In 1887 the vessel was in the Peel Park Museum,
Salford; now lost.
a) Parkinson 1881–2.
b) Yates 1887.
c) Garstang 1906, 244.

186 Salford
Clifton   SD 78110379
Incense cup together with bones and parts of skull dug up in 1788
from a bed of gravel on the banks of the river Irwell.
a) Pegge 1789, Plate IX, Fig. 4.
b) Garstang 1906, 244.
c) O.S. Records SD70SE3.

187 Salford
Irlam   SJ 7294 ?
Shaft hole Adze (disc group) found 1890: 4½ inches by 4 inches.
Group XV, well used. Found during excavations for Manchester
Ship Canal and put in Warrington Museum.
a) Harrison 1892, 250.
b) Garstang 1906, 227 and Plate II, No. 8.
c) Jackson 1936.
d) Roe 1979, 46.

188 Salford
Irlam   SJ 7294 ?
Middle Bronze Age looped and socketed bronze spearhead, found
in excavating Manchester Ship Canal 20–30 feet below surface in
1891. Overall length 5¾ inches; blade 3 inches long, 1⅛ inch wide.
Socket has small elongated loops at each side between blade and
butt. Manchester Museum.
a) *Manchester Weekly Times*, July 17 1891 & Fig.
b) Harrison 1892, 250.
c) Garstang 1906, 235 and Fig. 23.

d) Jackson 1936.
e) Davey & Forster 1975, Fig. 69.

189 Salford
Kersal Moor   SD 81640202
Sandstone spindle whorl (Neolithic) found in 1908 on a 'Neolithic
working floor' which had been discovered in 1886.
a) O.S. Records SD80SW4.

190 Salford
Winton   SJ 755997
Polished axe (Group VI) found June 1922 during building of new
Westwood estate, Winton, *c.* 5 feet down in clay in middle of
Westwood Crescent. 9¼ inches long, 3¼ inches wide at the widest,
greatest thickness 1¾ inches. Weight 2¼ lbs. Flattened sides. 'One
of the finest and most perfect specimens in the Manchester area.'
Manchester Museum.
a) Phelps 1922 and Fig.
b) Jackson 1936, Plate 7.3.
c) Manby 1965, 384.

191 Salford
Worsley   SD 725013
At 150 feet O.D. 'what appeared to be an ancient burial mound . . .
surrounded by a slight ditch' said to have been located on the break
of slope overlooking the valley between Ellenbrook and
Boothstown – now industrial waste ground.
a) Clare 1973, Vol. 2.

192 Trafford
Mode Wheel   SJ 799974
Bronze Age perforated axe-hammer of Scandinavian type found in
October 1890 during the digging of the Manchester Ship Canal at
Mode Wheel. 6½ inches in length, 3 inches wide, weight 1 lb. 6 oz.
In 1906 in Peel Park Museum, Salford. Battle axe, Stage IV? (Roe).
a) *Manchester Weekly Times* March 13, 1891.
b) Harrison 1892, 251.
c) Garstang 1906, 220 and Plate III (i).
d) Roe 1966.
e) O.S. Records SJ89NW58.

193 Trafford
Mode Wheel   SJ 799974
Late Bronze Age crescentic gold pendant, originally thought to be
a Roman 'bulla', found in May 1772 close to the Mode Wheel lock
of the Mersey and Irwell Navigation in gravel, 1 foot below the
surface, in the bed of the river. Lost.
a) Whitaker 1773, 79–81 and Fig.
b) Watkin 1883, 121 and Fig.
c) Phelphs 1915, Fig.
d) Challis & Harding 1975, 35.
e) Davey & Forster 1975, Fig. 155.
f) O.S. Records SJ89NW90.

194 Trafford
Throstle Nest   SJ 816964
Perforated gritstone axe-hammer, 12 inches long, found pre 1771.
a) Whitaker 1771.
b) Plant 1867–8.
c) Yates 1887, 330.
d) Garstang 1906, 225.
e) O.S. Records SJ89NW69.

195 Tameside
Droylsden, Back Lane   SJ 9198 ?
Polished stone axe found 'in the Moss'. No further information.
a) Harrison 1896.
b) Garstang 1906, 218.
c) Jackson 1934–5a.

196 Tameside
Mossley, Bucton Castle   SD 98920161
Defensive enclosure in strong promontory position, 1,123 feet O.D.,
but of uncertain age. Consists of artificially raised platform
surrounded by rampart with outer ditch on 3 sides. Original
entrance on north west. Roughly oval platform, 100 feet by 75
feet, has surrounding rampart showing signs of revetment. Apart
from the area to the south west, where the natural slopes are very
steep, a broad and deep ditch surrounds the work. Slight traces of
an additional rampart are visible on the south east side. Aikin

describes ruins 6–7 feet higher 'than the area' near the south east side – no longer visible. A road with traces of a pavement and 2 ditches (apparently outworks) are recorded leading to the castle on the northern side. Various ornaments and two gold bead chains have been found in the immediate vicinity. The earthwork is clearly a ringwork (Class B). Its strong, defensive position, however, and the former existence of an outer rampart beyond the limits of a possible counterscarp bank to the ditch suggest that the ringwork is superimposed on an Iron Age fort. Against this, however, is that the area of the feature is very small by hillfort standards.

a) Aikin 1795, 471 and Fig.
b) Garstang 1906, 516.
c) Preston 1954.
d) Forde-Johnston 1962, 11.
e) Forde-Johnston 1976.
f) O.S. Records SD90SE3.

197 Tameside
Mossley, Luzley   SD 9601
'Good specimen of a stone celt found near Luzley by Mr Radcliffe, postmaster of Mossley'.
a) *TLCAS* 14, 1896, 162.
b) O.S. Records SD90SE8.

198 Tameside
Mossley, Scout   SD 973013 ?
Stone hammer found when digging well. Brown quartzite with deep hollows which suggest unfinished perforations. $4\frac{1}{8}$ inches long, $2\frac{1}{2}$ inches wide, $1\frac{5}{8}$ inches thick. Ends bruised by use.
a) Jackson 1936 and Plate 8:1.

199 Tameside
Mossley, Warlow   SD 993026
Flint knife with typical Early Bronze Age pressure flaking found on Mossley side of county boundary.
a) Clark 1932, Fig. 4, 5.

200 Tameside
Slatepit Moor   SE 00000099
Edge polished discoidal flint knife (grooved ware date) found 1961 at 1,150 feet O.D. overlooking Carr Brook, a stray find. Grey flint, 2.6 inches by 2.4 inches, maximum thickness 0.4 inches. Cast in Tolson Memorial Museum, Huddersfield.
a) Davies 1961.
b) Manby 1974.

201 Tameside
Stalybridge   SJ 958986
'Quoit shaped implement, 6 inches in diameter with hole $1\frac{1}{2}$ inches wide in centre, found in glacial drift 20 feet below the surface under the railway station, and in the possession of the station master' (in 1887). Material is like clay-ironstone. Variously described as a fishing net weight and spindle whorl.
a) Plant 1867–8, 74.
b) Yates 1887, 331.
c) Garstang 1906, 227.
d) Jackson 1936.

202 Warrington
Kenyon   SJ 61949480
Barrow at 115 feet O.D.; 33 feet diameter, $3\frac{1}{2}$ feet high. Tanged awl ploughed up along with urn containing bones in 1826; 2 more urns (1 inverted) found 1903. Awl round in section, tapering to point at one end, flattened at the other, 2.2 inches long. Warrington Museum.
a) Harrison 1892, 250.
b) Garstang 1906, 241 and Fig. 25.
c) Davey & Forster 1975, Fig. 19 (awl).

203 Wigan
Leigh   SD 6500 ?
Highly polished Cumbrian axe found in 1912 2 feet 6 inches down in gravel. $9\frac{1}{4}$ inches long, $2\frac{3}{4}$ inches wide, $1\frac{3}{4}$ inches thick. Flattened sides. Leigh Museum.
a) Jackson 1936.
b) Manby 1965, 384.
c) O.S. Records SD60SE10.

204 Wigan
Leigh   SD 6500 ?
Bronze double looped socketed spearhead found in 1799. About 8 inches in length. Manchester Museum (0.7873).
a) Barrit 1800, Fig.
b) Garstang 1906, 235.
c) Davey & Forster 1975, Fig. 67.
d) O.S. Records SD60SE11.

205 Barnsley
Cawthorne   SE 2808 ?
Polished stone axe, $3\frac{1}{2}$ inches long: greenstone with oval section and flat sides. Cast in Tolson Memorial Museum; original reported to be in 'Oldham Museum'.
a) *CAGB* 4, 1959, 55.
b) *CAGB* 5, 1960, 10 and Fig.

206 Bradford
Bronze spearhead; small, well cast, looped and socketed. 9.7 cm long. Provenance unknown. Bradford M.B. Museums (NH 9.41).

207 Bradford
Allerton   SE 1234 ?
'Celt' of hard unpolished stone, 5 inches long, found by workmen digging foundations pre 1896.
a) O.S. Records SE13SW8.

208 Bradford
Apperley Bridge   SE193381
Bronze stop ridge axe, 7 inches long, 2 inches wide at the cutting edge. No details about finding. Bradford Museum (no accession number).
a) Cowling 1946, 110.
b) Watson 1952, 82.
c) *CAGB* 5, 1960, 26.

209 Bradford
Ashbourne Gardens   SE 167351
Flanged bronze axe (Arreton tradition) found 1931 c. 3 feet down when digging drains on the Ashbourne Gardens Estate. $4\frac{4}{5}$ inches long, $2\frac{1}{4}$ inches wide at the cutting edge, shank $1\frac{1}{8}$ inches long; pitted surface, with mottled green patina; flanges not straight but slightly inturned at bottom. Bradford Museum (40.34).
a) *CAGB* 4, 1959, 16–17 and Fig.
b) *CAGB* 5, 1960, 26.
c) Manby 1964.
d) O.S. Records SE13NE35.

210 Bradford
Baildon, Baildon Hill I   SE 1364839701
Site of probable round barrow, cremation and pottery, on south-west shoulder of Baildon Moor. Excavated 1900, and pottery fragments and cremations found. Now barely discernible.
a) O.S. Records SE13NW35.

211 Bradford
Baildon, Baildon Hill II   SE 14324026
Barrow (?) excavated 1955 on eastern shoulder of Baildon Hill. Boulder kerb 14 feet 6 inches diameter; finds – 3 small flint flakes and a shale disc. Other possible barrows (earth and stone mounds) in same area.
a) *CAGB* 1, 1956, 85.
b) O.S. Records SE14SW46.

212 Bradford
Baildon, Baildon Moor   SE 14344056
Neolithic axe found August 1914 on northern slopes of Baildon Moor between Pennythorn Hill and Hope Hill by the side of an old cart track. Rough, unpolished (weathered?) surface; $3\frac{1}{2}$ inches long. Diorite. Bradford Museum (NH 62.47).
a) *CAGB* 7, 1962, 20.
b) O.S. Records SE14SW44.

213 Bradford
Baildon, Birch Close   SE 13724187
Stone circle originally 27 yards in diameter; now gone.
a) *WYAU* 4414.317827.

214 Bradford
Baildon, Brackenhall Green   SE 1239 ?

Polished flint axe found; deposited in Bradford Museum (now lost).
a) O.S. Records SE13NW36.

215 Bradford
Baildon, Brackenhall Green   SE 1238 ?
Part of stone axe-hammer found September, 1903. Bradford
Museum (45/33).
a) *CAGB* 11, 1966, 37.
b) O.S. Records SE13NW36.

216 Bradford
Baildon, Brackenhall Green   SE 129391
Round barrow; no details.
a) *WYAU* 4413.2991.

217 Bradford
Baildon, Brackenhall Green   SE 129391
Earthwork 50 yards by 30 yards with inner and outer ring of
boulders and a packing of small stones. Iron Age enclosure?
a) Wood 1905.
b) Cowling 1946, 71.
c) *WYAU* 4413.2991.

218 Bradford
Baildon, Brackenhall Green   SE 1239
Bronze Age/Iron Age enclosures: small rectangular enclosures and
circular pounds on terrace between road and ravine. Not
identifiable now.
a) O.S. Records SE13NW36.

219 Bradford
Baildon, Brackenhall Green   SE 12903925
Iron Age sickle found April 1964. 2 fragments, very rusty, $\frac{3}{8}$ inch
wide, *c.* 8 inches long. Unusual version of normal Iron Age reaping
hook or unbalanced sickle. Bradford Museum (a.61/65).
a) *CAGB* 10, 1965, 108 and Fig.
b) O.S. Records SE13NW53.

220 Bradford
Baildon, Dobrudden   SE 13984003
Stone axe found September 1956: 3.3 inches long, 2.4 inches wide
at cutting edge, 1.1 inches wide at butt; 1 inch thick with squared
sides. Bradford Museum (L. 13.56).
a) *Yorkshire Observer* 12 Sept. 1956.
b) *CAGB* 2, 1956, 17.
c) O.S. Records SE14SW27.

221 Bradford
Baildon, Dobrudden   SE 13934000
Polished flint axe, partly broken, found near Dobrudden Farm and
presented to Bradford Museum 1949. Bradford Museum (NH
41–49).
a) *CAGB* 1, 1956, 105.
b) O.S. Records SE14SW30.

222 Bradford
Baildon, Dobrudden I (Figs. 33 and 34)   SE 13834030
One of a group of 6 (?) barrows north of Dobrudden Farm on the
western flanks of Baildon Hill, *c.* 825 feet O.D. Colls' Barrow 8.
Former ring barrow; almost defaced circular earthwork 50 feet in
diameter, and about 1 foot high. Near the centre was found an
upright urn, about 2 feet down, 9–10 inches in height and 12 inches
in diameter, ornamented on the upper part with incised criss cross
lines; filled with calcined bones.
a) Colls 1846.
b) Wardell 1881.
c) Wood 1905.
d) O.S. Records SE14SW45.

223 Bradford
Baildon, Dobrudden II (Figs. 33 and 34)   SE 13834030
One of group of 6 (?) barrows north of Dobrudden Farm on the
western flanks of Baildon Hill, *c.* 825 feet O.D. Colls' Barrow 9.
Contained a cremation.
a) Colls 1846.
b) Wood 1905.

224 Bradford
Baildon, Dobrudden III   SE 13764023
Bronze Age ring barrow (remains of) consisting of circular bank of

earth and boulders, almost obliterated.
a) O.S. Records SE14SW42.

225 Bradford
Baildon, Dobrudden (Figs. 33 and 34)   SE 138402
Bronze Age extensive settlement with field boundaries, ring banks
etc. In 1845 there were traces of earthworks running parallel to each
other at distances from 50 to 80 yards apart, and intersected by
other works of similar construction. The banks consisted of
drystone walls, 4–5 feet high and 8 feet wide at the base. Much of
them had already been removed for roadworks. In the vicinity
Iron Age field walls have been excavated (SE 136397).
a) Colls 1846 and Figs.
b) Wood 1905.
c) *CAGB* 2, 1957, 81.
d) Challis & Harding 1975.

226 Bradford
Baildon, Faweather Farm   SE 14124173
Polished stone axe found amongst rubble filling in a drystone wall
between Faweather and Birch Close in 1957. 6.5 inches long, 3
inches wide at the cutting edge, 1.8 inches wide at the butt, 1.2
inches thick. Group VII. Cutting edge badly chipped. Bradford
Museum (A.2.58).
a) *CAGB* 3, 1958, 18 and Fig.
b) O.S. Records SE14SW29.

227 Bradford
Baildon, Ferniehurst   SE 15703865
Socketed bronze axe found 1935 2 feet down in garden of 17
Midland Road, Ferniehurst. 2.2 inches long, socket 1.5 inches
square; unusual hole for rivet or securing pin in side. Badly
damaged. Bradford Museum (A.22.53.)
a) *CAGB* 5, 1960 and Fig.

228 Bradford
Baildon, Hope Hill   SE 142396 ?
Hope Hill cairn destroyed by golf course extension in 1904 when
urn containing human bones found together with flint flakes, a
bronze point and a perforated bone (ornament?). Greenwell
reputedly dug in the same area in the 1870s and 3 more urns are
said to have been found on the same hill.
a) *CAGB* 1, 1956, 101.

229 Bradford
Baildon, Pennythorne Hill I (Figs. 33 and 34) SE 14044068
Composite barrow/earth circle, 50 feet in diameter with ditch on
south and east sides. Colls' Barrow 10: in the centre were ashes,
bones and charcoal and a broken urn. 5 feet to the north west was
another urn, 2 feet below the surface, 9–10 inches in height, 7
inches in diameter, inverted with its bottom missing and filled with
calcined bones, charcoal and a barbed and tanged arrowhead;
ornamented with zig zag lines. This barrow was re excavated 1890
and yielded two vessels – a bucket urn and a food vessel. This Late
Bronze Age bucket urn was found in an uncertain relationship with
the barrow, and is 24.1 cm high, 22.8 cm diameter at the rim and
13.2 cm at the base.
a) Colls 1846.
b) Raistrick 1929, 363 and Fig.
c) Gilks 1973, 178.

230 Bradford
Baildon, Pennythorne Hill II (Pen Hill Barrow)   SE 13924098 ?
Probably more than one barrow site. In a cairn almost reduced to
ground level, when stones were removed in 1869, 1 foot down were
found a small quantity of ashes, charcoal and calcined bones, and
among them a small urn. Cowling described this as a late food
vessel. Wardell (1869) figured 3 vessels (2 urns and a food vessel).
The golf course was extended in December 1904 when workmen
destroyed the cairn, in the process uncovering an inverted collared
urn in the sandy subsoil, containing a cremation and a bronze
tanged knife/dagger. Fragments of another vessel, possibly an
incense cup, were found nearby. Food vessel is in Craven Museum,
Skipton; other finds in Bradford Museum (no accession number).
a) Wardell 1869, 23.
b) Preston !905, 97.
c) Cowling 1946, 66 and Fig.
d) *WYAU* 4413.409928 and 4414.309928.

231 Bradford
Baildon, Sandals School　　　　　　　　　　SE 15243917
Bronze Age palstave and axe-hammer found during digging of
foundations for the school in 1893. The axe-hammer was reburied
in the school yard. Palstave is in Bradford Museum (215/33).
a) Wood 1905.
b) *CAGB* 5, 1960, 26 and 70.
c) O.S. Records SE13NE17.

232 Bradford
Baildon, The Soldiers Trench　　　　　　　SE 13043908
Remains of 'stone circle' – bank with inner and outer rows of
stones, forming enclosure with rubble bank 1–2 feet in height,
much denuded and mutilated. Iron Age enclosure? – querns found
nearby.
a) Cowling 1946, 138.
b) O.S. Records SE13NW27.

233 Bradford
Bingley　　　　　　　　　　　　　　　　SE 10103898
Possible hut circle – an arc of 4 boulders with a related 5th, flush
with the ground. A circle including these stones would be *c.* 7 m in
diameter. There is no other evidence to suggest it is a hut circle.
Found in 1953.
a) O.S. Records SE13NW9.

234 Bradford
Bingley　　　　　　　　　　　　　　　　SE 101399
Possible Iron Age settlement: stone walls and banks of earth and
stone have been recorded on a site now occupied by school playing
fields and a cemetery extension. Iron Age querns were found
nearby.
a) Cowling 1946, 159.
b) O.S. Records SE13NW6.

235 Bradford
Bingley, Catstones Ring　　　　　　　　SE 06803808
Quadrangular earthwork, *c.* 16 acres, univallate with slight ditch.
Possibly a stock enclosure.
a) Wood 1905.
b) Challis & Harding 1975, 50.
c) O.S. Records SE03NE2.

236 Bradford
Bingley, College　　　　　　　　　　　SE 11224049
Axe-hammer with hour glass perforation found 4 feet down in
clay during excavations for new boiler house in 1953. Fine grained
sandstone; 20 cm long, 8.5 cm maximum width, 8.5 cm maximum
thickness. Bradford Museum (A.36.60).
a) *CAGB* 6, 1961, 26 and Fig.
b) O.S. Records SE14SW51.

237 Bradford
Bingley, Cottingley　　　　　　　　　　SE 120367
Iron Age mortar found at Stair Foot Farm near possible Iron Age
wall. Homestead site?
a) *CAGB* 11, 1966, 89.

238 Bradford
Bingley, Crosley Wood　　　　　　　　SE 117386
At 325 feet O.D. on south west facing slopes of Aire valley. Short
stretches of walling (probably remains of a rectilinear field system
for arable or pastoral farming) occur in vicinity of a near circular
enclosure, 200 feet in diameter with 8 feet thick boundary (at
SE 11863854). Latter has feature on north west section consisting
of 2 vertical stones, 2 feet apart, one 3 feet 6 inches and the other 1
foot 6 inches high, both inserted into the ground, known as Giles
Stile: part of reputed stone circle, but 1964–5 excavation suggested
they may be facing stones of wall. Wall structure of enclosure (and
other stretches of walling) originally consisted of double row of flat
boulders with filling of rubble – remains of stone revetment found
in 2 places and spread of rubble walling in others. Circular
enclosure originally a cattle pound? Finds from excavation
included pottery sherds, a shale disc, a few flint flakes and chert
fragments. Pottery evidence suggests Romano-British date;
possibly site may have originated during Iron Age. Finds
Bradford M.B. Museums (A.9.68).
a) Mayes 1967.
b) O.S. Records SE13NW9.

239 Bradford
Bingley, Eldwick Glen　　　　　　　　SE 123407
'Several earthworks forming a rectangular enclosure' near the
higher part of Eldwick Glen were levelled when the area was
enclosed and cultivated in 1864. The workmen found 2 'copper
spearheads' and a large egg shaped stone 14 inches long and 11½
inches in diameter. One 'spearhead' was 12 inches long (lost); the
other was in J. E. Preston's possession in 1874. Are the 2
'spearheads' the 2 socketed bronze axes which were found in
Eldwick during the 19th century?
a) O.S. Records SE14SW13 (earthworks).
b) *CAGB* 5, 1960, 26 (axes).
c) O.S. Records SE14SW13 (axes).

240 Bradford
Bingley, Gilstead Moor　　　　　　　　SE 129401
Chipped dark brown flint axe found 7th May 1882 in the grounds
of Hammondale House (now Netherdale House): 4½ inches long,
1¾ inches wide. Bradford M.B. Museums (445.32).
a) *CAGB* 5, 1960, 11 and Fig.
b) *CAGB* 11, 1966, 47.

241 Bradford
Bingley, Harden　　　　　　　　　　　SE 08603819
Axe-hammer found in garden of 18 Wilsden Road, Harden, in the
1940s. Coarse gritstone with cylindrical perforation: 17.5 cm in
length, 8.5 cm maximum width, 6.5 cm thick; 3¾ lbs. in weight.
Bradford M.B. Museums (A.69.61).
a) *Yorkshire Observer* Dec. 18th 1950.
b) *CAGB* 6, 1961, 36.
c) O.S. Records SE03NE1.

242 Bradford
Bingley, Harden Moor　　　　　　　　SE 07403867
Former Bronze Age ring or disc barrow, 25 feet in diameter, 18
inches high. Excavation in May 1959 produced an urn 12 inches
high and 9 inches in diameter, sherds of 2 or 3 other urns, calcined
bones, flints, charcoal and part of a pygmy vessel. 1905 report
described nearby 'cemetery' of small cairns (at SE 07553865), in all
comprising 20 'barrows' of varying sizes. In fact 4 small cairns are
the cemetery and consist of compact mounds of stone and earth;
the other mounds are probably quarry spoil heaps.
a) Wood 1905, 116–17.
b) *Bradford Telegraph and Argus* 13th May 1959.
c) Bradford M.B. Museums Index.

243 Bradford
Bingley, Harden, Ryecroft　　　　　　SE 077381
Iron Age limestone loom weight found on site of presumed lake
dwelling. Keighley Museum.

244 Bradford
Bingley, Peas Acre　　　　　　　　　　SE 10394158
Stone macehead found 3 feet below surface when drainage works
were being carried out in Peas Acre near Moorside (name of house)
pre 1936. Keighley Museum.
a) Cowling 1946, 64, Fig. 9.
b) O.S. Records SE14SW9.

245 Bradford
Bingley, Shipley Glen　　　　　　　　SE 1239 ?
Spindle whorl of fine sandstone, 4.7 cm in diameter, with hole 2.3
cm diameter in centre, found in stream in 1920s. Bradford M.B.
Museums (NH 2.52).

246 Bradford
Bingley, Shipley Glen　　　　　　　　SE 1239 ?
Iron Age mortar found.
a) *CAGB* 1, 1956, 65.
b) *CAGB* 2, 1957, 12.
c) *CAGB* 11, 1966, 89–90.

247 Bradford
Bolton　　　　　　　　　　　　　　　SE 1692735067
Very fine Neolithic axe of dark green stone found in garden of 1045
Bolton Road, Bolton, in August 1945; 4.1 inches long, 2.8 inches
wide, 1.6 inches thick. Group IV ('altered greenstone'). Bradford
Museum (A.6.55).
a) *Bradford Telegraph and Argus* Dec. 10th 1952.
b) O.S. Records SE17NE32.

248 Bradford
Bolton   SE 169351
Polished stone axe, 16.6 cm long, 6 cm wide, 4 cm thick (Group XVIII) found in garden of house on Bolton Road, Bolton in 1952. Bradford Museum (A 4.55).
a) *CAGB* 11, 1966, 63.

249 Bradford
Bull Royd   SE 13513367
Butt end of polished stone axe found in July 1966 in allotment at Bull Royd, Fairweather Green; fine grained, light fawn coloured stone.
a) *CAGB* 11, 1966, 78.
b) O.S. Records SE13SW19.

250 Bradford
Calverley   SE 2037
Butt end of polished stone axe found in 1958 in garden of house on Rockwood Road, Calverley; 4.4 inches long, 2.4 inches wide at maximum, 1.1 inches thick. Group VI. Bradford Museum.
a) *Bradford Telegraph and Argus* Nov. 8th, 1958.
b) Davies 1958, 73.
c) *CAGB* 5, 1960, 10 and Fig.
d) Manby 1965.

251 Bradford
Chellow Heights Reservoir   SE 117353
When reservoir being constructed in June 1921 sherds of 3 urns and an incomplete incense cup, 2 inches high and 3 inches diameter at its base, were found together with partly burnt bones (young female adult). Urn A: base of small urn $2\frac{1}{4}$ inches diameter; Urn B: later reconstructed, $10\frac{1}{2}$ inches high, $4\frac{1}{2}$ inches diameter at base, $8\frac{1}{2}$ inches diameter at mouth; Urn C: possibly 12 inches high, decorated with incised lines. All 3 urns of very coarse clay.
a) Rowe 1928.
b) Bradford M.B. Museums Index.

252 Bradford
Clayton   SE 128319
Polished stone axe found in garden of 6 Thornlea Grove, Clayton, in April 1951; 9.2 cm long, 5.7 cm wide, 2.5 cm thick. Group VI. Bradford Museum (NH 43.51).
a) *Yorkshire Observer* June 19th, 1951.
b) Bradford M.B. Museums Index.

253 Bradford
Clayton   SE 1131 ?
Iron Age mortar found.
a) *CAGB* 6, 1961, 2.
b) *CAGB* 11, 1966, 89–90.

254 Bradford
Cullingworth, Castlestead Ring   SE 05143625
Univallate, oval earthwork, 1.75 acres in extent; unknown purpose. Only north west quadrant extant, rest ploughed out but visible on aerial photographs. Excavation of nothern part in 1911 showed bank 6 feet high, 17 feet wide, outer ditch 11 feet wide and 4 feet deep. Slight counterscarping but no evidence of 2nd ditch, postholes or palisading.
a) Elgee & Elgee 1933, 119.
b) Challis & Harding 1975, 52.
c) O.S. Records SE03NE13.

255 Bradford
Cullingworth, Manywells Height   SE 063356
Iron Age (?) earthwork/enclosure visible on aerial photographs.
a) Challis & Harding 1975, 52.
b) *WYAU* 4403.6537.

256 Bradford
Cullingworth, Manywells Quarry   SE 065357
Grey flint axe (Beaker type?) with butt end retaining flaking marks, rest highly polished, found 1952. 4.4 inches long, 2.1 inches wide, 1 inch thick. Keighley Museum.
a) *Yorkshire Observer* Oct. 6th, 1952.
b) Bradford M.B. Museums Index.

257 Bradford
Eccleshill   SE 18063624

Early Bronze Age axe-hammer found in stone pier of steam crane at Stonehall Quarry in 1936: 25 cm long, 6.3 cm thick, weight $6\frac{1}{2}$ lbs. Hour glass perforation, fine grained sandstone, and decorated with 3 parallel grooves on each face. Bradford Museum (5.38).
a) *CAGB* 5, 1960, 10 and Fig.
b) Bradford M.B. Museums Index.

258 Bradford
Fagley   SE 188351
Polished stone axe found in garden of 41 Fenscote Crescent in 1968, 'hardly used'. 195 mm long, 65 mm wide, 38 mm thick. Group VII (?).
a) *Yorkshire Post* Nov. 14th, 1969.
b) *YAJ* 42, 1969, 239.
c) Bradford M.B. Museums Index.

259 Bradford
Farsley Common   SE 2135 ?
Bronze Age hoard reported: Wallington tradition?
a) Raistrick 1929, Plate 116.
b) Watson 1952, 83.
c) Gilks 1973b, 179.
d) O.S. Records SE23NW15.

260 Bradford
Greengates   SE 190373
Polished stone axe of facetted Langdale type found in garden at 28 New Line, Greengates, Eccleshill in 1976. 8 cm long, 5.3 cm wide, 2 cm thick. Bradford Museum (A 3.76).

261 Bradford
Idle   SE 17363648
Polished stone axe found in April 1908 in the grounds of a large house (Willowfield) now built upon at the junction of Wrose Road and Highfield Road, Five Lane Ends. 3.8 inches long, 1.75 inches wide at the cutting edge, 1 inch thick; light grey stone. Private possession.
a) *CAGB* 3, 1958, 37.
b) *CAGB* 5, 1960, 10.
c) Bradford M.B. Museums Index.

262 Bradford
Keighley   SE 0641 ?
Flint axe 3 inches long found 'near Keighley'.
a) *CAGB* 10, 1065, 29.

263 Bradford
Keighley   SE 0641 ?
Flat bronze axe (Arreton tradition) showing flange development, found 'in Keighley area'. Keighley Museum.
a) Manby 1964.

264 Bradford
Keighley, Black Hill   SE 050420 ?
Polished stone axe, very smooth with small chips on 2 cutting edges; Group VI. 20.2 cm long, 6.8 cm wide, 2 cm thick. Bradford M.B. Museums (7381).

265 Bradford
Keighley, East Morton   SE 0942 ?
Perforated, quartzite stone hammer in good condition, found 1900. Keighley Museum.
a) Cowling 1946, 64 and Fig. 4.
b) O.S. Records SE04SE6.

266 Bradford
Keighley, East Morton   SE 0942 ?
Neolithic spindle whorl found. Keighley Museum.

267 Bradford
Keighley, Holme House   SE 02854015
Stone axe found, compares with Fimber axe of Yorkshire Wolds. Keighley Museum.
a) Cowling 1946, 64.
b) *CAGB* 5, 1960, 10 and Fig.

268 Bradford
Keighley, Keighley Moor   SD 99433987
Small triangular axe found in July 1961 during digging of water channel. Pointed butt type, ground but not finely polished. Badly

decomposed because of acid soil conditions. Bradford M.B. Museums.
a) *CAGB* 6, 1961, 52.
b) O.S. Records SD93NE3.
c) Bradford M.B. Museums Index.

269 Bradford
Keighley, Morton, Howden Ridge   SE 09284201
Butt fragment of broad-butted, flat bronze axe found in 1880 in rocks near Carr House, Howden Ridge. Keighley Museum (7371).
a) Cowling 1946, 64.
b) Manby 1964.
c) *WYAU* 4404.922081.

270 Bradford
Keighley, North Dean Road   SE 04884109
Flaked and partly polished axe of pale brown flint, 12 cm long, 5 cm wide, 2 cm thick, found in July 1950 in stream on north side of North Dean Road near its confluence with Castle Hill Beck. 'Seamer' type axe (grooved ware date). Keighley Museum (84.50).
a) *CAGB* 4, 1959, 13 and Fig.
b) *CAGB* 5, 1960, 11 and Fig.
c) Manby 1974.

271 Bradford
Keighley, Riddlesden   SF 086418
Polished stone axe found in allotment behind St. Mary's Church. 12.3 cm long, 2.3 cm thick, 5.8 cm wide. Bradford M.B. Museums (26.68).
a) Bradford M.B. Museums Index.

272 Bradford
Keighley, Riddlesden   SE 087419
Stone axe-hammer found among water worn pebbles in garden at Cliffe Crescent, Bradford Road, in 1952. Keighley Museum (50.52).
a) *Yorkshire Observer* Oct. 6th, 1952.
b) Bradford M.B. Museums Index.

273 Bradford
Keighley, Station   SE 066412
3 cinerary urns containing cremations found during construction of railway 100 yards from Keighley Station; part of quern also found.
a) O.S. Records SE04SE4.

274 Bradford
Keighley, Steeton Moor   SE 020430
Stone axe found: slate, very smooth, slightly damaged at cutting edge. 15.1 cm long, 7 cm wide, 2.5 cm thick. Bradford M.B. Museums (7387).
a) Keen and Radley 1971.
b) Bradford M.B. Museums Index.

275 Bradford
Keighley, Sutton Moor   SE 0041 ?
Palstave found near Sutton-on-the-Moor. Keighley Museum.

276 Bradford
Keighley, Victoria Park   SE 05634203
Rough out Group VI axe found *c.* 1914 by workmen digging in Hawkholme Lane. Butt broken off during discovery. Flattish, wedge shaped, rounded end; large chip or depression on under side. 24 cm long, 9.3 cm wide at rounded end, 4.5 cm thick. Keighley Museum (7504).
a) Manby 1965, 384.
b) Keen & Radley 1971, 19, 27 and Fig. 20.
c) Manby 1979, Fig. 3, 1.
d) O.S. Records SE04SE20.
e) Bradford M.B. Museums Index.

277 Bradford
Lidget Green   SE 131324
Polished stone axe of facetted Langdale type found in April 1938 in Bulgreave Wood, Lidget Green, Horton; 10 cm long, 5.3 cm wide at cutting edge, 2.7 cm thick. Bradford Museum (NH 4.38).
a) *CAGB* 5, 1960, 11 and Fig.
b) *CAGB* 10, 1965, 77.

278 Bradford
Shipley, Hirst Wood   SE 127382

Iron Age settlement (?) at 300 feet O.D. on eastern slope of glacial moraine (with sandy soil and Millstone Grit erratics which were used for constructing). Sub circular enclosure with 8 feet thick stone wall: 40 feet external diameter, 10 feet internal diameter. Outer and inner retaining walls, infill of rubble. Central hearth excavated together with central posthole (supported conical roof?). Floor covered with rough paving of pebbles; hammerstones, rubbers, potboilers etc. found. Other circular huts and straight sided enclosures occur nearby.
a) *WYAU* 4413.2800.

279 Bradford
Shipley, Saltaire   SE 12543766
Polished flint axe found in 1938 in Branksome Drive, Nabwood, just above the River Aire. Grey flint; 11.5 cm long, 5.5 cm wide, 2 cm thick. Keighley Museum (119.41).
a) *CAGB* 5, 1960, 10.
b) O.S. Records SE13NW20.
c) Bradford M.B. Museums Index.

280 Bradford
Thornton, Lower Headley   SE 09943215
3 urns found in a field in 1880. Lost.
a) O.S. Records SE03SE4.

281 Bradford
Wilsden, Shay Gate   SE 101357
Circular enclosure, internal and external banks. Non defensive.
a) Challis & Harding 1975, 52.
b) O.S. Records SE13NW50.

282 Bradford
Wyke   SE 155268
Stone axe found in building site near the Crescent, Wyke, in May 1964. Surface very rough due to weathering. Light, fawn-grey colour; 3.5 inches long, 2.3 inches wide at cutting edge, 1 inch thick. Bradford Museum (11/64).
a) *CAGB* 9, 1964, 75 and Fig.
b) Bradford M.B. Museums Index.

283 Calderdale
Barkisland, Meg Dyke   SE 05021749
Square earthwork on eastern side of high spur, sides *c.* 53 yards long. Double rampart rising 6–7 feet above ditch bottom, latter being driven through solid rock in places. Northern angle originally rounded. North eastern side destroyed by quarrying, south eastern side by road construction. Uncertain age: it has been compared to other small sub rectangular enclosures, possibly used for stock control, as at Kirklees (291), although it may be a medieval vaccary.
a) Watson 1775, 48.
b) Petch 1924, 75 and Figs. 37–8.
c) Watson 1952, 48.
d) Challis & Harding 1975, 131.

284 Calderdale
Barkisland, Peat Pits   SE 050184
Stretches of mounds and ditches, one 100 yards long, another 30 yards in length.
a) Longbotham 1932, 163.

285 Calderdale
Barkisland, Ringstone Edge   SE 04431830
Alleged stone circle/ring work, *c.* 88 feet in diameter; mainly rubble bank. No trace of standing stones – said to have been removed in the 18th century. In 1907 partly destroyed on eastern and northern sides. Cinerary urn said to have been found prior to 1905. 1905 excavation found *c.* 20 feet in from the north eastern edge of the circle '5 separate interments', consisting of charred wood with apparently no bones. An urn was found south west of the centre of the circle, originally encased on 2 sides by upright stones with a flat stone on top, but at some time one of the supporting stones and the capstone had fallen and the cist was filled with earth. Urn *c.* 12 inches high, and was lying on its side. It had 'become softened' and was of 'rough and rude construction, consisting of clay mixed with small pebbles'.
a) Longbotham 1932, 167ff.
b) Watson 1952, 94.
c) Lunn 1966.
d) O.S. Records SE01NW12.

286 Calderdale
Barkisland, Ringstone Edge SE 04811871
Cluster of 7 possible grave mounds: small earth and stone mounds
0.3 to 4 m in diameter. One has 2 stones set in ground – remains of
retaining ring?
a) Watson 1952, 94.
b) O.S. Records SE01NW9.

287 Calderdale
Barkisland, Ringstone Edge Reservoir SE 050180
Unfinished Mesolithic tranchet flint axe (identified by Rankine)
found when water level of reservoir low in the summer of 1923.
$6\frac{5}{8}$ inches long, $2\frac{3}{4}$ inches wide at cutting edge, $1\frac{1}{2}$ inches wide at
butt; weight 1 lb 5 oz. Private possession; cast in Tolson
Memorial Museum, Huddersfield.
a) Petch 1924, 50, Fig. 20a.
b) Jackson 1936.
c) Watson 1952, 73.
d) Davies 1964.
e) O.S. Records SE01NW17.

288 Calderdale
Barkisland, Ringstone Edge Reservoir SE 047182
When water level low a number of stone circular pavings were
noted on the north west side. Hut circles?
a) Longbotham 1932, 160–1.

289 Calderdale
Brighouse, Hipperholme SE 128259 ?
Flat bronze axe of thin butted type found 1824; in good condition.
Tolson Memorial Museum, Huddersfield.
a) Manby 1965.
b) Varley 1977, 58.

290 Calderdale
Brighouse, Hoveringham Gravel Pit SE 165220
Late Bronze Age basal-looped, straight-based spearhead
(Wallington tradition) found at Cooper Bridge, 30 yards from the
north bank of the River Calder, 30 feet down during excavation of
sand and gravel in 1969. A short length of shaft had been
preserved and was held in position by a bronze pin (now lost).
Tolson Memorial Museum, Huddersfield (122.1.70).
a) *YAJ* 44, 1971, 191.

291 Calderdale
Brighouse, Kirklees Park SE 174217
Square or 5 sided enclosure, 2–3 acres in size, with bank and
external ditch. Originally thought to be Roman Fort (c.f. Oldfield
Hill, No. 377). For stock control? Iron Age/Medieval?
a) Roth 1906, 286.
b) Richmond 1924, 319.
c) Toomey 1966 and Fig.
d) Challis & Harding 1975, 50.
e) O.S. Records SE12SE3.

292 Calderdale
Brighouse, Rastrick SE 1422 ?
On an eminence, $\frac{1}{4}$ mile from River Calder, 'a big find of urns was
made in 1797 in a quarry. 20 urns measuring from 4 inches to 15
inches in diameter containing ashes and fragments of burnt human
bones . . . The large urns were 3 feet and the small ones $1\frac{1}{2}$ feet
below the surface, and they were surrounded by a black substance
supposed to be the remains of the fires in which the bodies were
burnt. Some of the urns were curiously ornamented, but most fell
to pieces before they could be got out of the earth. One of them
was inverted and the bones it contained were much better
preserved . . .'
a) *Leeds Mercury* Nov. 25th, 1797.
b) Roth 1906, 292–3.

293 Calderdale
Halifax (Fig. 13, i)
Food vessel, $6\frac{1}{4}$ inches high, $6\frac{2}{5}$ inches diameter at the rim and 3
inches at the base. One lug distinct; grey-buff, dark grey interior;
cord maggot and cord line decoration. No data as to provenance.
Bankfield Museum, Halifax AH 158 (on loan to Tolson Memorial
Museum, Huddersfield).
a) Roth 1906, Fig. 197.
b) Watson 1952, 86.
c) *WYAU* 4402.95 and Fig.

d) Tolson Memorial Museum Index.

294 Calderdale
Halifax, Haley Hill SE 1027 ?
Stone axe found near Haley Hill, 4 inches long, $2\frac{5}{8}$ inches wide at
cutting edge, butt broken; weight 8 oz. Later in Bankfield Museum,
Halifax (AH 635). (Same as 321?)
a) Watson 1952, 72.

295 Calderdale
Halifax, Holdsworth SE 082290
Possible remains of Neolithic settlement excavated: a structure
represented by two parallel ditches, 5 m apart, with inturned ends
separated by an entrance gap 1.25 m wide. The walls were of
vertical timbers set in the trenches and the spaces between probably
filled with stacked turf and/or split timbers. Flint waste and tools
also recovered. Possibly three stone axes had previously been
found in vicinity: a) highly polished example, $5\frac{1}{4}$ inches long, $1\frac{3}{4}$
inches wide at cutting edge, $1\frac{1}{2}$ inches wide at butt, found in 1892
in a field at Brigg Royd Farm, Holmfield (later in Bankfield
Museum, Halifax, AH 2009); b) another found below Windy Bank
Road (later in Bankfield Museum, Halifax, AH 494); c) highly
polished example, 5 inches long, found in clay field near Brigg
Royd.
a) Roth 1906, 299 and Fig. 206 (axe A).
b) Watson 1952, 70 (all 3 axes).
c) Gilks 1974, 7 (settlement).

296 Calderdale
Halifax, Holdsworth SE 082290
Bronze socketed axe, broken in antiquity: 8 cm long, 4.5 cm wide
at edge, butt 3.3 cm by 2 cm. Surface deeply pitted and covered
with thick green patina. Private possession.
a) *YAJ* 48, 1976, 2.

297 Calderdale
Halifax, Overgreen Royd SE 05172794
Iron Age (?) circular ditched enclosure, now consisting oa
superficial depression, barely discernible, with traces of a spread
outer bank. (c.f. 299).
a) O.S. Records SE02NE9.

298 Calderdale
Halifax Parish
2 socketed axes, no provenance. Bankfield Museum, Halifax
(A.9.3).
a) Watson 1952, 82.
b) Tolson Memorial Museum Index.

299 Calderdale
Halifax, Round Ring SE 05522941
Southern surviving angle of damaged sub rectangular enclosure;
probable Iron Age pastoral enclosure, remains consisting of a
superficial depression on high ground west of Mixenden. Compares
with other probable Iron Age enclosures nearby (eg 297).
a) O.S. Records SE02NE8.

300 Calderdale
Halifax, Skircoat SE 093236 ?
Middle Bronze Age wing flanged axe found in clay prior to 1775;
6 inches in length, weight 14 oz. Deposited in Bankfield Museum,
Halifax in 1832 (AH 21).
a) Watson 1775, 31.
b) Roth 1906, 296 and Fig. 199.
c) Petch 1924, 53 and Fig. 22.2.
d) Varley 1977.
e) O.S. Records SE02SE2.

301 Calderdale
Halifax, Skircoat, Heath SE 09372401 ?
3 urns found prior to 1775 'at the bottom of the walk leading to
the house called Heath in Skircoat'. They were 3 feet below the
surface, 3 feet apart and inverted; 2 were broken, the third
containing calcined bones and dust, was 8 inches high and 4 inches
diameter at the base. Lost.
a) Watson 1775, 61.
b) Watson 1952, 86.
c) Varley 1973.
d) O.S. Records SE02SE7.

302 Calderdale
Halifax, The Carrs SE 05542993
Small, single ditched, sub rectangular earthwork, an Iron Age (?)
pastoral enclosure, excavated by the Halifax Antiquarian Society.
Possible internal traverse. Badly mutilated by quarrying and water
courses.
a) O.S. Records SE02NE3.

303 Calderdale
Midgley, Castle Carr SE 021304 ?
Group of barrows illustrated 1842, but site not known now,
possibly destroyed in preparing reservoirs or may be under water.
a) Roth 1906, 305–6 and Fig. 219.
b) *WYAU* 4403.201432.

304 Calderdale
Midgley, Greave House SE 039258
2 urns found 1877 near 'the Roman Road' close to Greave House;
presented to Bankfield Museum, Halifax.
a) Roth 1906, 296.

305 Calderdale
Midgley, Han Royd SE 023267
Circular earthwork at *c.* 825 feet O.D.
a) Watson 1952, 49.
b) Challis & Harding 1975.

306 Calderdale
Midgley, Miller's Grave SE 01922839
Possible remains of cairn. Circular mound of loose stones base of
which is earth covered, 18 m diameter, 1.5 m high. Centre
mutilated; no finds.
a) Roth 1906, 286.
b) O.S. Records SE02NW5.

307 Calderdale
Mixenden SE 0628 ?
Large urn found at Mixenden Church which 'contained the
remains of more than one human body'; 20 inches high, 14 inches
diameter with narrow base. Urn 'placed mouth downwards on a
slab of stone and the space around it was filled with sand'.
a) Davis 1881.

308 Calderdale
Mixenden Moor SE 05862975 ?
'Hoard' found *c.* 1776 in peat diggings: comprised flanged bronze
axe/palstave, polished axe of 'black stone', battle-axe/axe-hammer
'of green pebble speckled with white', 3 barbed-and-tanged
arrowheads and 'a hollow gouge or scoop of hard grey stone'.
Contents suggest a homesteader's possessions. Lost.
a) Roth 1906, 302–4 and Figs. 212–16.
b) Petch 1924, 50.
c) Varley 1977.

309 Calderdale
Ovenden, Mount Zion SE 06792974
Collared urn discovered in February 1877 in the grounds of Mount
Zion Chapel, 2 feet below the surface. A slab of stone was found
and beneath it a square cist formed of 4 upright stones containing
the urn, inverted and surrounded by gravel. The vessel is 19 inches
high, 13 inches diameter at mouth and 4 inches at base; its 'neck is
ornamented with dots', and it contained the broken, cremated
bones of an adult female. Bankfield Museum, Halifax (AH 54)
(now on loan to Tolson Memorial Museum, Huddersfield).
a) Roth 1906, 293–4 and Fig. 193.
b) Watson 1952, 87.
c) Varley 1968.
d) O.S. Records SE02NE4.

310 Calderdale
Rishworth, Booth Dean SE 0216 ?
Stone axe recorded: 10½ inches long, 3¼ inches wide at cutting
edge, weight 3 lbs 14 oz.
a) Petch 1924, 50.
b) Watson 1952, 70.
c) O.S. Records SE01NW7.

311 Calderdale
Rishworth, Booth Moor SE 0116 ?
Flanged bronze axe with stop ridge (Arreton tradition), 5 inches

long, 2½ inches wide, found high on Booth Moor 'above (ie north
west of) the Darby Bar and Platt's Shooting Box'. Private
possession; cast in Rochdale Museum.
a) Wrigley 1911, 19–20 and Plate C.
b) Kendall & Roth 1912.
c) Petch 1924, 53 and Fig. 22.
d) Watson 1952, 82.
e) Manby 1964.
f) Varley 1977.

312 Calderdale
Rishworth, Castle Dean SE 004161 ?
Thin butted flint axe, polished at cutting edge only, found in
August 1921; 4¾ inches long, 1½ inches wide at cutting edge,
weight 2¾ oz. Private possession.
a) *YAJ* 26, 1921, 304–5.
b) Petch 1924, 50 and Fig. 20a.
c) Watson 1952, 70.
d) O.S. Records SE01NW15.

313 Calderdale
Rishworth, Castle Dean SE 004161 ?
Bronze Age jet stud or dress toggle found March 1914 by H. P.
Kendall. ⅞ inch diameter; polished on top and bottom faces, tool
marks in the groove. Bankfield Museum, Halifax (on loan to
Tolson Memorial Museum, Huddersfield). A grey pottery stud
also found on a different occasion: ¾ inch diameter, ⅜ inch thick.
Tolson Memorial Museum, Huddersfield (34.41.64).
a) Priestley 1936 (jet stud).
b) Tolson Memorial Museum Index (both finds).

314 Calderdale
Rishworth, Cat Hill SD 998172
Polished axe of non ophitic quartz dolerite found *c.* 1890, exact
provenance unknown. 14.7 cm long, 6.7 cm wide at cutting edge,
3.1 cm wide at butt; weight 1 lb 6 oz. Originally deposited in
Bankfield Museum; later thought to be lost, but now found in
material on loan to Tolson Memorial Museum, Huddersfield
(AH 2597).
a) Watson 1952, 71.
b) Tolson Memorial Museum Index.

315 Calderdale
Rishworth, Dog Hill SE 003171 ?
2 Bronze Age flint knives (food vessel period?): one described in
1912 as 'dark, translucent flint, 56 mm long, 22 mm wide, 3 mm
thick; very fine work'; other described 1963 as 'plano-convex
knife of brown flint picked up on peat bank 5 inches above
mineral soil'. Tolson Memorial Museum, Huddersfield.
a) Kendall & Roth 1912, Fig. 34.
b) *YAJ* 41, 1963, 173.

316 Calderdale
Rishworth, Flint Hill SD 989171
Shale armlet found on south west side of hill at 1,375 feet O.D. in
1929: in 4 pieces in clayey subsoil under peat. 73 mm internal
diameter, 6.5–8 mm thick, 95 mm external diameter. Kimmeridge
shale, perfectly circular and like early Iron Age type found at
Glastonbury. (Cf. also No. 169.) Rochdale Museum.
a) Price 1929–31.
b) Jackson 1929–31, Fig. 1.

317 Calderdale
Rishworth Moor SE 0017 ?
Spindle whorl found 1912; 37 mm diameter, made from 'hard,
local shale'.
a) Kendall & Roth 1912, Fig. 43.
b) Petch 1924, 37.

318 Calderdale
Rishworth Moor SE 0017 ?
Stone axe-hammer of medium grained sandstone with hour glass
perforation; 17.5 cm long, 7.8 cm wide, 6.3 cm thick. Bankfield
Museum, Halifax (AH 2011) (on loan to Tolson Memorial
Museum, Huddersfield).
a) Kendall & Roth 1912.
b) Tolson Memorial Museum Index.

319 Calderdale
Rishworth Moor SE 0017 ?

Stone axe 'found at site of barrow'; $2\frac{7}{8}$ inches long, $2\frac{1}{4}$ inches wide at cutting edge, $2\frac{5}{8}$ inches wide at butt; weight $4\frac{1}{4}$ oz.
a) Petch 1924, 50.
b) Watson 1952, 73.

319a Calderdale
Rishworth, Moselden   SE 0316 ?
Flake of brown flint with polished facets: probably struck from a polished flint axe. Tolson Memorial Museum, Huddersfield (34.39.64).
a) Tolson Memorial Museum Index.

320 Calderdale
Rishworth, Thief Clough   SD 98971666
Late Bronze Age (?) bronze knife, tanged with one rivet hole, 2.8 inches long. Pitted green and brown; slight mid rib. A surface find *c.* 1940. Tolson Memorial Museum, Huddersfield (A.111.57).
a) Tolson Memorial Museum Index.
b) O.S. Records SD91NE12.

321 Calderdale
Shelf, Green Lane Hall   SE 128284
Stone axe found in 1908. (Same as 294?)
a) *CAGB* 6, 1961, 53.

322 Calderdale
Shelf, Upper Westercroft (Fig. 35)   SE 117273
Hoard of bronze implements found in quarry in 1856, 2 feet down. Contents: looped palstave (lost); 4 transitional palstaves; looped palstave; 'late' palstave (unfinished); basal-looped spearhead, straight based type; point of large leaf-shaped spearhead blade; broken spearhead socket; side-looped spearhead (lost). Tin bronze, ie Wallington tradition, though late palstave shows Wilburton influence. May be a trader's deposit because of the inclusion of an unfinished palstave. The implements are much decayed due to soil conditions. Tolson Memorial Museum, Huddersfield (on loan from Bankfield Museum, Halifax, AH 2270–9).
a) Roth 1906, 297 and Figs. 201–4.
b) Burgess 1968, Fig. 6.
c) Varley 1977.
d) Tolson Memorial Museum Index.

323 Calderdale
Sowerby   SE 0423 ?
Looped palstave (Wallington tradition) found in early 19th century; $5\frac{1}{2}$ inches long. Presented in 1833 to Halifax Museum.
a) Roth 1906, 296 and Fig. 200.
b) Petch 1924, 53 and Fig. 22.3.
c) Watson 1952, 31.
d) Burgess 1968.
e) Varley 1977.
f) O.S. Records SE02SW1.

324 Calderdale
Sowerby Bridge, Crow Wood   SE 068242
Polished stone axe with faceted oval section found last century; 21.2 cm long, 7.5 cm wide at cutting edge, 7.4 cm wide at butt. Surface has weathered dull white to buff-grey, and there are numerous scars and areas of abrasion on both sides of blade. Deposited in Bankfield Museum, Halifax (AH 651) and later thought to be lost, but now in material on loan to Tolson Memorial Museum, Huddersfield.
a) Watson 1952, 71.
b) *YAJ* 51, 1979, 3.
c) Tolson Memorial Museum Index.

325 Calderdale
Stansfield Moor   SD 9228 ?
2 bronze harness rings (Iron Age). Tolson Memorial Museum, Huddersfield.

326 Calderdale
Todmorden   SD 9324 ?
Half of a perforated hammer head reported.
a) Kendall & Roth 1912.

327 Calderdale
Todmorden, Blackheath (Fig. 36)   SD 94352545
Embanked circle 100 feet in diameter at 940 feet O.D. excavated in July 1898. Bank *c.* 3 feet wide contained 'large stones set at more

or less regular intervals with charcoal near all of them and one of them blackened as if by fire'. A central urn was surrounded 2 feet away 'by a ring of deposits, 2 having urns and the others either having no urn or showing signs only of disintegrated pottery'. *c.* 10 feet from the centre was another 'series of deposits radially arranged, but all in the eastern half of the circle'. Apart from the urn found in the bank in the north western part of the circle, all the pottery finds occurred in the eastern half. An extensive area of charcoal, 1–2 inches thick, occurred north of centre, and the excavator considered that the cremations had been carried out here. 2 deep pits occurred *c.* 16 feet from the centre, 1 in the north eastern quadrant, the other in the south eastern, and it was thought that the clay for the urns was dug from these, the vessels being tempered with pounded sandstone grit of which a great quantity was found in the north western part of the circle. There was a 'curiously baked surface' near the pit in the south eastern section, and there were 3 other areas where the floor was 'hard baked and red, with pieces of charcoal amongst the general red', one such area in the western part having a floor 'looking like disintegrated pottery closely trodden together'. Just inside the bank at the cardinal points were 4 'cairns' – probably originally in the form of semi-circles: the one to the south contained a great deal of charcoal within the semi-circle, the others had around them 'partly banked clay or disintegrated pottery'. The excavator considered these to represent the 'kilns' where the pottery had been fired. An incomplete ring of stones was found in the south western quadrant. The urns were 'not deeply placed, some only 6 inches from the surface, none deeper than 18–24 inches, and all of them without exception were set in the ground upright on their bases'. A group of the urns had flat stones set on edge around them, as if to 'set them out from the others'.
Finds: 1) Central urn, 11 inches high, 8 inches diameter at rim, collar $3\frac{1}{4}$ inches deep ornamented by impressed cord; body plain. Very fine texture and well baked. Contained bones but no charcoal, and pygmy vessel $4\frac{1}{4}$ inches in diameter at maximum, mouth 3 inches wide, 3 inches high, cord ornamentation all over and pierced by 2 holes 1 inch apart near base. Inside pygmy vessel were bronze knife/dagger 3 inches long, a bronze pin $1\frac{3}{4}$ inches long, and a bone pin (minus point) $5\frac{1}{2}$ inches long. 2) Very coarse urn, $8\frac{1}{2}$ inches high, ornamented all over with 'irregularly placed punctures'. Contained charcoal and small fragments of bone. 3) Pygmy vessel, coarser and thicker than example in Urn 1, ornamented by 9 irregular rows of impressed cord; almost the same diameter from top to bottom and pierced by 2 holes $1\frac{1}{4}$ inches apart. 4) 'Rudely made urn' 8 inches high, 7 inches wide, decorated by herring bone cord ornamentation. Contained charcoal and small fragments of bone. 5) Well proportioned urn, 12 inches high, $9\frac{1}{4}$ inches diameter at mouth and $4\frac{1}{2}$ inches at base, collar 4 inches deep. Collar decorated by 'upright rows of punctures'. Contained bones of adult male. Around this urn were fragments of a possible 'covering vessel inverted over it'. 6) Urn with covering vessel (latter broken by spade), containing pygmy vessel 'lying obliquely within'. Urn 10 inches high, 8 inches diameter at mouth and $3\frac{1}{2}$ inches at base, collar 3 inches deep. No ornamentation, pot being well baked and bright red in colour. Covering vessel 'may have been a food vessel with bulging sides and different outline from the urn', and was ornamented by incised lines (Fig. 15, ii). Pygmy vessel 'insufficiently baked and began to crumble on exposure'. It contained dry, grey powder and had a double puncture at the base, the holes being 1 inch apart. It rested on bones which filled $\frac{2}{3}$ of the urn and were those of an adult female. Among the bones were 4 segmented faience beads, all with 8 segments, 3 spherical beads ornamented with grooves, some large amber beads and 9 beads of jet or shale, 2 bone pins, flint flakes and a leaf-shaped arrowhead. 7) Urn 10 inches high, $7\frac{1}{4}$ inches diameter at mouth and $3\frac{1}{2}$ inches at base, ornamented on collar and body by comb decoration. Contained bones and fragments of a bone pin (Fig. 15, ii). 8) Pygmy vessel, $2\frac{3}{4}$ inches high, 4 inches diameter at maximum, 3 inches diameter at mouth, with 2 small perforations at base, $\frac{1}{2}$ inch apart. Incised decoration. 9) Urn in bank on north west, possibly in a cist. It contained charcoal and small pieces of bone and 2 knife like flints. 10) Base of urn found in bank at southern point of circle. Other decomposed urns were found and some cremations deposited in circular holes without a vessel. One of the decomposed urns contained a scraper $1\frac{1}{2}$ inches long. Other finds included a whetstone, many flint flakes, cores, chippings, several flint scrapers and knife-like blades, and many chert fragments, 3 polishers. Finds in Todmorden Library.
a) Full report by J. L. Russell in Roth 1906, 307–22 and Figs. 220–9.

b) Law 1898.
c) Fishwick 1903, Figs. 1–4 (urn and 'incense cups').
d) Watson 1952, 89–92.
e) Stone & Thomas 1956, 80 (identification of beads in Urn 6).

328 Calderdale
Todmorden, Ramsden Clough   SD 915213
Polished stone axe found under 4 feet of peat on clay bed in reservoir works in 1880s; oval section, flat sides, 9.1 inches long, 3 inches wide at cutting edge, 1.6 inches wide at butt, 1.7 inches thick; weight 2 lbs 7½ oz. Group VI. Bacup Museum.
a) March 1887.
b) Manby 1963.
c) O.S. Records SD92SW5.

329 Calderdale
Wadsworth, Cockhill I   SD 010275
In May 1897 burials discovered at quarry when pieces of urns rolled down. Bones were found in a grave which was *c.* 6 feet long, 14–18 inches wide and *c.* 2 feet deep; it was aligned north–south and contained much charcoal. 'In the ends of the grave were about 6 inches of charred wood and bones mixed together at the bottom'. Flints were also found and 'the larger half of a small earthenware vessel' (ie urn fragments). The flints included a knife, 51 mm long, 23 mm wide and 7 mm thick: very worn.
a) Roth 1906, 306.
b) Kendall & Roth 1912, Fig. 33 (knife).

330 Calderdale
Wadsworth, Cockhill II   SD 01332739
Remains of barrow, 1.160 feet O.D.: circular bank of earth and stone, 1–2 feet high, *c.* 132 feet diameter, with slight indications of inner ditch on north west side. Central mound – of no significance (partly excavated in 1930s by Watson who discovered no evidence that it was a burial mound, though half a quern was found). 'Excavation' of the feature in the 19th century by Wilkinson resulted in the discovery of parts of a broken urn which contained the cremated remains of 2 persons (adult and child), and an 'incense cup which bore traces of ornamentation' (also in a fragmentary condition). Several flint arrowheads and scrapers were found. At one time 2 more circular banks existed in the vicinity but these were destroyed by quarrying. A short distance away a number of small mounds were also reported, *c.* 15 feet in diameter, and 18 inches high in the centre, 'which appeared to have been staked around'. No evidence of these exists at the present day (due to quarrying activities).
a) Wilkinson 1897.
b) Wilkinson 1903.
c) Roth 1906, 306.
d) Watson 1952.
e) O.S. Records SE02NW6.

331 Calderdale
Wadsworth, New Laithe   SD 96253153
Hut circle 35 feet wide with kerbed rubble walls.
a) Challis & Harding 1975, 44.
b) O.S. Records SD93SE5.
c) *WYAU* 3493.612515.

332 Calderdale
Wainstalls, Robin Hood's Penny Stone   SE 04642874
Said to have been surrounded by a stone circle which was broken up for building purposes. Nothing survives.
a) Crabtree 1836, 28.
b) O.S. Records SE02NW1.

333 Calderdale
Wainstalls, Robin Hood's Penny Stone   SE 04642874
Early Bronze Age battle-axe found near Robin Hood's Penny Stone 1872; 25 cm in length, 10 cm wide at rounded top, 5 cm thick. Made from fine grained sandstone; the cutting edge when viewed from the side is convex, and there is a cylindrical perforation 4 cm in diameter 5 cm from the top of the implement. Deposited in Bankfield Museum, Halifax; thought lost, but recently found in Bankfield material on loan to Tolson Memorial Museum, Huddersfield.
a) Roth 1906, 302 and Fig. 211.
b) Watson 1952, 76.
c) *YAJ* 51, 1979, 3.
d) O.S. Records SE02NW12.

334 Calderdale
Wainstalls, Sleepy Lowe   SE 03612936
Modern cairn possibly overlying an earlier one. A barrow 'near Sleepy Law was opened by Rev. John Watson: covered with thin pieces of shale laid regularly like the tiles of a roof and the hollow beneath contained nothing but charcoal and the burnt remains of a body'.
a) Davis 1881.
b) O.S. Records SE02NW9.

335 Calderdale
Walsden   SD 9322 ?
Early Bronze Age axe-hammer, 8½ inches long, 2⅝ inches thick. Deposited in Bankfield Museum, Halifax.
a) Roth 1906, 302.
b) Watson 1952, 76.

336 Calderdale
Walshaw Dean   SD 96553358
Stone circle discovered 1902 during reservoir construction (evidence now submerged). '10 irregular stones of local rock, varying considerably in size, one 1.9 m long standing 76 cm above the clay when the peat was removed. The circle is 11 m in diameter. Inside the circle is a rough curved wall, 3.7 m in diameter, whose presence may be fortuitous'.
a) *HAS* 1902.
b) Roth 1906, 304–5 and Figs. 217 and 218.
c) Watson 1952, 89.
d) O.S. Records SD93SE4.

337 Calderdale
Warley, Hollins   SE 04742587
Greenstone axe found in digging foundations of a barn; 4 inches long and between 1–1⅝ inches wide. Lost.
a) Roth 1906, 298.
b) Petch 1924, 50.
c) O.S. Records SE02NW2.

338 Calderdale
Warley, Tower Hill (Fig. 13, iii)   SE 05472604
Several urns with cremations and a pygmy vessel recorded in 1848: a) urn half embedded in soil, 13–14 inches high, containing cremation; b) a few yards away, another urn containing bones and ashes but very decomposed; c) nearby, another urn 7 inches high, 6⅛ inches diameter at rim and 3⅝ inches at base, contained bones and ashes accompanied by a pygmy vessel, and these contents were 'protected by a lid'; the fabric of the urn is reddish-brown (outside) with darker grey tones on the collar and body: collar decorated with filled triangles of cord impressions, neck covered with acute lattice striations produced by a sharp pointed instrument and bordered on shoulder by a series of shallow pits produced by the rounded end of a stick; d) tripartite collared urn, 9⅞ inches high, 6⅞ inches diameter at rim and 4⅛ inches at base; fabric is hard buff-brown with darker brown tones; collar is decorated with herring bone motif, while neck is covered with lattice striations, bordered on the shoulder by a series of shallow pits produced by the rounded end of a stick. Fragments of other urns and cremations were also found. Urn C is comparable with the collared urn found in association with food vessels at Harland Edge (Riley 1966). Urns C and D, together with fragment of pygmy vessel at Tolson Memorial Museum, Huddersfield (on loan from Bankfield Museum, Halifax, AH 146–7).
a) Roth 1906, 294–6 and Figs. 195–6.
b) Watson 1952, 87.
c) Gilks 1968.
d) Gilks 1973.
e) Tolson Memorial Museum Index.
f) O.S. Records SE02NE10.

339 Calderdale
Widdop   SD 93153260
Battered flint axe found (part of Mesolithic tranchet axe?). Private possession.
a) *WYAU* 3493.321650.

340 Craven
Cowling Parish
Axe-hammer of fine grained, dark-grey sandstone with large hour glass perforation and hollow from perforation towards the cutting edge. 23 cm long, 10 cm wide, 7.5 cm thick; 2.5 cm minimum

diameter of perforation; weight 7 lbs. Bradford M.B. Museums (213.33).
a) Bradford M.B. Museums Index.

341 Craven

Ickornshaw Moor   SD 971394
Mesolithic tranchet axe found near summit in 1936 on Airedale side of watershed. Dull, cherty-looking flint with light brown patina; 6.5 inches long, 2.2 inches wide, 1.1 inches thick. Flat dressing on ventral surface is said to compare with Thames axes. Bradford M.B. Museums (121.68).
a) Davies 1964, Fig. 2.

342 Craven

Ickornshaw Moor   SD 9640 ?
Flat bronze axe (Migdale) found 1912. Keighley Museum; cast in Tolson Memorial Museum, Huddersfield.
a) Raistrick 1929, 359.
b) Manby 1964.
c) Davey & Forster 1975, Fig. 11.
d) Bradford M.B. Museums Index.

343 Kirklees

Almondbury, Castle Hill   SE 15251405
Butt of polished stone axe found in 1939 during excavations of hill fort; 3¾ inches long, volcanic ash or silicified tuff. Tolson Memorial Museum, Huddersfield (20.8.74).
a) Keen & Radley 1971.
b) Tolson Memorial Museum Index.

344 Kirklees

Almondbury, Castle Hill (Fig. 20)   SE 152140
8 acre hill fort on isolated plateau site at 800 feet O.D. with magnificent views over the surrounding countryside. Almost all the earthworks now visible are of the twelfth century A.D., but they preserve the lines of earlier ramparts. Excavated 1936–9 (mainly defences) with further excavations 1969–70 and 1972 in order to clarify some of the problems and to obtain material for C14 dating. Before this dating evidence was available, the fort was interpreted as a defence of the first centuries B.C. and A.D., destroyed by the Romans. The earthworks are now known to be sited on a Neolithic occupation floor, dated to just before 2,000 b.c. The date of the first establishment of the fort and the sequence of rebuilding and enlargement are still being debated. Phase I – simple univallate enclosure occupying the southern half of the plateau. This subsequently fell into decay and a land surface developed over the ruins, stone kerbed huts 25 feet in diameter being built. Phase II – univallate fort, roughly same site as Phase I. Phase III – bivallate fort enclosing whole of plateau, ie twice area of original. This phase dated to 555 ± 100 b.c. (I 4542). Phase IV – multivallate structure enclosing parts of lower slopes. Rampart construction involved different techniques at different times, including slab revetted forms with clay core laid between timber and turf rafts, stone revetted ramparts with timber laced core, and ramparts with dump construction (these being the final forms). Edge set slab rampart is paralleled by inner rampart at Portfield (155) where pottery indicates a Late Bronze Age date. Fort finally destroyed by fire (much evidence of vitrification in ramparts), most likely around 500 B.C., and the site was abandoned. Substantial extension or annexe incorporated in final fort with connecting hollow way.
a) Varley 1948, 46ff.
b) Challis & Harding 1975, 116–21.
c) Varley 1976.
d) O.S. Records SE11SE1.

345 Kirklees

Batley   SE 2276024768
Neolithic axe head found in garden at Horner Crescent, Carlinghow Lane, 1 foot down, in March 1960. Felsite?
a) Archaeological Index, Huddersfield Library.

346 Kirklees

Cleckheaton   SE 1825 ?
Polished stone axe reported, exact provenance not known. Group XVIII.
a) Tolson Memorial Museum Index.

347 Kirklees

Denby, Castle Hill   SE 20370695

Earthwork with L-shaped rampart, rounded angles and ditch 10–12 feet wide – remains of originally square enclosure. Once thought to have originated as a medieval vaccary, but recent finds suggest it began as a Late Neolithic/Early Bronze Age enclosure (leaf-shaped arrowheads, scrapers, axe fragments etc. found in early 1970s), later overlain by small Iron Age farmstead. The cutting edge and part of the waist of a re-chipped axe of grey-green andesitic tuff (Group VI), and a butt fragment of a larger axe with facetted sides of fine grained lamprophyre (Group XV) were ploughed up in the interior in 1970–1. Tolson Memorial Museum, Huddersfield (11.1.71 and 10.1.71 respectively).
a) Petch 1924, 72 and Figs. 34 and 35.
b) *YAJ* 44, 1972, 217.
c) Gilks 1974.

348 Kirklees

Denby, Cumberworth, Piper Well   SE 2209 ?
Earthwork?
a) Petch 1924, 75–6.

349 Kirklees

Denby, High Flatts   SE 212074
Polished stone axe found 1854: wedge shaped, 6¾ inches long, 3¼ inches wide at cutting edge tapering to 2inches at the butt end, 1¾ inches thick; weight 2 lbs 9 oz. Morehouse mentioned another 'large British weapon' 1 mile to the west.
a) Morehouse 1861, 3 and 244 and Fig.
b) Petch 1924, 50.
c) Watson 1952, 72.
d) O.S. Records SE20NW1.

350 Kirklees

Farnley Tyas   SE 17291350
Polished stone axe ploughed up in 1966 at Beech Farm, Field Lane; rounded sides, 7¾ inches long, 3 inches wide at cutting edge, 2 inches wide at butt; weight 2 lbs 3 oz. Group VII. Tolson Memorial Museum, Huddersfield (23.1.66).
a) Earnshaw 1966.
b) Tolson Memorial Museum Index.
c) O.S. Records SE11SE12.

351 Kirklees

Featherbed Hill
Stone axe reported.
a) Petch 1924, 50.

352 Kirklees

Gomersal, Birkenshaw   SE 21112836
Neolithic porcellanite axehead found in November 1963 during excavation of supposed Roman road, 2 feet below the surface. Batley Museum.
a) *YAJ* 41, 1969, 165.
b) *WYAU* 4422.181316.
c) O.S. Records SE22NW8.

353 Kirklees

Heckmondwike, Norristhorpe   SE 20952262
Polished stone axe ploughed up in the autumn of 1907. Borrowdale andesitic ash; 4¼ inches long, 2 inches wide at cutting edge, 1 inch wide at butt, 1¼ inches thick. Lost.
a) *YAJ* 20, 1909, 104.
b) Petch 1924, 46.
c) Watson 1952, 73.

354 Kirklees

Holmfirth, Cartworth Moor   SE 1305
Bronze spearhead with small side loops found 1811 in peat digging. 5.6 inches long with dark green patina; socket and loops broken. Tolson Memorial Museum, Huddersfield (60.13.47).
a) Morehouse 1861, 8–9 and Fig.
b) Radley 1967.
c) Tolson Memorial Museum Index.
d) O.S. Records SE10NW2.

355 Kirklees

Holmfirth, Digley   SE 105061 ?
Earthwork, oval in shape.
a) Archaeological Index, Huddersfield Library.

356 Kirklees
Holmfirth, Hepworth, Pikelow   SE 178072
Stone axe found 1830; 7 inches long, 3 inches wide at cutting edge;
weight 2 lbs 10 oz.
a) Morehouse 1861, 3.
b) Petch 1924, 50.
c) Watson 1952, 73.

357 Kirklees
Holmfirth, Holme Moss   SE 0904 ?
Early Bronze Age stone macehead found October 1916. Bradford
Museum (L 71/47).
a) *CAGB* 4, 1959, 54.
b) O.S. Records SE00SE2.

358 Kirklees
Holmfirth, New Mill, Hornhill   SE 17300862
Butt fragment of polished greenstone axe, rounded sides, 5⅛ inches
long. Tolson Memorial Museum, Huddersfield (A.22.58).

359 Kirklees
Holmfirth, Ramsden Clough   SE 119051
Greenish-grey mottled stone axe (altered dolerite, Group XIII)
found on eastern side of Riding Wood Reservoir in 1966; 10 cm
long, 7 cm wide at cutting edge, 3 cm thick. Tolson Memorial
Museum, Huddersfield (91.1.67).
a) *YAJ* 41, 1969, 239.
b) Tolson Memorial Museum Index.

360 Kirklees
Holmfirth, Wooldale   SE 154102
Fragment of Neolithic polished axe (Group VI?). Tolson Memorial
Museum, Huddersfield (1950.0).
a) *YAJ* 52, 1980, 181.
b) Tolson Memorial Museum Index.

361 Kirklees
Honley   SE 134115
Hoard of Early Iron Age and Roman objects and coins contained
within hollow bone, including bronze harness rings, Roman coins,
brooch etc. Probably represents personal wealth of a Brigantian
tribesman, hidden soon after A.D. 73. The coins are foreign to the
locality. Tolson Memorial Museum, Huddersfield.
a) Toomey 1966.
b) *WYAU* 4412.328411.

362 Kirklees
Honley, Hagg Wood   SE 14931026
Group of 7 cairns with adjacent ring bank. Excavation by
Huddersfield and District Archaeological Society of some of the
cairns produced hardly any datable material, although one cairn
did reveal features typical of some Bronze Age barrows. Beneath
the cairn were found the remains of a hut or shelter with a
succession of small hearths and a group of stone packed postholes.
a) Lunn 1963.
b) Lunn 1966.
c) *YAJ* 42, 1970, 242.
d) *WYAU* 4412.4093; 4412.4055; 4412.409436.

363 Kirklees
Honley, Slate Pits Wood   SE 116107
11 cairns and partly destroyed ring bank 52 feet in diameter
surveyed in 1963 by Huddersfield and District Archaeological
Society.
a) Lunn 1966.

364 Kirklees
Honley Wood   SE 12431204
Extensive earthworks/cairn complex, located by Huddersfield and
District Archaeological Society.
a) *Huddersfield Dist. Archaeol. Soc. Bull.* 1963, 2.
b) *WYAU* 4412.1125.

365 Kirklees
Huddersfield, Crosland Moor   SE 12351408 ?
Earthworks almost obliterated in 1926, described in 1775 as
comprising 'a couple of remains at a very short distance, one 77
yards by 64 yards, the other 98 yards by 87 yards. The vallum of
the latter is 6 yards and about 1 foot wide. The smaller has the
appearance of square angles, the larger is rounded at the corners.

3 ancient millstones were found in the larger, each 1 foot in
diameter, and 11 hollow places, 2–3 yards long apiece and ¾ of a
yard deep.' Now only a slight depression and a slight oval mound
remains; aerial photographs show an obvious cropmark – a
curvilinear enclosure.
a) Watson 1775, 275.
b) Petch 1924, 72.
c) O.S. Records SE11SW5.

366 Kirklees
Huddersfield, Dalton   SE 1727316965
Stone axe with cutting edge badly fractured found in 1957 in black
subsoil above yellow clay in the garden of 6 Windsor Drive,
Dalton. Group VI; oval section, rounded sides, butt only survives,
3.8 inches long, original length *c.* 5 inches. Tolson Memorial
Museum, Huddersfield (33.1.57).
a) *CAGB* 3, 1958, 4 and Fig.
b) Keen & Radley 1971.
c) O.S. Records SE11NE14.

367 Kirklees
Huddersfield, Dalton   SE 1716 ?
Bronze axe reported. No further information.
a) Cowling 1946, 65.
b) *WYAU* 4411.7655.

368 Kirklees
Huddersfield, Damside
Stone axe reported.
a) *Huddersfield Examiner* June 28th, 1887.
b) Watson 1952, 71.

369 Kirklees
Huddersfield, Fixby Park   SE 13231987
Neolithic flint axe found 1931.
a) Archaeological Index, Huddersfield Library.

370 Kirklees
Huddersfield, Moldgreen   SE 160164
Part polished stone axe with oval section and flat sides found in
Birkhouse Lane, 3½ inches long, 1⅓ inches wide at cutting edge;
weight 3¾ oz. Tolson Memorial Museum, Huddersfield (A.20.58).
a) Petch 1924, 50.
b) Watson 1952, 72.
c) Manby 1964.

371 Kirklees
Kirkburton   SE 19951279
Early Bronze Age axe-hammer/battle-axe of fine micaceous
sandstone, twice pierced (both hour glass perforations), found in
garden of Dene House, Tanshaw Road, in a rock crevice. Tolson
Memorial Museum, Huddersfield (A.24.58).
a) Petch 1924, 47 and Fig. 21.
b) Watson 1952, 76.
c) Keen & Radley 1971.
d) O.S. Records SE11SE6.

372 Kirklees
Marsden, Cupwith Hill   SE 032141 ?
Flint axe, 4½ inches long; weight 5 oz. (Possibly the same as 375?)
a) Petch 1924, 50.
b) Watson 1952, 71.

373 Kirklees
Marsden, March Hill   SE 007130
Flint knife, 49 mm long, 16 mm wide, 3 mm thick; dark flint,
cutting edges very worn. Also a 'large tool' of grey flint, 99 mm
long, 36 mm wide, 16 mm thick; much worn.
a) Kendall & Roth 1912, Figs. 36 and 40.

374 Kirklees
Marsden, Pule Hill   SE 03221036
4 Bronze Age food vessels (including 1 footed vessel) and a pygmy
vessel were found by G. Marsden in 1896 on the summit of the hill,
c. 1,400 feet O.D. The vessels were all lying on their sides in small,
rock cut cavities and a barbed-and-tanged arrowhead accompanied
one of the burials; also found were scrapers, a stone disc, flakes
and microliths (not all contemporary with the burials). Excavation
in 1899 found no signs of a barrow (hilltop possibly denuded? or a
flat cemetery?), but 3 cavities in the rock were discovered, 3 feet

long, 2 feet wide, and at the bottom were bones, charcoal and flints. 4 of the vessels have survived: a) footed food vessel, 3.6 inches high, 6.9 inches diameter at the rim, hard gritty buff ware with reddish-grey tone; maggot cord line decoration; one perforated lug remaining; b) type 2 food vessel, 3.8 inches high, 4.6 inches diameter at the rim and 2.4 inches at the base; gritty buff ware with reddish tone and grey patches; cord maggot impressions; c) type 1a food vessel, 5.5 inches high, 5.2 inches diameter at the rim; smooth grey buff to brown; fine incised decoration; 2 oppositely placed lugs; d) pygmy vessel, 3.2 inches high, 2.2 inches diameter at the rim, 3.5 inches at the base; hard reddish buff to grey; scaled exterior; incised and stick end decoration; 2 perforations in base, 1½ inches apart. Tolson Memorial Museum, Huddersfield (A.13.58–A.16.58).

a) Clark 1902, 38–42.
b) Wrigley 1911, 51–6 and Plate L.
c) Petch 1924, 56–9 and Figs. 24 and 25.
d) Watson 1952, 95–7.
e) Manby 1969.

375 Kirklees
Marsden, Stonefolds Quarry   SE 04351231
Flint axe reported. (NB: 'A Celtic battle axe of flint was found some years ago on the moor above Stonefolds' (Sykes 1906, 15). Same as above, and possibly 372?).
a) Jackson 1936.
b) Archaeological Index, Huddersfield Library.

376 Kirklees
Meltham Moor   SE 0807 ?
Polished flint axe found in 1846 'c. 300 yards from the boundary between Holme and Netherthong', ie on Little Moss? Brown banded flint, 5½ inches long, 2 inches wide at the cutting edge and 1 inch at the butt. Tolson Memorial Museum, Huddersfield (A.21.58).
a) Morehouse 1861, 6 and Fig.
b) Petch 1924, 50.
c) Watson 1952, 72.
d) Tolson Memorial Museum Index.
e) O.S. Records SE00NE2.

377 Kirklees
Meltham, Oldfield Hill   SE 08731010
1 acre, D shaped enclosure at c. 900 feet O.D. Originally thought to be a Roman fort, it was first 'excavated' by A. Wrigley in 1909 with indeterminate results. Richmond sectioned the banks and examined the entrance in 1923. Most recent excavations in 1970s. Rampart of rubble and earth 7 feet wide faced with drystone walling; original height c. 10 feet; V shaped rock cut ditch, 5½ feet deep and 6 feet wide, and a counterscarp bank similar to inner rampart with drystone revetment surviving to 4 courses. North east entrance had double timber gateway. Pre rampart palisade trench on at least 2 sides of the enclosure with vertical posts 2 feet apart. Finds include 2 stone discs, rough out beehive quern, iron slag and very small fragments of pottery. Site dated to Iron Age because of lack of Roman material. Apparently also an extra enclosure contiguous with eastern rampart which could be a cattle pound (?).
a) Richmond 1924.
b) Toomey 1966.
c) Challis & Harding 1975, 132.
d) Toomey 1976.

378 Kirklees
Meltham, Royd Edge   SE 09100965
1 acre sub rectangular enclosure at c. 1,000 feet O.D. defined by inner ditch and outer bank, discovered 1960. Surrounded by stone revetted rubble rampart and inner rock cut ditch similar to no. 377. Entrances on east and west, latter spanned by double timber gate with central stop. Deliberately broken stone put down to consolidate entrance way and among it was found a fragment of a beehive quern. Earlier occupation indicated by inner palisaded enclosure on a rather different alignment which partly destroyed an earlier circular hut. Finds include flint chippings, clinker and baked clay scraps, and a lead spindle whorl. Late pre Roman Iron Age?
a) YAJ 42, 1968, 114, 244 and 392.
b) Challis & Harding 1975, 133–4.

379 Kirklees
Meltham, West Nab   SE 077088

Bronze Age plano-convex flint knife found among boulders on northern side of West Nab: 1⅞ inches long, flaked from good quality dark brown flint. Tolson Memorial Museum, Huddersfield.
a) CAGB 5, 1960, 6 and Fig.

380 Kirklees
Mirfield   SE 212204
Haft-flanged axe found between Church and Motte in December 1970 in ground made in 19th century. Private possession.
a) YAJ 44, 1972, 218.

381 Kirklees
Mirfield, Lower Hopton   SE 20151918
Flint flake from Mesolithic tranchet axe found August 1965 at foot of slope at 175 feet O.D. c. 400 feet from River Calder in brown clay (a hillwash deposit), 18 inches down. 6¼ inches long, dense mottled flint. Tolson Memorial Museum, Huddersfield.
a) CAGB 9, 1964, 106 and Fig.

382 Kirklees
Mirfield, Upper Heaton   SE 177192
Bronze Age flint knife. Tolson Memorial Museum, Huddersfield.

383 Kirklees
Outlane, Lee Hill   SE 09081835
Iron Age (?) circular earthwork (overlooking Roman fort) with stone and earth rampart and outer rock cut ditch; 80 yards in diameter, 1.5 acres. Fortified farmstead? In 1775 it was reported that 'a bank or trench beginning a little way from this runs up Lindley Moor', though this had gone by 1924. Remains of 2 possible barrows formerly existed on hill top at c. 935 feet O.D., outside the earthwork.
a) Watson 1775, 58.
b) Petch 1924, 74–5.
c) Preston 1954.
d) Toomey 1960.
e) O.S. Records SE01NE3.
f) WYAU 4401.980385.

384 Kirklees
Slaithwaite   SE 0714 ?
Unpolished flint axe; 3⅞ inches long, 1½ inches wide at cutting edge.
a) O.S. Records SE01SE5.

385 Kirklees
Slaithwaite, Blackmoorfoot   SE 09691311
Stone cist recorded, later covered by reservoir.
a) Petch 1924, 60.

386 Kirklees
Slaithwaite, River Colne   SE 0714 ?
Perforated polished stone hammer found in river bed; oval socket. 5½ inches long, 2¾ inches wide, 1½ inches thick; weight 1 lb 5⅓ oz. Tolson Memorial Museum, Huddersfield (A.25.58).
a) Petch 1924, 49 and Fig. 21.
b) Watson 1952, 76.

387 Kirklees
Storthes Hall   SE 18341214
Neolithic/Bronze Age sandstone grain roller found 1957 and identified by British Museum. Tolson Memorial Museum, Huddersfield (29.1.57).
a) CAGB 3, 1958, 8.

388 Kirklees
Thunder Bridge   SE 184110
Battle axe of Codford St. Peter Stage V type, 'Late Earlier Bronze Age', found on spoil derived from recutting of ditch adjacent to Station Road. Kite shaped, 15.2 cm long, 7.6 cm maximum width; expanded 'blade' and convex, parallel sided butt, 5.2 and 4.4 cm deep respectively. All edges gently rounded and polished. Hour glass perforation just below centre, 3 cm across rim and 1.7 cm at centre; weight 769 gm. Tolson Memorial Museum, Huddersfield (1586–6).
a) YAJ 52, 1980, 179.

389 Kirklees
Woodsome Hall   SE 18051476
Stone axe (Group IX) found 50 yards from the gate of Woodsome

Hall in 1886; 4½ inches long, 2 inches wide at cutting edge; weight 9 oz. Tolson Memorial Museum, Huddersfield (A.18.58).
a) Croft 1886.
b) Petch 1924, 50.
c) Watson 1952, 73.
d) *YAJ* 40, 1960, 41.
e) Keen & Radley 1971.
f) *WYAU* 411.5300.
g) Tolson Memorial Museum Index.

390 Leeds
Bramhope   SE 268248
'Cumbrian type' polished stone axe, pointed oval section, light buff grey-green in colour; 15.6 cm long, 6.9 cm wide at cutting edge, 3.3 cm wide at butt, 3.3 cm thick. Tolson Memorial Museum, Huddersfield (13.1.73).
a) *YAJ* 46, 1974, 141.
b) Tolson Memorial Museum Index.

391 Leeds
Bramley, Hough Hill   SE 245335
Urn exposed and broken to fragments during quarrying at Hough End in December 1879; filled with calcined bones and placed in dish shaped hollow, 2–3 feet deep.
a) Wardell 1881.
b) Rayner 1887, 2.

392 Leeds
Chapeltown   SE 3037 ?
Stone axe-hammer found 2 feet down in clay at Battle Bridge in 1879; hour glass perforation, 8¾ inches long, 3¾ inches wide, 2¾ inches thick; weight 5¼ lbs.
a) Wardell 1881.
b) *WYAU* 4433.07.

393 Leeds
Churwell   SE 27952900
Middle Bronze Age hoard found in cutting being dug on line of Leeds–Dewsbury railway in May 1846: it included 2 spearheads and 5 palstaves. 1 spearhead was 10¾ inches long, the other (broken) was 4 inches in length. 1 of the palstaves had not been trimmed since being taken from the mould. 1 palstave (19 oz. in weight) is in Bradford Museum (214/33); 3 palstaves (including unfinished example) and 1 socketed spearhead are in Leeds Museum.
a) Wardell 1881.
b) Holmes 1882.
c) Clark 1909 and Fig.
d) *CAGB* 12, 1965, 7 (palstave at Bradford).

394 Leeds
Cookridge   SE 254402
Sherds of beaker found in garden at Tinshill Drive in 1960 together with flint scrapers and flakes. Vessel belongs to Clarke's Developed Southern British Group: 21.7 cm high, 15.7 cm diameter at rim, 9.6 cm diameter at base. Leeds Museum.
a) Gilks 1973, 176 and Fig. 4.2.

395 Leeds
Hunslet, Carr Moorside   SE 3031
Bronze Age hoard including '12–14 celts' found in May 1881 2 feet 6 inches down 'in field between Carr Moor Side and Dewsbury Road, south west of Hunslet Moor'. Included in the hoard were 8 transitional palstaves, 1 socketed axe and 1 looped spearhead. Most of the finds went to the Leeds Museum, but individual items lost their identity when the Museum was bombed during the last war; some items were lost in the bombing.
a) Wardell 1881.
b) Holmes 1882.
c) Raistrick 1929, Plate 116.
d) Watson 1952, 83.
e) Burgess 1968, 60–1.
f) *WYAU* 4433.0120; 4433.0141; 4433.010052.

396 Leeds
Kirkstall Road   SE 2735 ?
Late Bronze Age socketed axe with multiple mouth mouldings. Leeds Museum.
a) Clark 1909.
b) Raistrick 1929, 336.

c) Burgess 1968, 66 and Fig. 11.3.
d) O.S. Records SE23SE8.

397 Leeds
Morley   SE 2627 ?
Large, heavy bronze palstave 'found near Morley', 7 inches long, weight 21¾ oz. 'Unused and in the same rough and unfinished condition as when it left the mould'.
a) Wardell 1881.
b) Watson 1952, 82.

398 Leeds
Morley   SE 2627 ?
Straight based, basal-looped spearhead. Leeds Museum.
a) Raistrick 1929, Plate 116.
b) Watson 1952, 83.
c) Radley 1967.
d) Burgess 1968, 67.

399 Leeds
Morley, West Ardsley   SE 26872597
Early Bronze Age axe-hammer found 1956 on freshly ploughed land. Leeds Museum (D140.1964).
a) O.S. Records SE22NE7.

400 Leeds
Neville Street   SE 2933
Stone axe, from Borrowdale? Leeds Museum. (NB: the polished stone axe labelled 'Neville Street' in Leeds Museum is not the one illustrated as such in the Thoresby Society Publication XV, facing p. 219, No. 7, and its provenance is therefore doubtful. It has a rounded cutting edge, thin square butt and very straight sides; oval section with squared sides. Cutting edge badly damaged, and the implement has been re used as a whetstone; 5.2 inches long, 2.1 inches wide, 1 inch thick).
a) Alcock 1959 and Fig.
b) Keen & Radley 1971.

401 Leeds
Potter Newton   SE 2936 ?
Axe-hammer found between Potter Newton and Meanwood.
a) *WYAU* 4423.9655.

402 Leeds
Rawdon   SE 209393
Stone axe found *c.* 3 feet below surface in clay on north side of Acacia Park Estate near the golf course in 1935. Langdale stone. (NB: O.S. Records SE23NW1: polished stone axe found 1935 at SE 20103859, 6 inches long, 2 inches wide, 1½ inches thick, with slight imperfections on cutting edge. Same as above?).
a) *CAGB* 5, 1960, 10.
b) *CAGB* 12, 1967, 12.
c) O.S. Records SE23NW18.

403 Leeds
Rawdon, Billing   SE 218398
Early Bronze Age flanged axe. Cast in Keighley Museum.
a) Wood 1905.
b) Raistrick 1929, Plate 116.
c) Watson 1952, 82.
d) O.S. Records SE23NW8.

404 Leeds
Rawdon, Billing   SE 21593979
Iron Age gold torque found *c.* 1780 on ' the lofty ridge' at Billing; consisted of 2 plain rods twisted together and tapering to a point at the ends. Sent to British Museum; lost.
a) Wardell 1881, 52.
b) Holmes 1888.
c) Cowling 1946, 126.

405 Leeds
Rawdon, Cragg Wood   SE 20903880
3 bronze flanged axeheads found 'under large stone' in 1866 and given to Bradford Philosophical Society (later to Museum). Largest was 7 inches long, 2 inches wide at cutting edge with well defined flanges; second was 5 inches long; third was merely a fragment. All were corroded and pitted.
a) *CAGB* 5, 1960, 70 and Fig.
b) O.S. Records SE23NW2.

406 Leeds

Stonegate Road   SE 297383

Highly polished 'Cumbrian' stone axe found in garden of Castle View, a house on Stonegate Road; rounded cutting edge, thin square butt, oval section with squared sides. 8.6 inches long, 3.0 inches wide, 1.7 inches thick. Leeds Museum.

a) Alcock 1959 and Fig.

b) Manby 1965.

407 Leeds

Wortley   SE 2732 ?

Half of a large sandstone macehead, 3.45 inches long. Geological Museum, London (M 106).

a) Roe & Radley 1964.

b) *WYAU* 4423.7255.

408 Leeds

Yeadon   SE 2040 ?

Socketed axe recorded.

a) Raistrick 1929, Plate 116.

b) Watson 1952, 83.

409 Leeds

Yeadon   SE 2040?

c. 1775 large urn found.

a) Wardell 1881.

410 Yeadon

Yeadon Moor   SE 215415

Bronze palstave found on Yeadon Moor exhibited at Bradford in 1882 and 1889. Much decayed; no further details.

a) Wardell 1881.

b) Holmes 1888.

c) *WYAU* 4424.8155.

411 Wakefield

Netherton   SE 27821640

Mesolithic tranchet axe of mottled grey flint with thin white cortex found 1963 in gravel diggings. 17.4 cm long, 5 cm wide, 3.7 cm thick. Tolson Memorial Museum, Huddersfield; cast in Wakefield Museum.

a) Davies 1964, Fig. 1.

b) O.S. Records SE21NE5.

412 Wakefield

Woolley Edge, Beacon Field   SE 3013 ?

Flint axe (Beaker age?), 2.4 inches long. Dark, grey-blue flint, polished cutting edge. Tolson Memorial Museum (A.23.58).

a) Tolson Memorial Museum Index.

Figure 30. Plan of Cairn Circle, at Burnley, Mosley Height (48). (After Bennett 1950–1).

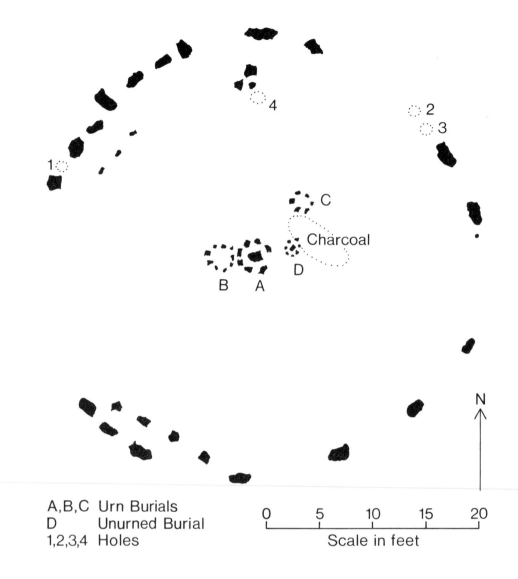

A,B,C Urn Burials
D   Unurned Burial
1,2,3,4 Holes

Scale in feet

0   5   10   15   20

Figure 31. Artist's impression and sketch plan of Ring Work at Burnley, Hell Clough III (46). (After Bennett 1946).

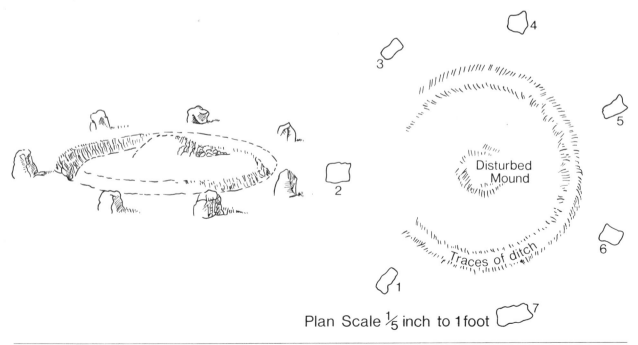

Plan Scale ⅕ inch to 1 foot

Figure 32. Plan of Cairn at Heywood, Wind Hill (165). (After Tyson 1980).

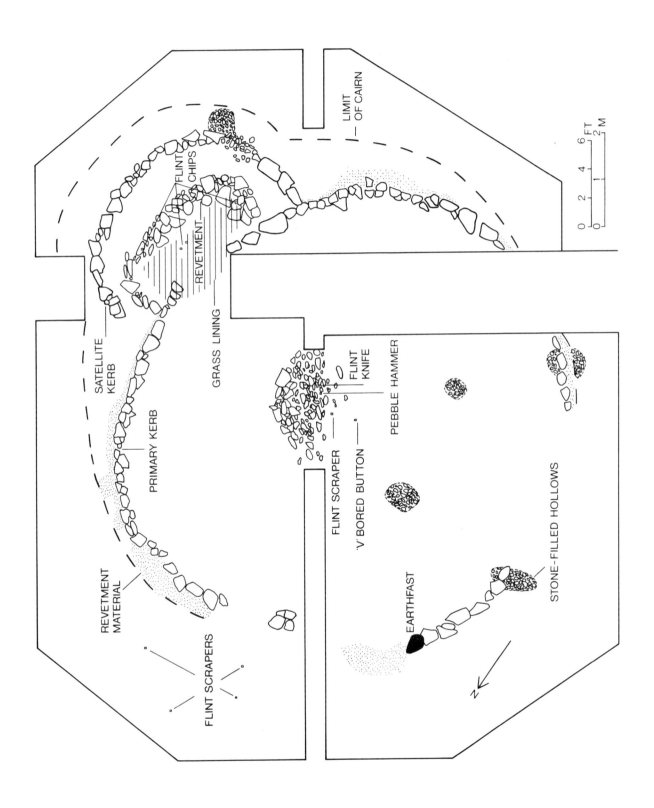

Figure 33. Map of Rombalds Moor and Baildon Common showing extent of area included in text. (After Colls 1846).

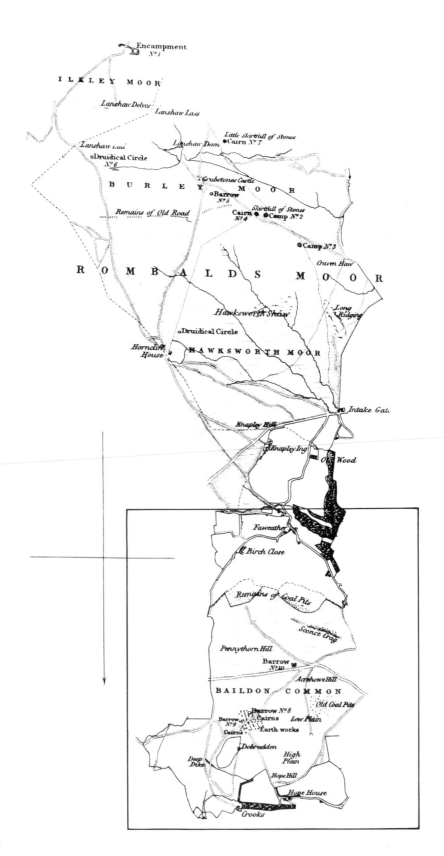

British Remains on Rombalds Moor & Baildon Common — Yorkshire.

Reduced from Plans of the Ordnance Survey of England.

Published by the Society of Antiquaries of London, 23rd April 1846.

Figure 34. Plans of Barrows, Enclosures and possible Field Systems (Reaves?) on Baildon Common and Rombalds Moor. (After Colls 1846).
(Note: The Field Systems have now disappeared).

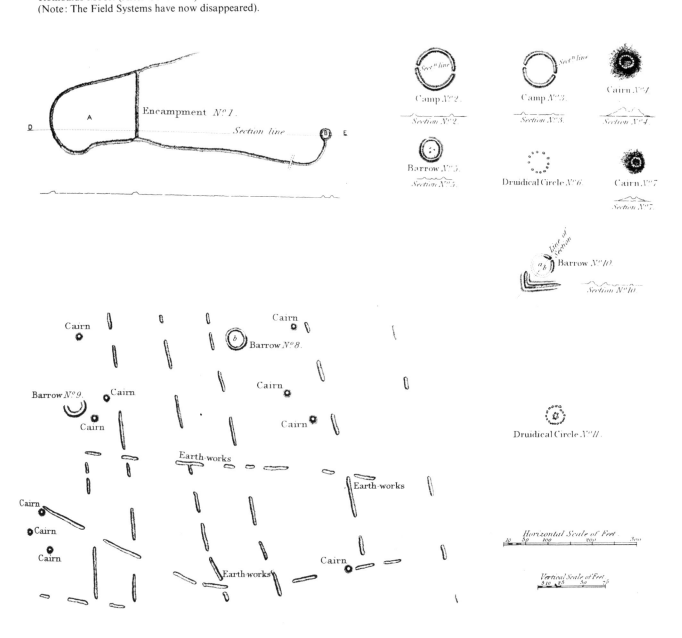

Plans & Sections of British Remains on Rombalds Moor and Baildon Common   Yorkshire

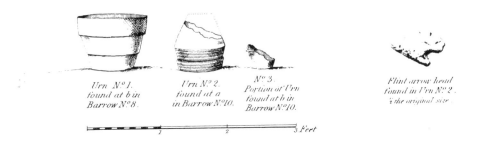

Figure 35. Hoard of Bronze implements from Shelf, Calderdale. (After Burgess 1968).

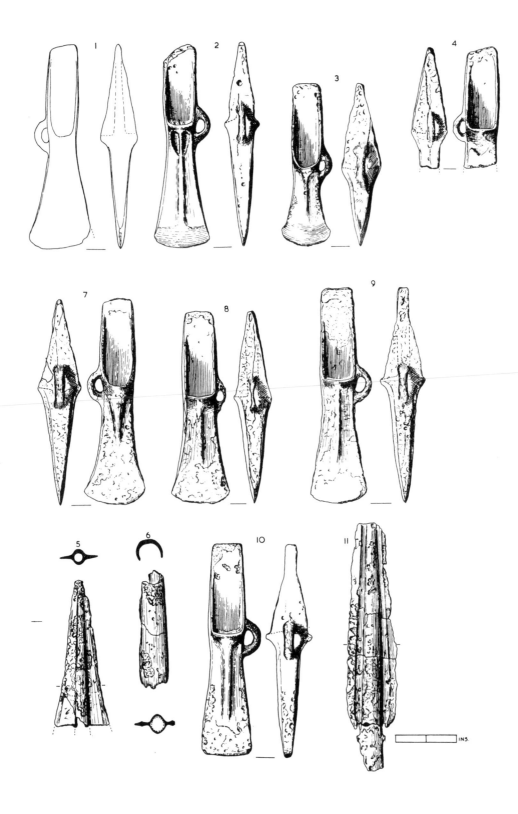

Figure 36. Plan of Cairn Circle at Todmorden, Blackheath (327). (After Roth 1706).

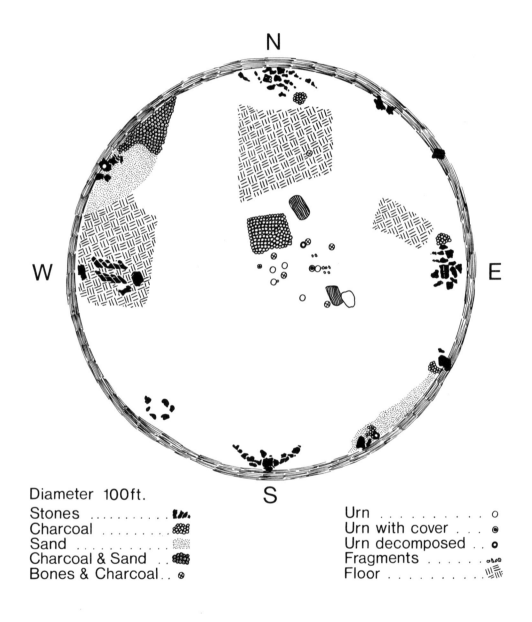

Diameter 100ft.

Stones ....
Charcoal ....
Sand ....
Charcoal & Sand ..
Bones & Charcoal.. ⊗

Urn .... ○
Urn with cover ... ◉
Urn decomposed .. ○
Fragments ......
Floor ....

Appendix 3
Museums with Central Pennine Material
Bibliography

1 Tolson Memorial Museum, Huddersfield
This museum possesses by far the most comprehensive collection of Central Pennine material, including some on loan from the Bankfield Museum, Halifax, and most of this is on display. The *Mesolithic* period is represented by a great variety of flint implements and other material (including a large collection of Buckley material as well as other collections). *Neolithic* material includes many leaf/lozenge arrowheads, transverse arrowheads and scrapers from the local moors, together with polished stone axes from the Huddersfield area. The *Bronze Age* collection includes arrowheads, stone axe-hammers, food vessels and urns, bronze implements of various kinds (including the Shelf hoard). There is also a small collection of *Iron Age* material from the vicinity.

2 Bradford Metropolitan Council Museums
The Manor House Museum (Ilkley), Cartwright Hall (Bradford) and Cliffe Castle (Keighley) have material mainly from an area extending from the river Wharfe in the north to Bradford in the south, and from the eastern end of Rombalds Moor to the Lancashire border. Central Pennine material is to be found on display in the two last named museums, and includes stone and flint axes of *Neolithic* age; pottery, stone and metal implements from the *Bronze Age*; and some *Iron Age* material. At the Manor House Museum (in store) is a well catalogued collection of *Mesolithic*, *Neolithic* and *Bronze Age* flints, axes etc. from, in particular, the Rombalds Moor and Keighley areas.

3 Towneley Hall Museum, Burnley
A well displayed collection of local finds includes *Bronze Age* pottery etc. (in particular the Mosley Height finds) and an excellent display of flint implements (*Mesolithic*, *Neolithic* and *Bronze Age*). The museum possesses the Bennett Collection (Mosley Height excavation finds, stone axes, axe-hammers, bronze implements, urns and a large collection of flints); the Magson Collection (a good selection of flint implements, mainly from the Blackstone Edge–Rishworth–Dean Clough–Shore Moor–Thieveley area); the Beattie Collection (flints from the Burnley–Rossendale area).

4 Bolton Museum
A small collection of *Mesolithic* flints – some of local origin, others Buckley flints from March Hill. Most of the remainder of the small collection of local material consists of *Bronze Age* finds (including a little pottery, a few bronze and stone implements, and the finds from the Noon Hill excavations), together with a few *Neolithic* polished stone axes.

5 Rochdale Museum
Several collections of *Mesolithic*, *Neolithic* and *Bronze Age* flint implements, mainly from the local moors. The remainder of the material consists of a few local stone axes (*Neolithic* and *Bronze Age*), the finds from the Hades Hill barrow, bones and other material from the Worsthorne district, and a few of the important local *Iron Age* finds.

6 Blackburn Museum
A small collection of local material, almost entirely on display. It includes *Neolithic* axes and *Bronze Age* stone, metal and pottery together with replicas of the Portfield hoard.

7 Manchester Museum
Very little Central Pennine material is on display, but in store are many stone, metal and pottery finds from the area. The W. H. Sutcliffe collection (which also includes some Buckley material) consists of a variety of *Mesolithic* flints from the Pennines, together with graphite and iron pyrites, and some *Mesolithic* material from the sandy lowland areas immediately north of the city; there are also some *Neolithic* and *Bronze Age* arrowheads in the collection.

8 Bury Museum
A small collection, all on display, includes the finds from the excavations of the *Bronze Age* barrows at Wind Hill, Whitelow and Bank Lane, together with an urn from near the parish church and a local quern.

9 Bacup Museum
Collections of *Mesolithic* flints, *Neolithic* and *Bronze Age* flint arrowheads, all from the surrounding moorlands, together with many unprovenanced examples. Also the late Neolithic Tooter Hill adze and a few polished stone axes.

10 Saddleworth Museum
Several small collections of flint implements, with good representatives from the *Mesolithic*, *Neolithic* and *Bronze Age* periods (including some Buckley material). A very small number of other local finds, mainly lithic in character.

11 Merseyside County Museums, Liverpool
A collection assembled by Francis Buckley is in store. He gave a comprehensive and fully representative collection of Pennine *Mesolithic* flints (mainly from March Hill) to the museum in 1938. These were destroyed when the museum was burnt out in 1941, and Buckley sent a further collection in 1944, endeavouring to supply a variety of both broad and narrow blade implements. In 1950 his widow gave the Museum the residue of his collection together with his map and notebooks. The latter were transferred to the Tolson Memorial Museum, Huddersfield, in 1957. The flints include finds from the principal Central Pennine *Mesolithic* sites such as Warcock Hill, Windy Hill, White Hill, March Hill and other neighbouring moorlands, together with a large number of unprovenanced flints and a little *Neolithic* and *Bronze Age* material.

12 Other Central Pennine Material
Small collections are scattered in a number of institutions which are not necessarily museums. DARWEN LIBRARY has some local *Bronze Age* urns, TODMORDEN LIBRARY holds some of the finds from the Blackheath excavation, while RADCLIFFE LIBRARY has one or two local *Bronze Age* implements. Isolated examples of Central Pennine material can also be found in the museums at WARRINGTON, SKIPTON, and PRESTON. The WAKEFIELD MUSEUM has a well displayed collection of local material, of which the *Mesolithic* flints from Woolley Edge together with some Buckley-donated flints are of relevance. Finally, the LEEDS CITY MUSEUM possesses stone and metal implements and pottery from the extreme eastern part of the Central Pennine area.

Bibliography

Abram, W. A.   (1877)   *A History of Blackburn, Town and Parish*. Blackburn
                (1879–80)   Discovery of an Ancient British Urn at Blackburn, *Local Gleanings*, 82–5
Addy, S. C.   (1908)   The Names of the Derbyshire and Staffordshire Barrows, *Derbyshire Archaeol. J.*, 103–41
Aikin, J.   (1795)   *A Description of the Country from Thirty to Forty Miles round Manchester*. London
Aitken, J.   (1875)   Remarks upon a Flint Arrow Tip and some Flint Flakes, *Trans. Manchester Geol. Soc.* 14, 284–8
Alcock, L.   (1950)   The Henge Monument of the Bull Ring, Dove Holes, Derbyshire, *Proc. Prehist. Soc.* 16, 81–6
              (1958)   Polished Stone Axes of Lake District Origin from Leeds, *Yorkshire Archaeol. J.* 39, 391–4
Andrew, S.   (1901)   Bronze Implement from Thornley, near Lees, *Trans. Lancashire Cheshire Antiq. Soc.* 19, 240–1
Anon.   (1886)   Account of Flint Implements found on Bull Hill near Haslingden, *Trans. Lancashire Cheshire Antiq. Soc.* 4, 304–7
ApSimon, A. M.   (1959)   Food Vessels, *Univ. London Inst. Archaeol. Bull.* 1, 24–36
Ashbee, P.   (1960)   *The Bronze Age Round Barrow in Britain*. London
              (1970)   *The Earthen Long Barrow in Britain*. London
              (1978)   *The Ancient British*. Norwich.
Atherden, M. A.   (1976)   The impact of Late Prehistoric Cultures on the Vegetation of the North York Moors, *Trans. Inst. Brit. Geogr. New Series* 1, 284–300
Baldwin, W.   (1903)   Some Prehistoric Finds from Ashworth Moor and Neighbourhood, *Trans. Manchester Geol. Soc.* 28, 108–13
Ball, D. F.   (1975)   Processes of Soil Degradation: a Pedological Point of View, *The Effect of Man on the Landscape: the Highland Zone* (eds J. G. Evans S. Limbrey & H. Cleere), 20–7. Counc. Brit. Archaeol. Res. Rep. 11
Barnes, B., Edwards, B. J. N., Hallam, J. S., and Stuart, A. J.   (1971)   The Skeleton of a Late-Glacial Elk associated with Barbed Points from Poulton-le-Fylde, Lancashire, *Nature* 232, 488–9
Barrit, T.   (1800)   Account of some Antiques lately found in the River Ribble &c., *Mem. Proc. Manchester Lit. Phil. Soc.* 5 (2), 527–34
Bartley, D. D.   (1962)   The Stratigraphy and Pollen Analysis of Lake Deposits near Tadcaster, Yorks., *New Phytol.* 61, 277–87
              (1975)   Pollen Analytical Evidence for Prehistoric Forest Clearance in the upland area west of Rishworth, West Yorkshire, *New Phytol.* 74, 375–81
              (1976)   Extwistle Moor, Lancashire, *Radiocarbon* 18, 257
Bennett, W.   (1946)   *History of Burnley*, vol. 1. Burnley
              (1950–1)   Report on Excavations near Burnley, *Trans. Lancashire Cheshire Antiq. Soc.* 62, 204–8
Binford, L. R.   (1968)   Post-Pleistocene Adaptation, *New Perspectives in Archaeology* (eds S. R. & L. R. Binford), 313–41. Chicago
Birks, H. J. B.   (1963–4)   Chat Moss, Lancashire, *Mem. Proc. Manchester Lit. Phil. Soc.* 106, 22–45
              (1964)   Late-Glacial Deposits at Bagmere Cheshire and Chat Moss Lancs., *New Phytol.* 64, 270–85
              (1965)   Pollen Analytical Investigations at Holcroft Moss, Lancs., and Lindow Moss, Cheshire, *J. Ecol.* 53 (2), 299–314
Blundell, J. D.   (1965–6)   A Note on a Bronze Axe found at Great Harwood, Lancs., *Trans. Lancashire Cheshire Antiq. Soc.* 76, 222–3
Blundell, J. D. and Longworth, I. H.   (1967–8)   A Bronze Age Hoard from Portfield Farm, Whalley, Lancs., *Brit. Mus. Quart.* 32, 8–14
Bonsall, C.   (1975)   British Antiquity 1974–5: Review of Palaeolithic/Mesolithic publications, *Archaeol. J.* 132, 302–9
Booth, J.   (1963)   Preliminary Excavation of the Barrow on Noon Hill, Belmont, Lancs. (August 1958), *J. Bolton & District Arch. Soc.* 1, 4–8
Bowman, G.   (1909)   Note on a Bronze Palstave found at Openshaw, Manchester, *Trans. Lancashire Cheshire Antiq. Soc.* 27, 146–7
Bradley, R.   (1972)   Prehistorians and Pastoralists in Neolithic and Bronze Age England, *World Archaeol.* 4, 192–204
              (1978a)   Colonisation and Land Use in the Late Neolithic and Early Bronze Age, *The Effect of Man on the Landscape: the Lowland Zone* (eds S. Limbrey & J. G. Evans), 95–103. Coun. Brit. Archaeol. Res. Rep. 21
              (1978b)   *The Prehistoric Settlement of Britain*. London
Briggs, C. S.   (1976)   Notes on the Distribution of some Raw Materials in Later Prehistoric Britain, *Settlement and Economy in the Third and Second Millenia B.C.* (eds C. Burgess & R. Miket), 267–82. Brit. Archaeol. Rep. 33
Britton, D.   (1963)   Traditions of Metal Working in the Later Neolithic and Early

Bromehead, C. E. N., Edwards, W., Wray, D. A., and Stephens, J. V. (1933)	Bronze Age of Britain, *Proc. Prehist. Soc.* 29, 258–325 *Geology of the Country around Holmfirth and Glossop.* London
Buckland, P. C. and Dolby, M. J. (1973)	Mesolithic and Later Material from Misterton Carr, Notts: an Interim Report, *Trans. Thoroton Soc. Nottinghamshire* 77, 5–33
Buckley, F. (MS. 1920–48)	*Notebooks* and *Drawing Books.* Tolson Memorial Museum, Huddersfield
(1921)	*A Microlithic Industry, Marsden, Yorkshire.* Privately Printed
(1922)	Yorkshire Gravers, *Proc. Prehist. Soc.* 3, 542–7
(1923)	Some Recent Discoveries in our Local Flints, *Oldham Chronicle*, Dec. 15
(1924a)	*A Microlithic Industry of the Pennine Chain.* Privately Printed
(1924b)	Use of Pygmy Flints, *Antiq. J.* 4, 47–8
(1948)	From Harpoon to Fish Hook, *The Archer* (Works J. of Rt. Fletcher & Sons Ltd., Stoneclough and Greenfield), 2 (6), 210–11
Bulleid, A. (1968)	*The Lake-Villages of Somerset*, 6th ed. Street
Bu'Lock, J. D. (1958)	The Pikestones: a Chambered Long Cairn of Neolithic Type on Anglezarke Moor, Lancs., *Trans. Lancashire Cheshire Antiq. Soc.* 68, 143–5
(1961)	The Bronze Age in the North-West, *Trans. Lancashire Cheshire Antiq. Soc.* 71, 1–42
(1965–6)	Some Notes on the Planeswood Hoard of Gold and Bronze Objects of the Late Bronze Age, *Trans. Lancashire Cheshire Antiq. Soc.* 76, 218–21
Bu'Lock, J. D. and Rosser, C. E. P. (1960)	Winter Hill, a Composite Cairn of the Bronze Age, *Trans. Lancashire Cheshire Antiq. Soc.* 70, 66–73
Burgess, C. B. (1968)	*Bronze Age Metalwork in Northern England c. 1000–700 B.C.* Newcastle
(1969)	Some Decorated Socketed Axes in Canon Greenwell's Collection, *Yorkshire Archaeol. J.* 46, 267–71
(1970)	The Bronze Age, *Current Archaeol.* 19, 208–15
(1974)	The Bronze Age, *British Prehistory: a New Outline* (ed. C. Renfrew), 165–232. London
(1976a)	Britain and Ireland in the Third and Second Millenia B.C.: a Preface, *Settlement and Economy in the Third and Second Millenia B.C.* (eds C. Burgess & R. Miket), i–iii. Brit. Archaeol. Rep. 33
(1976b)	The Beaker Phenomenon: Some Suggestions, *Settlement and Economy in the Third and Second Millenia B.C.* (eds C. Burgess & R. Miket), 309–23. Brit. Archaeol. Rep. 33
Burl, A. (1976)	*The Stone Circles of the British Isles.* London
Burleigh, R., Hewson, A., and Meeks, N. (1976)	British Museum Natural Radiocarbon Measurements, VIII, *Radiocarbon* 18, 16–42
Butler, L. A. S. (1967)	Prehistoric Archaeology, *Leeds and its Region* (eds M. W. Beresford & G. R. J. Jones), 89–93, Leeds
Butterfield, A. (1939)	Structural Details of a Long Barrow on Black Hill, Bradley Moor, West Yorkshire, *Yorkshire Archaeol. J.* 34, 222–7
Butterworth, A., and Lewis, G. D. (1978)	*Prehistoric and Roman Times in the Sheffield Area*, 3rd ed. Sheffield
Carroll, D. M., Hartnup, R., and Jarvis, R. A. (1979)	*Soils of South and West Yorkshire.* Harpenden
Case, H. (1969)	Neolithic Explanations, *Antiquity* 43, 176–86
Challis, A. J. and Harding, D. W. (1975)	Later Prehistory from the Trent to the Tyne, *Brit. Archaeol. Rep.* 20, 2 vols
Chaplin, R. R. (1975)	The Ecology and Behaviour of Deer in Relation to their Impact on the Environment of Prehistoric Britain, *The Effect of Man on the Landscape: the Highland Zone* (eds J. G. Evans, S. Limbrey & H. Cleere), 40–2. Counc. Brit. Archaeol. Res. Rep. 11
Charles, W. N., McCowan, D. and East, K. (1977)	Selection of Upland Swards by Red Deer (Cervus elephas L.) on Rhum, *J. Applied Ecol.* 14, 55–64
Childe, V. G. (1940)	*Prehistoric Communities of the British Isles.* London
Churchill, D. M. (1962)	The Stratigraphy of the Mesolithic Sites III and IV at Thatcham, Berkshire, England, *Proc. Prehist. Soc.* 28, 362–70
Clare, T. (1973)	*Aspects of the Stone Circles and Kindred Monuments of North West England.* Unpublished M.A. thesis, University of Liverpool, 2 vols.
Clark, E. K. (1902)	Excavations at Pule Hill, near Marsden, *Yorkshire Archaeol. J.* 16, 38–42
(1909)	Leeds in Prehistoric Times, *Thoresby Soc. Pub.* 15, 212–21
Clark, J. G. D. (1932)	*The Mesolithic Age in Britain.* Cambridge
(1936)	*The Mesolithic Settlement of Northern Europe.* Cambridge
(1938)	Reindeer Hunters' Summer Camps in Britain?, *Proc. Prehist. Soc.* 4, 229
(1954)	*Excavations at Star Carr.* Cambridge
(1972)	*Star Carr: a Case Study in Bio-Archaeology.* Reading, Mass.
(1977)	*World Archaeology in New Perspective*, 3rd ed. Cambridge
Clark, J. G. D. and Rankine, W. F. (1939)	Excavations at Farnham, Surrey (1937–8): the Horsham Culture and the Question of Mesolithic Dwellings, *Proc. Prehist. Soc.* 5, 61–118
Clarke, D. L. (1970)	*Beaker Pottery of Great Britain and Ireland*, 2 vols. Cambridge
(1976)	Mesolithic Europe: the Economic Basis, *Problems in Economic and Social Archaeology* (eds G. de G. Sieveking, I. H. Longworth & K. E. Wilson), 449–81. London

Clement, L.   (1874)   Roman Remains in Marsden, Briercliffe and Extwistle, *Trans. Burnley Lit. Sc. Club* 1, 78–81

Coles, J. M.   (1971)   The Early Settlement of Scotland: Excavations at Morton, Fife, *Proc. Prehist. Soc.* 37 (2), 284–366

Colls, J. M. N.   (1846)   Letter upon some Early Remains discovered in Yorkshire, *Archaeologia* 31, 299–307

Conway, V. M.   (1947)   Ringinglow Bog, near Sheffield, *J. Ecol.* 34, 149–81
            (1954)   Stratigraphy and Pollen Analysis of Southern Pennine Blanket Peats, *J. Ecol.* 42, 117–47

Coombs, D. G.   (1976)   Excavations at Mam Tor, Derbyshire, 1965–1969, *Hillforts: Later Prehistoric Earthworks in Britain and Ireland* (ed. D. W. Harding), 147–52. London

Coppock, J. T.   (1976)   *An Agricultural Atlas of England and Wales*, 2nd ed. London
Courtney, T. W.   (1978)   *A Stone Age Site: Unstone, Derbyshire*. North Derbyshire Archaeological Committee

            (1979)   Unstone, Derbyshire: Summary Report, *Proc. Prehist. Soc.* 45, 339
Cowie, T. G.   (1978)   Bronze Age Food Vessel Urns in Northern Britain, *Brit. Archaeol. Rep.* 55

Cowling, E. T.   (1936)   Flint Implement Sites in Mid-Wharfedale, *Yorkshire Archaeol. J.* 33, 35–48

            (1946)   *Rombalds Way: a Prehistory of Mid-Wharfedale*. Otley
            (1973)   A Mesolithic Flint Site: the Sandbeds, Otley, Yorkshire, *Yorkshire Archaeol. J.* 45, 1–12

            (1976)   Neolithic and Bronze Age Graving and Scoring Tools from Mid-Wharfedale, *Yorkshire Archaeol. J.* 48, 27–34
Cowling, E. T. and   Two Mesolithic Riverside Sites in Yorkshire, *Yorkshire Archaeol. J.*
Stickland, A. J.   (1947)   36, 455–62
Crabtree, J.   (1836)   *A Concise History of the Parish and Vicarage of Halifax*. Halifax
Croft, W. R.   (1886)   Discovery of Stone and Flint Weapons and other Implements near Huddersfield, *Yorkshire Archaeol. J.* 9, 255–6

Crowe, P. R.   (1962)   Climate, *Manchester and its Region* (ed. C. F. Carter), 17–46. Manchester

Cummins, W. A.   (1980)   Stone Axes as a Guide to Neolithic Communications and Boundaries in England and Wales, *Proc. Prehist. Soc.* 46, 45–60

Cundill, F. R.   (1976)   Late Flandrian Vegetation and Soils in Carlingill Valley, Howgill Fells, *Trans. Inst. Brit. Geogr. New Series* 1, 301–9

Cunliffe, B.   (1978)   *Iron Age Communities in Britain*, revised ed. London
Davey, P. J.   (1976)   The Distribution of Bronze Age Metalwork from Lancashire and Cheshire, *J. Chester Archaeol. Soc.* 59, 1–13

Davey, P. J. and   *Bronze Age Metalwork from Lancashire and Cheshire*, Worknotes 1,
Forster, E.   (1975)   University of Liverpool
Davidson, D. A.   (1972)   Terrain Adjustment and Prehistoric Communities, *Man, Settlement and Urbanism* (eds P. J. Ucko, R. Tringham & G. W. Dimbleby), 17–22. London

Davies, J.   (1958)   Some Stone Axes of Lake District Origin, *CAGB* 3, 73–5
            (1959a)   Prehistoric Graphite on the Yorkshire Moors, *CAGB* 4, 6–8
            (1959b)   The Ghostly Saw of White Hill, *CAGB* 4, 19–20
            (1961)   A Polished Discoidal Flint Knife from Slatepit Moor, Lancs., *Trans. Lancashire Cheshire Antiq. Soc.* 71, 160–2

            (1963a)   A Stone Axe of Irish Origin from Wharfedale, *CAGB* 8, 111–14
            (1963b)   A Mesolithic Site on Blubberhouses Moor, Wharfedale, West Riding of Yorkshire, *Yorkshire Archaeol. J.* 41, 61–70

            (1964)   Tranchet Axes from West Yorkshire, *CAGB* 9, 68–73
Davies, J. and   Mesolithic Flint Axes from the West Riding of Yorkshire,
Rankine, W. F.   (1960)   *Yorkshire Archaeol. J.* 40, 209–14
Davies, M.   (1941–3)   A Preliminary Survey of Local Upland Peat Deposits in relation to the Mesolithic Occupation of the Area around Rochdale, *Trans. Rochdale Lit. Sc. Soc.* 21, 83–97

Davis, J. W.   (1881)   On the Discovery of Chipped Flints beneath the Peat on the Yorkshire Moors, near Halifax, *Yorkshire Archaeol. J.* 6, 125–8

Dawes, N.   (1851–2)   British Burial Places near Bolton, County Lancaster, *Trans. Hist. Soc. Lancashire Cheshire* 4, 130–2

Deans, T.   (1933)   Tardenoisian Sites on Oxenhope Moor, *Naturalist*, 223–7.
Devis, C. H.   (1867–8)   Stone Hammer found at Collyhurst, Manchester, *Trans. Manchester Geol. Soc.* 7, 49–50

Dimbleby, G. W.   (1961)   The Ancient Forest of Blackamore, *Antiquity* 35, 123–8
Earnshaw, J.   (1966)   A Polish Stone Axe from Farnley Tyas, *Huddersfield Dist. Archaeol. Soc. Bull.* 18, 6–7

Earp, J. R., Poole, E. G. and   *Geology of the Country around Clitheroe and Nelson*. London
Whiteman, A. J.   (1961)
Edwards, B. J. N.   (1969)   Lancashire Archaeological Notes, Prehistoric and Roman, *Trans. Hist. Soc. Lancashire Cheshire* 121, 99–108

Edwards, W. and   *British Regional Geology: The Pennines and Adjacent Areas*, 3rd ed.
Trotter, F. M.   (1954)   London
Elgee, F.   (1930)   *Early Man in North East Yorkshire*. Gloucester
Elgee, F. and   *The Archaeology of Yorkshire*. London
Elgee, H. W.   (1933)
Evans, J. G.   (1971)   Notes on the Environment of Early Farming Communities in Britain, *Economy and Settlement in Neolithic and Early Bronze Age Britain and Europe* (ed. D. D. A. Simpson), 11–26. Leicester

	(1975)	*The Environment of Early Man in the British Isles.* London
Eyre, S. R.	(1966)	The Vegetation of a South Pennine Moorland, *Geography as Human Ecology, Methodology by Example* (eds S. R. Eyre & G. R. J. Jones), 147–73. London
Feather, S. W. and Manby, T. G.	(1970)	Prehistoric Chambered Tombs of the Pennines, *Yorkshire Archaeol. J.* 42, 396–7
Fell, C. I.	(1964)	The Cumbrian Type of Polished Stone Axe and its Distribution in Britain, *Proc. Prehist. Soc.* 30, 39–55
Fishwick, H.	(1889)	*The History of the Parish of Rochdale.* Rochdale
	(1903)	Discovery of Ancient British Barrow in Todmorden, in the County of Lancaster, *The Reliquary and Illustrated Archaeologist* 9, 276–9
Fleming, A.	(1971)	Bronze Age Agriculture on the Marginal Lands of North-East Yorkshire, *Agr. Hist. Rev.* 19, 1–24
	(1976)	Early Settlement and the Landscape in West Yorkshire, *Problems in Economic and Social Archaeology* (eds G. de G. Sieveking, I. H. Longworth & K. E. Wilson), 359–73. London
	(1978)	The prehistoric landscape of Dartmoor. Part 1: South Dartmoor, *Proc. Prehist. Soc.* 44, 97–123
Forde-Johnston, J.	(1962)	The Iron Age Hillforts of Lancashire and Cheshire, *Trans. Lancashire Cheshire Antiq. Soc.* 72, 9–46
	(1976)	*Hillforts of the Iron Age in England and Wales.* Liverpool
Franks, J. W. and Johnson, R. H.	(1964)	Pollen Analytical Dating of a Derbyshire Landslip: the Cown Edge Landslips, Charlesworth, *New Phytol.* 63, 209–16
Freeman, T. W., Rodgers, H. B. and Kinvig, R. H.	(1966)	*Lancashire, Cheshire and the Isle of Man.* London
French, G. J.	(1894)	The Stone Circles on Chetham's Close, *Trans. Lancashire Cheshire Antiq. Soc.* 12, 42–51
Garstang, J.	(1906)	Early Man, *Victoria County History of the County of Lancaster* (eds W. Farrer & J. Brownbill), I, 211–56. London
Gilks, J. A.	(1968)	Two Middle Bronze Age Cinerary Urns from Tower Hill, Warley, W.R., *Yorkshire Archaeol. J.* 42, 119–20
	(1973a)	The Neolithic and Early Bronze Age Pottery from Elbolton Cave, Wharfedale, *Yorkshire Archaeol. J.* 45, 41–54
	(1973b)	Bronze Age Pottery and a Basal-Looped Spearhead from West Yorkshire, *Yorkshire Archaeol. J.* 45, 175–9
	(1974)	*A Neolithic Occupation Site at Castle Hill, Denby, near Huddersfield, Yorkshire,* West Yorkshire Metropolitan County Archaeological Research Committee
	(1977)	A Collared Urn and Pebble Mace Head of the Early Bronze Age from Brownhill, Saddleworth, *Yorkshire Archaeol. J.* 49, 45–9
Green, H. S.	(1980)	The Flint Arrowheads of the British Isles, *Brit. Archaeol. Rep.* 75
Greenfield, E.	(1960)	The Excavation of Barrow 4 at Swarkeston, Derbyshire, *Derbyshire Archaeol. J.* 80, 1–48
Greenhalgh, T.	(1871)	Druidical Circle in the Township of Turton, Parish of Bolton le Moors, South Lancs., *J. Brit. Archaeol. Ass.* 27, 524–6
	(1880)	Note on Druidical or Stone Circle on Cheetham Close, Turton, *J. Brit. Archaeol. Ass.* 36, 444
Grimshaw, B.	(1916)	The Edgeworth Palstave, *Trans. Hist. Soc. Lancashire Cheshire,* 31, 208–9
Guilbert, G.	(1977)	The northern Welsh Marches: some recent developments, *The Iron Age in Britain – a Review* (ed. J. Collis), 41–50. Sheffield
Hadfield, A.	(1807)	On Burial Urns found near Breightmet Hill, *Gentleman's Magazine* 77 (2), 1097–8
Hall, B. R. and Folland, C. J.	(1970)	*Soils of Lancashire.* Harpenden
Hallam, A. M.	(1964)	A Collared Urn of the Middle Bronze Age from Chorley, Lancashire, *Trans. Lancashire Cheshire Antiq. Soc.* 74, 188–91
Hallam, J. S.	(1960)	*The Mesolithic of the Central Pennines.* Unpublished M.A. thesis, University of Liverpool, 2 vols.
	(1970)	The Prehistory of Lancashire, *Archaeol. J.* 127, 232–7
Harding, D. W.	(1970)	The 'New' Iron Age, *Curr. Archaeol.* 20, 234–40
Harding, D. W. (ed.)	(1976)	*Hillforts: Later Prehistoric Earthworks in Britain and Ireland.* London
Hardwick, C.	(1865–6)	Ancient British Remains at Over Darwen, *Trans. Hist. Soc. Lancashire Cheshire* 6, 273–8
Harrison, W.	(1892)	Archaeological Finds in Lancashire, *Trans. Lancashire Cheshire Antiq. Soc.* 10, 249–52
	(1896)	*An Archaeological Survey of Lancashire.* Westminster
Hawke-Smith, C. F.	(1979)	Man-Land Relations in Prehistoric Britain: the Dove–Derwent Interfluve, Derbyshire, *Brit. Archaeol. Rep.* 64
Heathcote, J. P.	(1961)	The Prehistory of North Derbyshire, *Archaeol. J.* 118, 207–9
Hibbert, F. A., Switsur, V. R. and West, R. G.	(1971)	Radio-carbon dating of Flandrian pollen zones at Red Moss, Lancashire, *Proc. Roy. Soc. London,* B. 177, 161–76
Hicks, S. P.	(1971)	Pollen Analytical Evidence for the Effect of Prehistoric Agriculture on the Vegetation of North Derbyshire, *New Phytol.* 70, 647–67
	(1972)	The Impact of Man on the East Moor of Derbyshire from Mesolithic Times, *Archaeol. J.* 129, 1–21
Higham, N. J.	(1979)	An Aerial Survey of the Upper Lune Valley, *The Changing Past: some recent work in the Archaeology of Northern England* (ed. N. J. Higham), 31–3. Manchester

Holliday, R. (1967)	Agriculture and Soils, *Leeds and its Region* (eds M. W. Beresford & G. R. J. Jones), 62–88. Leeds
Holmes, J. (1882)	Recent Discovery of Bronze Celts, *Yorkshire Archaeol. J.* 7, 143–4
(1888)	Notes on the Discoveries of Bronze Implements etc. in the West Riding, *Proc. Yorkshire Geol. Soc.* 9, 427–32
Hunt, D. (1978)	*Aspects of the Bronze Age in the Rossendale Hills and the Adjacent Lowlands of Lancashire.* Unpublished M.A. thesis, University of Durham
Jackson, J. W. (1928)	Flint Adze from Bacup, *Antiq. J.* 8, 90
(1929–31)	On the Discovery of a Shale Armlet on Flint Hill, near Blackstone Edge, *Trans. Rochdale Lit. Sc. Soc.* 17, 71–3
(1934–5a)	The Prehistoric Archaeology of Lancashire and Cheshire, *Trans. Lancashire Cheshire Antiq. Soc.* 50, 65–106
(1934–5b)	The Prehistory of the Manchester Region, *Year Book, Ancient Monuments Society, Manchester*, 48–53
(1936)	Contributions to the Archaeology of the Manchester Region, *North Western Naturalist*, 11, 110–19
(1968)	A large Cinerary Urn and Roman Coil found at Glossop, *Derbyshire Archaeol. J.* 88, 96–7
Jacobi, R. M. (1976)	Britain Inside and Outside Mesolithic Europe, *Proc. Prehist. Soc.* 42, 67–84
(1978a)	Population and Landscape in Mesolithic Lowland Britain, *The Effect of Man on the Landscape: the Lowland Zone* (eds S. Limbrey & J. G. Evans), 75–85. Counc. Brit. Archaeol. Res. Rep. 21
(1978b)	Northern England in the Eighth Millenium bc: an essay, *The Early Postglacial Settlement of Northern Europe* (ed. P. Mellars), 295–332. London
Jacobi, R. M., Tallis, J. H. and Mellars, P. A. (1976)	The Southern Pennine Mesolithic and the Ecological Record, *J. Archaeol. Sci.* 3, 307–20
Jarman, M. R., Vita-Finzi, C. and Higgs, E. S. (1972)	Site Catchment Analysis in Archaeology, *Man, Settlement and Urbanism* (eds P. J. Ucko, R. Tringham and G. W. Dimbleby), 61–6. London
Jewell, P. (1963)	Cattle from British Archaeological Sites, *Man and Cattle* (eds A. E. Mourant & F. E. Zeuner), 80–101. Royal Anthropological Institute of Great Britain and Ireland, Occasional Paper 18
Johnson, R. H. (1965a)	The Glacial Geomorphology of the West Pennine Slopes from Cliviger to Congleton, *Essays in Geography for Austin Miller* (eds J. B. Whittow & P. D. Wood), 58–94. Reading
(1965b)	A study of the Charlesworth Landslides, near Glossop, *Trans. Inst. Brit. Geogr.* 37, 111–26
(1969)	The Glacial Geomorphology of the area around Hyde, Cheshire, *Proc. Yorkshire Geol. Soc.* 37, 189–230
Jones, G. R. J. (1961)	Settlement Patterns in Anglo-Saxon England, *Antiquity* 35, 221–32
Jones, R. L. (1976)	The Activities of Mesolithic Man: Further Palaeobotanical Evidence from North-East Yorkshire, *Geoarchaeology* (eds D. D. Davidson & M. A. Shackley), 355–67. London
Jones, R. L., Cundill, P. R. and Simmons, I. G. (1979)	Archaeology and Palaeobotany on the North York Moors and their Environs, *Yorkshire Archaeol. J.* 51, 15–22
Keen, L. and Radley, J. (1971)	Report on the Petrological Identification of Stone Axes from Yorkshire, *Proc. Prehist. Soc.* 37 (1), 16–37
Kendall, H. P. and Roth, H. L. (1912)	Local Prehistoric Implements, *Bankfield Museum Notes, Halifax*, 12
King, A. (1969)	*A Study of Early Settlement in Upper Ribblesdale and the Adjacent Uplands.* Unpublished M.A. thesis, University of Liverpool
Kirkman, A. C. (1843)	Ancient British Collar, found in Lancashire, *Gentleman's Magazine*, 19
Law, R. (1881–2)	On the Discovery of Flint Implements on the High Hills, near Rochdale, *Trans. Manchester Geol. Soc.* 16, 287–9
(1898a)	Discovery of Burial Urns at Todmorden, *J. Brit. Archaeol. Ass. New Series* 4, 277–82
(1898b)	Archaeological Discovery at Todmorden, *Trans. Lancashire Cheshire Antiq. Soc.* 16, 169–72
Law, R. and Horsfall, J. (1882)	Discovery of Flint Implements on the Hills between Todmorden and Marsden, *Proc. Yorkshire Geol. Soc.* 8, 1–15
(1886–8)	An Account of Small Flint Implements found beneath Peat on Several Elevated Points of the Pennine Chain, lying between Huddersfield and Oldham, *Trans. Manchester Geol. Soc.* 19, 599–603
Leach, G. B. (1912–13)	Prehistoric Relics from the Hills lying due East of Burnley, *Trans. Rochdale Lit. Sci. Soc.* 11, 18–22
(1951)	Flint Implements from the Worsthorne Moors, Lancs., *Trans. Hist. Soc. Lancashire Cheshire* 103, 1–22
Lewis, G. D. (1966)	Some Radio Carbon Dates for the Peak District, *Derbyshire Archaeol. J.* 86, 115–17
(1970)	*The Bronze Age in the Southern Pennines.* Unpublished M.A. thesis, University of Liverpool
Littleborough Archaeological Society (1972)	Snoddle Hill Investigations, *LAS* 1, 3–9
(1976)	The Excavation of some Sites of the Mesolithic Period, *LAS* 2, 2–10
Longbotham, A. T. (1932)	Prehistoric Remains in Barkisland, *Trans. Halifax Antiq. Soc.*, 153–82

Longworth, I. H. (1961)	The Origins and Development of the Primary Series in the Collared Urn Tradition in England and Wales, *Proc. Prehist. Soc.* 27, 263–306
Luck, J. R. (1894)	An Account of the Opening of a Large Tumulus near Stonyhurst, Lancashire, *Trans. Lancashire Cheshire Antiq. Soc.* 12, 30–41
Lunn, N. (1963)	An Account of Recent Fieldwork in the Honley area, including a Preliminary Account on Excavations at Hagg Wood in 1963, *Huddersfield Dist. Archaeol. Soc. Bull.* 13
(1966)	Bronze Age Man in the Pennines, *Huddersfield Dist. Archaeol. Soc. Bull.* 18, 1–5
Lynch, F. (1966)	The Pikestones, Anglezarke, Lancashire, *Proc. Prehist. Soc.* 32, 347–8
Manby, T. G. (1957)	Food Vessels of the Peak District, *Derbyshire Archaeol. J.* 77, 1–29
(1962)	Some Mesolithic Sites in the Peak District and Trent Basin, *Derbyshire Archaeol. J.* 82, 10–23
(1963)	A Large Greenstone Axe from Ramsden Clough, Todmorden, *CAGB* 8, 54–8
(1964a)	Food Vessels from Derbyshire, *Derbyshire Archaeol. J.* 84, 117–20
(1964b)	Early Bronze Age Axes from Yorkshire, *Yorkshire Archaeol J.* 41, 344–55
(1965)	The Distribution of Rough-out 'Cumbrian' and Related Stone Axes of Lake District Origin in Northern England, *Trans. Cumberland Westmorland Antiq. Archaeol. Soc.* 65, 363–404
(1965–6)	A Beaker from Extwistle Moor, *Trans. Lancashire Cheshire Antiq. Soc.* 76, 224–5
(1967)	*The Neolithic Cultures of the North of England.* Unpublished M.A. thesis, University of Liverpool
(1969)	Bronze Age Pottery from Pule Hill, Marsden, W.R. Yorkshire and Foot Vessels of the Early Bronze Age from England, *Yorkshire Archaeol. J.* 62, 273–82
(1970)	Long Barrows of Northern England: Structural and Dating Evidence, *Scot. Archaeol. Forum*, 1–27
(1974)	Grooved Ware Sites in Yorkshire and the North of England, *Brit. Archaeol. Rep.* 9
(1979)	Typology, materials and distribution of flint and stone axes in Yorkshire, *Stone Axe Studies* (eds T. H. McK. Clough & W. A. Cummins), 65–81. Counc. Brit. Archaeol. Res. Rep. 23
March, H. C. (1886)	A Cinerary Urn, *Rochdale Lit. Sci. Soc. Ann. Rep.*
(1887a)	Types of Sepulchral Urn, *Trans. Lancashire Cheshire Antiq. Soc.* 5, 272–86
(1887b)	*The Early Neolithic Floor of East Lancashire.* Privately Printed
Martin, S. (1844)	Discovery of a Roman Urn near Burnley in Lancashire, *Archaeologia* 30, 553–4
Maxim, J. L. (1912–13)	Querns and other Corn-Grinding Stones in Rochdale and District, *Trans. Rochdale Lit. Sci. Soc.* 11, 72–83
(1923–5)	Recent Discoveries of Corn-Grinding Stones and Corn Mills in Rochdale and District, *Trans. Rochdale Lit. Sci. Soc.* 15, 111–20
(1928)	An Interesting Antiquarian Discovery, *North Western Naturalist*, 3, 21–2
(undated)	*Prehistoric Relics of Old Rochdale*, Mss. Rochdale Central Library
May, J. (1976)	*Prehistoric Lincolnshire.* Lincoln
Mayes, P. (1967)	Excavations at Crosley Wood, Bingley, *Yorkshire Archaeol. J.* 42, 19–23
Megaw, J. V. S. and Simpson, D. D. A. (1979)	*Introduction to British Prehistory.* Leicester
Mellars, P. A. (1969)	Radiocarbon Dates for a New Creswellian Site, *Antiquity* 43, 308–310
(1973)	The Affinities of the Sandbeds Mesolithic Site, *Yorkshire Archaeol. J.* 45, 13–18
(1974)	The Palaeolithic and Mesolithic, *British Prehistory: a New Outline* (ed. C. Renfrew), 41–99. London
(1976a)	Fire Ecology, Animal Populations and Man: a Study of some Ecological Relationships in Prehistory, *Proc. Prehist. Soc.* 42, 15–45
(1976b)	Settlement Patterns and Industrial Variability in the British Mesolithic, *Problems in Economic and Social Archaeology* (eds G. de G. Sieveking, I. H. Longworth & K. E. Wilson), 375–99. London
Millward, R. and Robinson, A. (1975)	*The Peak District.* London
Moore, C. M. and Cummins, W. A. (1974)	Petrological Identification of Stone Implements from Derbyshire and Leicestershire, *Proc. Prehist. Soc.* 40, 59–78
Morehouse, H. J. (1861)	*The History and Topography of the Parish of Kirkburton.* Huddersfield
Morrison, A. (1980)	*Early Man in Britain and Ireland: An Introduction to Palaeolithic and Mesolithic Cultures.* London
O'Kelly, M. J. (1972)	Further radio-carbon dates from Newgrange, Co. Meath, Ireland, *Antiquity* 46, 226–7
Oldfield, F. (1965)	Problems of Mid-Post-Glacial Pollen Zonation in Part of North-West England, *J. Ecol.* 53, 247–60
Pacitto, A. L. (1968)	The Excavation of Two Bronze Age Burial Mounds at Ferry Fryston in the West Riding of Yorkshire, *Yorkshire Archaeol. J.* 42, 295–305

Palmer, J.   (1966)   Landforms, Drainage and Settlement in the Vale of York,
                             Geography as Human Ecology, Methodology by Example (eds S. R.
                             Eyre & G. R. J. Jones), 91–121. London

           (1967)   Landforms, *Leeds and its Region* (eds M. W. Beresford & G. R. J.
                             Jones), 16–29. Leeds

Parkinson, R.   (1881–2)   The Broughton Park Cinerary Urn, *Manchester Lit. Club Rep. Proc.*
                             8, 48–50

Pegge, S.   (1789)   Discoveries in Opening a Tumulus in Derbyshire, and Note on Find
                             at Clifton, *Archaeologia* 9, 189–92

Pennington, W.   (1970)   Vegetational History in the North-West of England: a Regional
                             Synthesis, *Studies in the Vegetational History of the British Isles*
                             (eds D. Walker & R. G. West), 41–79. Cambridge

           (1975)   The Effect of Neolithic Man on the Environment of North-West
                             England: the Use of Absolute Pollen Diagrams, *The Effect of Man
                             on the Landscape: the Highland Zone* (eds J. G. Evans, S. Limbrey &
                             H. Cleere), 74–85. Counc. Brit. Archaeol. Res. Rep. 11

Petch, J. A.   (1924)   *Early Man in the District of Huddersfield.* Huddersfield

Phelps, J. J.   (1915)   A Gold Pendant of Early Irish Origin, *Trans. Lancashire Cheshire
                             Antiq. Soc.* 33, 192–200

           (1922)   Stone Implement found at Winton, Eccles, *Trans. Lancashire
                             Cheshire Antiq. Soc.* 40, 43–4

Pigott, M. E. and   Stratigraphy and Pollen Analysis of Malham Tarn and Tarn Moss,
Pigott, C. D.   (1959)   *Field Studies* 1, 84–101

Pitts, M. W. and   Some Aspects of Change in Flaked Stone Industries of the
Jacobi, R. M.   (1979)   Mesolithic and Neolithic in Southern Britain, *J. Archaeol. Sci.* 6,
                             163–77

Plant, J.   (1867–8)   Remarks on a Stone Axe found in the Valley of the Mersey at
                             Flixton, near Manchester in 1846, *Trans. Manchester Geol. Soc.* 7,
                             65–75

Platt, S. S.   (1898–1900)   Stone Axe Hammer found at Low House Farm, near Milnrow,
                             Trans. Rochdale Lit. Sci. Soc. 7, 95–7

           (1909–11)   Stone Celt or Axe found at Castle Hill, Rochdale, *Trans. Rochdale
                             Lit. Sci. Soc.* 10, 22–5

Powell, T. G. E.   (1952)   Excavation of a Circular Enclosure at Broadbank, Briercliffe, Lancs.,
                             Trans. Hist. Soc. Lancashire Cheshire 104, 145–51

Powell, T. G. E., Oldfield, F.   Excavations in Zone VII Peat at Storrs Moss, Lancashire, England,
and Corcoran, J. X. W. P.   *Proc. Prehist. Soc.* 37, 112–37
               (1971)

Prag, A. J. N. W.   (1977)   The Edgeworth Palstave Rediscovered, *Trans. Lancashire Cheshire
                             Antiq. Soc.* 79, 123–4

Preston, F. L.   (1954)   The Hill-Forts of the Peak, *Derbyshire Archaeol. J.* 74, 1–31

Preston, W. E.   (1905)   Cinerary Urn from Penythorne Hill, Baildon Moor, *Bradford Sci. J.*
                             1, 97

Price, J. H.   (1929–31)   Discoveries on the Hills around Rochdale, *Trans. Rochdale Lit. Sci.
                             Soc.* 17, 38–49

           (1932–4)   A Pre-Roman Iron Spearhead, *Trans. Rochdale Lit. Sci. Soc.* 18, 73

Priestley, J. H.   (1936)   Local Flints and the Prehistoric Sequence, *Trans. Halifax Antiq. Soc.*
                             93–129

Radley, J.   (1963a)   One Ultimate Form of the 'Petit Tranchet' Derivative Arrowhead,
                             Yorkshire Archaeol. J. 41, 203–8

           (1963b)   Recent Prehistoric Finds in the Peak District, *Derbyshire Archaeol J.*
                             83, 96–101

           (1964)   Late Upper Palaeolithic and Mesolithic Surface Sites in South
                             Yorkshire, *Trans. Hunter Archaeol. Soc.* 9, 38–50

           (1965a)   Significance of Major Moorland Fires, *Nature* 205, 1254–8

           (1965b)   A Ring-Bank on Beeley Moor, *Derbyshire Archaeol. J.* 85, 126–31

           (1966a)   Fifty Arrow-Heads from the Gritstone Moors of the South
                             Pennines, with a Consideration of other Arrow-Heads from the
                             Peak District, *Trans. Hunter Archaeol. Soc.* 9, 110–14

           (1966b)   Glebe Low, Great Longstone, *Derbyshire Archaeol. J.* 86, 54–69

           (1966c)   A Bronze Age Ring-Work on Totley Moor and other Bronze Age
                             Ring-Works in the Pennines, *Archaeol. J.* 123, 1–26

           (1967)   New Bronze Age Spear-Heads from Yorkshire and a Provisional List
                             of Yorkshire Spear-Heads, *Yorkshire Archaeol. J.* 42, 15–19

           (1968a)   The Origins of the Arbor Low Monument, *Derbyshire Archaeol. J.*
                             88, 100–3

           (1968b)   A Mesolithic Structure at Sheldon, with a Note on Chert as a Raw
                             Material on Mesolithic Sites in the South Pennines, *Derbyshire
                             Archaeol. J.* 88, 26–36

           (1970)   The Mesolithic Period in North-East Yorkshire, *Yorkshire Archaeol.
                             J.* 42, 314–24

           (1974)   The Prehistory of the Vale of York, *Yorkshire Archaeol. J.* 46, 10–22

Radley, J. and   An Occupied Cave of the Bronze Age, Bunker's Hill Wood, Beeley,
Cooper, L.   (1966)   *Derbyshire Archaeol. J.* 86, 93–8

           (1968)   A Neolithic Site at Elton, an Experiment in Field Recording,
                             Derbyshire Archaeol. J. 88, 37–46

Radley, J. and   Mesolithic Sites in South West Yorkshire, *Yorkshire Archaeol. J.* 41,
Marshall, G.   (1963)   81–97

           (1964)   Maglemosian Sites in the Pennines, *Yorkshire Archaeol. J.* 41,
                             394–402

Radley, J. and Mellars, P. (1963)	Hail Mary Hill: a Mesolithic Site in the Rother Valley, *Trans.* *Hunter Archaeol. Soc.* 8, 307–11
(1964)	A Mesolithic Structure at Deepcar, Yorks., England, and the Affinities of its Associated Flint Industries, *Proc. Prehist. Soc.* 30, 1–24
Radley, J. and Plant, M. (1967)	Two Neolithic Sites at Taddington, *Derbyshire Archaeol. J.* 87, 149–54
Radley, J. and Simms, C. (1967)	Wind Erosion in East Yorkshire, *Nature* 216, 20–2
Radley, J., Tallis, J. H. and Switzur, V. R. (1974)	The Excavation of Three 'Narrow Blade' Mesolithic Sites in the South Pennines, England, *Proc. Prehist. Soc.* 40, 1–19
Raistrick, A. (1929)	The Bronze Age in West Yorkshire, *Yorkshire Archaeol. J.* 29, 354–65
(1931)	Prehistoric Burials at Waddington and at Bradley, West Yorkshire, *Yorkshire Archaeol. J.* 30, 248–55
(1933a)	The Correlation of Glacial Retreat Stages across the Pennines, *Proc.* *Yorkshire Geol. Soc.* 22, 199–214
(1933b)	The Distribution of Mesolithic Sites in the North of England, *Yorkshire Archaeol. J.* 31, 141–56
(1939)	Iron Age Settlements in West Yorkshire, *Yorkshire Archaeol. J.* 34, 115–50
Raistrick, A. and (1962) Holmes, P. F.	Archaeology of Malham Moor, *Field Studies* 1, 73–100
Ramm, H. G. (1957)	A Survey of the Combs Moss Hill-Fort, *Derbyshire Archaeol. J.* 77, 49–53
Rayner, S. (ed.) (1887)	*The History of Pudsey.* London
Richmond, I. A. (1924)	Excavations at Meltham, near Huddersfield, *Yorkshire Archaeol. J.* 27, 319–20
(1925)	*Huddersfield in Roman Times.* Huddersfield
Riley, D. N. (1966)	An Early Bronze Age Cairn on Harland Edge, Beeley Moor, *Derbyshire Archaeol. J.* 86, 31–53
(1980)	Recent Air Photographs of Duggleby Howe and the Ferrybridge Henge, *Yorkshire Archaeol. J.* 52, 174–8
Roe, F. E. S. (1966)	The Battle-Axe Series in Britain, *Proc. Prehist. Soc.* 32, 199–245
(1979)	Typology of stone implements with shaftholes, *Stone Axe Studies* (eds T. H. McK. Clough & W. A. Cummins), 23–48. Counc. Brit. Archaeol. Res. Rep. 23
Roe, F. E. S. and Radley, J. (1968)	Pebble Mace Heads with Hour-Glass Perforations from Yorkshire, Notts. and Derbyshire, *Yorkshire Archaeol. J.* 42, 169–77
Roose, T. (1894)	Great Edge Settlement on Extwistle Moor, *Trans. Lancashire* *Cheshire Hist. Soc.* 12, 108–10
Roth, H. L. (1906)	*The Yorkshire Coiners 1767–1783 and Notes on Prehistoric Halifax.* Halifax
Rowe, J. H. (1928)	An Ancient Burial at Chellow, near Heaton, *The Heaton Review* 2
Shaw, G. (1889)	Celt and Urns Discovered in Saddleworth in 1844, *Local Notes and* *Gleanings: Oldham and Neighbourhood in Bygone Times* (ed. G. Shaw), 3, 153–5. Oldham
Simmons, I. G. (1969a)	Pollen Diagrams from the North York Moors, *New Phytol.* 68, 807–27
(1969b)	Environment and Early Man on Dartmoor, Devon, England, *Proc.* *Prehist. Soc.* 35, 203–19
(1975)	Towards an Ecology of Mesolithic Man in the Uplands of Great Britain, *J. Archaeol. Sci.* 2, 1–15
(1979)	Late Mesolithic Societies and the Environment of the Uplands of England and Wales, *Univ. London Inst. Archaeol. Bull.* 16, 111–29
Simmons, I. G. and Cundill, P. R. (1969)	Vegetation History during the Mesolithic in North-East Yorkshire, *Yorkshire Archaeol. J.* 42, 324–7
Simpson, D. D. A. (1971)	Beaker Houses and Settlements in Britain, *Economy and Settlement* *in Neolithic and Early Bronze Age Britain and Europe* (ed. D. D. A. Simpson), 131–52. Leicester
Simpson, F. G. and Richmond, I. A. (1941)	The Roman Fort on Hadrian's Wall at Benwell, *Archaeologia* *Aeliana*, 4th Series, 19, 1–43
Smith, A. G. (1970)	The Influence of Mesolithic and Neolithic Man on British Vegetation: a discussion, *Studies in the Vegetational History of the* *British Isles* (eds D. Walker & R. G. West), 81–96. Cambridge
Smith, I. F. (1974)	The Neolithic, *British Prehistory: a New Outline* (ed C. Renfrew), 100–36. London
(1979)	The Chronology of British Stone Implements, *Stone Axe Studies* (eds T. H. McK. Clough & W. A. Cummins), 13–22. Counc. Brit. Archaeol. Res. Rep. 23
Smith, R. T. (1979)	Environmental Issues in Landscape Studies, *Landscape History* 1, 16–28
Sparks, B. W. and West, R. G. (1972)	*The Ice Age in Britain.* London
Spencer, A. (1950)	Bronze Age Settlement in Radcliffe? *Lancashire Life* 2 (1), 4–5
(1950–1)	Preliminary Report on Archaeological Investigations near Radcliffe, Lancs., *Trans. Lancashire Cheshire Antiq. Soc.* 62, 196–203
Spencer, J. (1893)	Glaciated Boulders in Calderdale, *Naturalist*, 75–9
Spratt, D. A., Goddard, R. E. and Brown, D. R. (1976)	Mesolithic Settlement Sites at Upleatham, Cleveland, *Yorkshire* *Archaeol. J.* 48, 19–26
Spratt, D. A. and	Prehistoric Activity and Environment on the North York Moors, *J.*

Simmons, I. G. (1976)	*Archaeol. Sci.* 3, 193–210
Stone, J. F. S. and Thomas, L. C. (1956)	Use and Distribution of Faience in Ancient East and Prehistoric Europe, *Proc. Prehist. Soc.* 22, 37–84
Stonehouse, W. P. B. (1972)	Rocher Moss South: Report on a Recently Excavated Mesolithic Flint Site in Saddleworth, *Saddleworth Hist. Soc. Bull.* 2, 36–40
(1976)	Red Ratcher: The Excavation of a Mesolithic Site in the Peak National Park, *Saddleworth Hist. Soc. Bull.* 6, 15–22
(1978)	White Hassock: Prehistoric Arrowheads? *Saddleworth Hist. Soc. Bull.* 8, 1–3
(1980)	Rocher Moss South 2: A Later Mesolithic Site in Saddleworth, *Saddleworth Hist. Soc. Bull.* 10, 21–4
Stonehouse, W. P. B. and Barnes, B. (1980)	The Medlock Flint Adze, *Saddleworth Hist. Soc. Bull.* 10, 41–3
Sutcliffe, W. H. (1896–7)	A Neolithic Trader's Store of Graphite, *Trans. Rochdale Lit. Sci. Soc.* 5, 63–4
(1898–1900)	Hades Hill Barrow, *Trans. Rochdale Lit. Sci. Soc.* 6, 56–63
(1899)	Urns found in East Lancs. and the Implements associated with the Men who made them, *Trans. Burnley Lit. Sci. Club* 17, 171–7
Sutcliffe, W. H. and Parker, J. (1899)	Note on Discoveries at Hades Hill, Wardle, *Trans. Lancashire Cheshire Antiq. Soc.* 17, 233–4
Switsur, V. R. and Jacobi, R. M. (1975)	Radiocarbon Dates for the Pennine Mesolithic, *Nature* 256, 482–4
Sykes, D. F. (1906)	*The History of the Colne Valley*. Slaithwaite
Tallis, J. H. (1964)	The Pre-Peat Vegetation of the South Pennines, *New Phytol.* 63, 363–73
(1975)	Tree Remains in Southern Pennine Peats, *Nature* 256, 482–4
Tallis, J. H. and McGuire, J. (1972)	Central Rossendale: the Evolution of an Upland Vegetation I. The Clearance of Woodland, *J. Ecol.* 60, 721–37
Tallis, J. H. and Switsur, V. R. (1973)	Studies on Southern Pennine Peats, VI: A Radiocarbon Dated Pollen Diagram from Featherbed Moss, Derbyshire, *J. Ecol.* 61, 743–51
Taylor, C. C. (1980)	The Making of the English Landscape – 25 years on, *The Local Historian* 14, 195–201
Taylor, J. A. (1973)	Chronometers and Chronicles: a Study of Palaeo-Environments in West Central Wales, *Progr. Geogr.* 5, 250–334
(1975)	The Role of Climatic Factors in Environmental and Cultural Changes in Prehistoric Times, *The Effect of Man on the Landscape: the Highland Zone* (eds J. G. Evans, S. Limbrey & H. Cleere), 6–19. Counc. Brit. Archaeol. Res. Rep. 11
Thompson, F. H. (1967)	The Roman Fort at Castleshaw, Yorkshire (W.R.): Excavations 1957–64, *Trans. Lancashire Cheshire Antiq. Soc.* 77
Thomson, W. H. (1947)	On a Perforated Stone Hammer found in Alexandra Park, Manchester, *Trans. Lancashire Cheshire Antiq. Soc.* 59, 219–20
Tinsley, H. M. (1975)	The Former Woodland of the Nidderdale Moors (Yorkshire) and the Role of Early Man in its Decline, *J. Ecol.* 63, 1–27
(1976)	Cultural Influences on Pennine Vegetation with Particular Reference to North Yorkshire, *Trans. Inst. Brit. Geogr. New Series* 1, 310–22
Tinsley, H. M. and Smith, R. T. (1974)	Ecological Investigations at a Romano-British Earthwork in the Yorkshire Pennines, *Yorkshire Archaeol. J.* 46, 23–33
Tonks, L. H., Jones, R. C. B., Lloyd, W., Sherlock, R. L. and Wright, W. B. (1931)	*The Geology of Manchester and the South-East Lancashire Coalfield.* London
Toomey, J. P. (1960)	The Earthwork at Lee Hill, Huddersfield: an Iron Age Hill Farm?, *Huddersfield Dist. Archaeol. Soc. Bull.* 6, 8
(1962)	Newly Discovered Earthwork at Royd Edge, Meltham, *Huddersfield Dist. Archaeol. Soc. Bull.* 10
(1966)	Iron Age Man in the Pennines, *Huddersfield Dist. Archaeol. Soc. Bull.* 19, 1–8
(1976)	*An Iron Age Enclosure at Oldfield Hill, Meltham.* Huddersfield
Tyson, N. (1980)	Excavation of a Cairn at Wind Hill, Heywood, Lancashire, *GMAG Publication* 1
Tyson, N. and Bu'Lock, J. D. (1957)	The Iron Age Fortifications at Planes Wood, Whalley, *Trans. Lancashire Cheshire Antiq. Soc.* 67, 115–17
Varley, R. A. (1968)	A Collared Urn from Ogden, W.R., *Yorkshire Archaeol. J.* 42, 126–7
(1973)	Bronze Age Finds from Skircoat, Halifax, *Yorkshire Archaeol. J.* 45, 173–4
(1977)	Bronze Axes from Calderdale, *Yorkshire Archaeol. J.* 49, 51–8
Varley, W. J. (1932)	Early Man in the Cheshire Plain, *J. Chester N. Wales Archaeol. Soc.* 29, 50–65
(1938)	The Bleasdale Circle, *Antiq. J.* 18, 154–71
(1948)	The Hillforts of the Welsh Marches, *Archaeol. J.* 105, 41–66
(1964)	*Cheshire before the Romans.* Chester
(1976)	A Summary of the Excavations at Castle Hill, Almondbury 1939–1972, *Hillforts: Later Prehistoric Earthworks in Britain and Ireland* (ed. D. W. Harding), 119–31. London
Varley, W. J. and Jackson, J. W. (1940)	*Prehistoric Cheshire.* Chester
Waddington, W. A. and Wilkinson, T. (1886)	Prehistoric Remains in the Neighbourhood of Burnley, *Trans. Burnley Lit. Sci. Club* 4, 89–97

Wainwright, G. J.   (1960)   Three Microlithic Industries from South-West England and their Affinities, *Proc. Prehist. Soc.* 26, 193–201

Walker, D.   (1956)   A Site at Stump Cross, near Grassington, Yorks., and the Age of the Pennine Microlith Industry, *Proc. Prehist. Soc.* 22, 23–8

Walker, J. W.   (1935)   Mesolithic Flints from the Wakefield District, *Yorkshire Archaeol. J.* 32, 170–1

(1939)   *Wakefield: Its History and People.* Wakefield

Wardell, J.   (1869)   *Historical Notices of Ilkley, Rumbald's Moor and Baildon Common.* Leeds

(1881)   *Historical Notices of Ilkley, Rombald's Moor, Baildon Common . . .,* 2nd ed. Leeds

Waterman, D. M., Kent, B. W. J. and Stickland, H. J.   (1955)   Two Inland Sites with 'Iron Age A' Pottery in the West Riding of Yorkshire, *Yorkshire Archaeol. J.* 38, 383–97

Watkin, W. T.   (1883)   *Roman Lancashire.* Liverpool

Watson, G. G.   (1952)   *Early Man in the Halifax District.* Halifax

Watson, J.   (1775)   *History and Antiquities of the Parish of Halifax.* London

Whatton, W. R.   (1833–4)   Ancient Instrument of Brass at Rochdale in Lancashire, *Archaeologia* 25, 595

Whitaker, J.   (1771)   *The History of Manchester.* London

(1773)   *The History of Manchester,* 2nd ed. London

Whitaker, T. D.   (1872)   *An History of the Original Parish of Whalley and Honor of Clitheroe,* 4th ed., 2 vols. London

Whittle, A. W. R.   (1978)   Resources and Population in the British Neolithic, *Antiquity* 52, 34–43

(1980)   Two Neolithics? *Curr. Archaeol.* 70 and 71, 329–34, 371–3

Wilkinson, T.   (1893)   Extwistle Moor, Burnley, *Trans. Lancashire Cheshire Antiq. Soc.* 11, 156–61

(1897)   Prehistoric Remains from Wadsworth Moor, near Hebden Bridge, *Trans. Lancashire Cheshire Antiq. Soc.* 15, 214–15

(1903)   On a Prehistoric Drinking Vessel found near Burnley, *Report of the British Association,* London (1904), 808–9

(1904)   Local Prehistoric Man, *Trans. Halifax Antiq. Soc.* 1–8

(1911a)   Interesting Discovery near Burnley, *Lancashire Naturalist* 4, 223

(1911b)   Remains of an Earth Circle at Hell Clough, *Lancashire Naturalist* 4, 237–40

(1912)   Stone Axe Hammer found near Radcliffe, *Lancashire Naturalist* 5, 64

Wilkinson, T. and Tattersall, J. F.   (1889)   *Memories of Hurstwood, Burnley, Lancashire.* Burnley

Willett, F.   (1952–3)   A Scandinavian Flint Axe from Manchester, *Trans. Lancashire Cheshire Antiq. Soc.* 63, 191–3

Willett, F. and Seddon, T.   (1952–3)   Excavations in Everage Clough, Burnley, 1951, *Trans. Lancashire Cheshire Antiq. Soc.* 63, 194–200

Wood, B.   (1905)   Prehistoric Antiquities of the Bradford District, *Bradford Antiq. New Series* 2, 113–23

Woodhead, T. W.   (1906)   Ecology of Woodland Plants in the Neighbourhood of Huddersfield, *J. Linnaean Soc.* 37, 333–406

(1929)   History of the Vegetation of the Southern Pennines, *J. Ecol.* 17, 1–31

(1931)   *Climate, Vegetation and Man in the Huddersfield District.* Huddersfield

Woodman, P. C.   (1978)   The Mesolithic in Ireland, *Brit. Archaeol. Rep.* 58

Wray, D. A., Stephens, J. V., Edwards, W. N. and Bromehead, C. E. N.   (1930)   *The Geology of the Country around Huddersfield and Halifax.* London

Wright, W. B., Sherlock, R. L., Wray, D. A., Lloyd, W. and Tonks, L. H.   (1927)   *The Geology of the Rossendale Anticline.* London

Wrigley, A.   (1911)   *Saddleworth: its Prehistoric Remains.* Oldham

Wymer, J. J.   (1962)   Excavations at the Maglemosian Sites at Thatcham, Berkshire, England, *Proc. Prehist. Soc.* 28, 329–61

Wymer, J. J. (ed.)   (1977)   Gazetteer of Mesolithic Sites in England and Wales, *Counc. Brit. Archaeol. Res. Rep.* 20

Wynne, M. E.   (1959)   *The Role of the River Mersey in the Bronze Age.* Unpublished M.A. thesis, University of Liverpool, 2 vols

Yates, G. C.   (1887a)   Broughton Hall Urn, *Trans. Lancashire Cheshire Antiq. Soc.* 5, 296–7

(1887b)   Stone Implements, *Trans. Lancashire Cheshire Antiq. Soc.* 5, 320–31

(1895)   Bronze Implements of Lancashire and Cheshire, *Trans. Lancashire Cheshire Antiq. Soc.* 13, 124–38

Work Notes Series

Work Notes Series

Work Notes 1
Bronze Age Metalwork from Lancashire and Cheshire
(*out of print*)

Work Notes 2
Catalogue of the Prehistoric Metalwork in Merseyside County Museums

Work Notes 3
Man and the Changing Landscape
A study of Occupation and Palaeo Environment in the Central Pennines

Work Notes 4
Thomas Gann: A Pioneer of Mayan Archaeology in British Honduras
A Catalogue of Mayan Antiquities deposited in Merseyside County Museums

Catalogue of the Prehistoric Metalwork in the Merseyside County Museums

Joseph Mayer, a jeweller and goldsmith in Liverpool in the mid-nineteenth century, collected a wide and important range of objects of art and antiquity. Among the provenanced items of prehistoric metalwork he bought are the Ulceby bit-ring, 'Mayer' mirror and Trawsfynydd tankard, all outstanding and internationally famous examples of Iron Age craftsmanship. Other British prehistoric bronzes were purchased by Mayer from the Faussett family in 1854, and from W. H. Rolfe in 1857. These add significantly to our knowledge of the Bronze Age since almost all have a recorded provenance.

A fine selection of Central European bronzes was acquired by Mayer as part of he Fejérváry/Pulszky collection in about 1855, including swords, daggers and axes, as well as brooches and bracelets.

Many of the items of art and antiquity he obtained were displayed by Mayer in his own Museum in Liverpool. In 1867 he presented the major part of his entire collection to Liverpool, and it has been housed ever since then in the Museum in William Brown Street. Later donations by societies and individuals have increased the range and variety of specimens but, for antiquities at least, Mayer's collection remains of central importance.

This catalogue is the first complete and detailed study of the Museums' collection of prehistoric metalwork, with each item described and illustrated. Introductory notes on the history and documentation of the collection are followed by the catalogue itself. The first part includes all the provenanced items arranged according to location, and the second part contains the unprovenanced material arranged according to type, providing an outline of the development of metal tools, weapons and ornaments. One appendix gives all known details of specimens which were lost in the Blitz of May 1941 before adequate record had been made; the other appendix discusses the Felsted, Essex, 'hoard'.

Susan Nicholson

Published 1981

Thomas Gann: A Pioneer of Mayan Archaeology in British Honduras
A Catalogue of Mayan Antiquities deposited in Merseyside County Museums.

Dr T. W. F. Gann was trained in medicine in London and Liverpool, and served as District Medical Officer in British Honduras from 1894 to 1923. Between 1919 and 1938 he was also lecturer in Central American Archaeology at the Liverpool Institute of Archaeology. He was involved with several excavations in Central America with the British Museum and the Carnegie Institute, Washington DC, and on his own behalf, and has been acknowledged for his 'discovery' of sites in the Mayan area.

Gann wrote extensively: six popular books as well as articles in the London Illustrated News. These, together with papers in scientific journals, provide information on his excavations.

The material excavated by him was dispersed during his lifetime, or after his death, to institutions and to friends. At Merseyside County Museums, (formerly Liverpool City Museums), there are a number of collections donated by Gann either directly to the Museum or on loan from the former Institute of Archaeology, University of Liverpool. In total more than one thousand items, mostly pottery, were received, including single items of great importance such as the Kendal jades and the Santa Rita mural.

This will be the first comprehensive catalogue made of the collections at the Museum. These are of particular importance at the present time because of renewed archaeological excavations in Belize (British Honduras) and interest in Gann's published material.

The contents include notes on Gann himself and on the sites at which he excavated. The main catalogue describes all the Gann material deposited at the Museum. A select bibliography lists works both by and about Gann. Other Central American Pre-Columbian material at the Museum is summarised in an appendix. A second appendix briefly describes collections of artefacts and archives from Gann's excavations held by other museums.

Yvonne Schumann

To be published 1983

Merseyside County Museums
William Brown Street
Liverpool L3 8EN
051-207 0001